D1613073

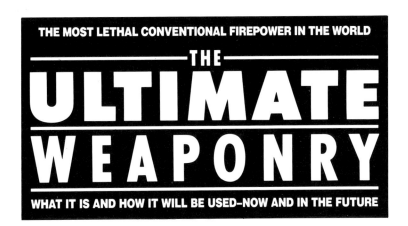

THE MOST LETHAL CONVENTIONAL FIREPOWER IN THE WORLD

THE ULTIMATE WEAPONRY

WHAT IT IS AND HOW IT WILL BE USED–NOW AND IN THE FUTURE

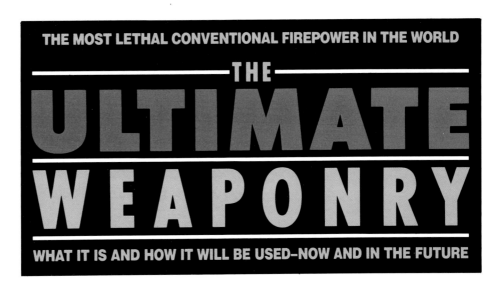

THE MOST LETHAL CONVENTIONAL FIREPOWER IN THE WORLD

THE ULTIMATE WEAPONRY

WHAT IT IS AND HOW IT WILL BE USED–NOW AND IN THE FUTURE

PADDY GRIFFITH

CONSULTANT DR JOHN PIMLOTT

GUILD PUBLISHING

LONDON · NEW YORK · SYDNEY · TORONTO

First published in Great Britain in 1991
by Sidgwick & Jackson Limited
Cavaye Place
London SW10 9PG

Copyright © 1991 Brown Packaging Limited

This edition published 1991
by Guild Publishing
by arrangement with
Sidgwick & Jackson Limited

CN 5219

Printed by Eagle Colour Books Ltd,
Blantyre, Scotland.

Bound by the Bath Press, Bath, Avon

Editorial: Roger Ford, John Boteler, Chris Marshall, Rory Bridson
Picture Reasearch: Stasz Gnych
Design: Steve Wilson

Technical Illustrations: Graham Bingham
Battlefield overviews: Harry Clow

Picture Acknowledgments

Roger Ford 193 B/R. Robert Hunt Library 54 T/L, 121 T/R, 161
T. Hugh MacManners 26/27, 46 B/L, 49 B/R, 54 B/L, 61 B/R, 98
C/L, 130 B/R, 134 C/T, 137 T, 143 B, 148 B, 149 L, 158/9, 178/9,
189. 216 T, 217 B. Military Picture Library 111 B/R, 118, 124
B/L, 132 T/R. TRH Pictures 19 C/T, 20 T, 25 L, 31 T/R, 33 B/R,
34 B, 36 T/L, 37 C/B, 38 B/L, 40 B/R, 40 B/R, 42 B/L, 52 B, 55
T, 58/9, 59 T/L, 64 B/L, 65 B/R, 66 B, 71, 73 T/L, 76 T/L, 77 C/L,
82 C/B, 82 B/R, 89 B, 90 T/R, 92/93, 97 T, 100 T, 104, 115 T,
116 B/L, 119 B/L, 127 T, 128/9, 133 C, 141 B, 142 T, 152 T/R,
160 B/L, 162 B, 165 B, 166, 168 C/L, 168 B/R, 182 B/R, 187 T,
187 B/R, 188 B/L, 190, 197, 200, 201, 208/9,211, 214, 215 B, 215
C, 218, 219. TRH Pictures/DOD. 10 T/R, 11 T, 91 B/R, 108 B/R,
117 T/L, 126 B, 131 T/L, 144 C, 194 C/B. TRH Pictures/USAF 22
C/L, 24 T/R, 39 T/L, 46 B/R, 60 T, 64 T, 73 C/R, 86/87, 102 B/R,
103 B/R, 106/107, 116 R, 125 T, 192 T, 195 T. TRH Pictures/US
Army 40 T/L, 42 L, 44/45, 125 T, 140, 150, 155 T/L, 155 B, 172
B, 194. TRH Pictures/Y Debay 122 T, 145 C/R, 164 T, 178 T/L.

CONTENTS

FOREWORD

by

General Sir John Hackett,

GCB; (KCB; CB); CBE; (MBE); DSO and BAR; MC; DL; FRSL

FEW would see in the title of this book any claim that in man's unceasing conflicts with other men, and the effort to bring into use more and more effective weapons of war, we have now reached finality, or even that it is in sight. Already we are at a stage where the wholly unrestrained use of the weapons now available could result in the virtual extinction of all human life upon this planet, but development of weapon systems and the research upon which it is based goes on. The search for greater effectiveness, accuracy, mobility, lethality and destructive power in offensive weapon systems persists in growing intensity. Even marginal improvements can be of high value and are eagerly sought after. In defence, whether of whole systems or parts of systems, or of objectives vital to an enemy, complete invulnerability lies like a will-o-the wisp beyond the horizon. We reduce vulnerability in any way we can. We do it, if possible, by evasion of attack, by protection against attack if it comes, by reactive response, preferably leaving the attacker worse off than before his attempt, by deception, by the use of obscurity and night vision, by the use of stealth techniques for the reduction, or complete elimination, if that were possible, of tell-tale invitations to attack. We use any means available, longing for the unattainable, the complete invisibility imagined only as in the gift of Wagner's *Tarnhelm*. We improve our communications, our information handling capability, our engineering and logistical technology and anything that can help towards the ultimate goal in battle - the unchallenged presence of an infantry soldier, armed only with a handheld weapon, upon a vital piece of real estate.

What this book offers, in the restless, endless search for the ultimate, is a valuable review of the present state of the art and a glimpse of some of the directions in which our search may now be moving. The contributors are not senior officers. The book does not emanate from the Royal Military College of Science at Shrivenham, where the technical training of officers in the Army, and a considerable part of the RAF, at University level, is now concentrated. This book has been put together by operators at the working level, men whose business is not so much to design and develop weapon systems as to make the very best use of what is put into their hands, while teaching others to do the same, and offering at the same time invaluable user comment on what they see developing.

It is a book which comes out of the Sandhurst stable, where the emphasis is less on the higher technology of war than on warlike practice in the field at lower working levels of command. It need hardly be stressed that in warfare it is at the lower levels of command that decision has to be sought. Without success in squadrons, batteries and companies, failure overall is quite inevitable. A survey of the state of the game as seen by highly experienced eyes at this level, deliberately avoiding authoritative input from above, must therefore be of great value, both to the battlefield practitioner and to the non-military observer who wants to know what, in this complex, costly and quickly changing scene, it is all about.

Men have been fighting other men from time immemorial, first with hand and foot and head in close physical contact and with such help as could be found in sticks and stones, and then with more effective tools. What Homer called the "pitiless bronze and grey iron" came into use. Flung spears and missiles from bow and sling were followed by armour and the use of animals. Gunpowder, steam, internal combustion, heavier-than-air flight, rations now canned and no longer on the hoof, electrics and electronics, automatic weapons - these are only some of the many inovations which have totally changed the whole aspect of warfare over only a very few centuries. Nuclear fissions and fusion brought in to war a radical change in kind, and with the development of chemical and biological weapons the ultimate in weaponry may be thought to have already been reached. Conflict will not cease however, and, although self-preservation may dictate avoidance of the ultimate, improvement in warlike techniques will continue to be sought. This book tells us, from the users point of view, where we have got to and where we seem to be going.

Very many topics offer themselves for enquiry and comment. Is the tank dead? What of air power and the land battle? Is the helicopter now the queen? Are we moving towards an empty battlefield, reshaped by the engineer, in which systems fight systems with minimal human involvement? What of artillery, and new systems replacing the antiquated practice of throwing at the chosen target containers packed with high exlosives? When do we see the railgun, and particle beam weaponry? The questions are legion and high among them is the future of command and control in a world increasingly dominated by automatic processes. One thing has to be remembered. Automatic data processing has reduced the area within which an intuitive human decision alone is valid. It cannot eliminate it. In the war of systems against systems, which increasingly becomes the pattern of warfare in our time, we must beware of the mortal danger lurking in the automatic response. Man must remain the final arbiter and at all costs resist becoming the powerless slave of his own ingenuity.

It is all the more important to survey current trends and progress in weapons technology because of the vast range of possibilities now opening up. These are far greater than can be exploited with the funds now available, or likely to become so, in any part of the world. This is, at least in part, the result of the feverish efforts of the Soviet Union to match the military strength of the USA and the huge impetus thus lent everywhere to military research and development. The historian is likely to see here a main cause of the disintegration of the USSR. Elsewhere an important result has been embarrassment in the determination of procurement priorities. They will tell you at the Royal Military College of Science of ten or twenty highly promising developments all now on the back burner for lack of funding. The Strategic Defence Initiative is very far from being the only sufferer here. The growing imperative of hard choices in procurement policy emphasizes the importance of well informed opinion at the level of the user about what is on offer, among growing numbers of options, all at soaring cost.

The appearance of this provocative book is most timely. It will lead the enquiring reader, military or civilian, to the asking of some awkward and important questions.

INTRODUCTION

In the two decades since 1970 there has been a quiet and largely unnoticed revolution in the technological resources that soldiers – from generals right down to the poor bloody infantry – have on hand for fighting their battles. This is a revolution that makes the Americans' vaunted high-technology helicopter army of the Vietnam years look distinctly obsolescent – and even perhaps entirely obsolete.

Below: Fist of steel in an iron glove. A British armoured brigade on exercise on the North German plain

Since the Americans withdrew from Vietnam, a huge number of 'emerging technology' (ET) weapons have been invented. Several have already been deployed, and almost all have been at least partially tested. The likely performance of each individual weapon is therefore reasonably well known. But we do not yet know exactly how all this sophisticated new equipment will hang together and interact in a real high-technology conflict. We do not know how they may be countered in real combat, or which of them will be the true war winners and which will turn out to be white elephants.

For example: will modern 'instant' air-scattered minefields be more or less effective against the latest main battle tanks (MBTs) and their mine counter-measures than were the laboriously hand-laid mines of 1941-5 against the very different tanks of half a century ago? Will battlefield lasers eventually turn out to be most important as direct fire weapons, as target designators, as secure communication links, or as blinding agents – and what precautions may practically be taken against them? Will the optimum combat aircraft of the future be manned or unmanned, sophisticated (but few) or 'cheap 'n' cheerful' (but plentiful) – and how easily will they defeat the air defence array they are likely to encounter? Will the anti-tank gun of the future rely on kinetic energy (KE), as in the past, or on plasma beams and other assorted possible new death rays?

But perhaps the major question is whether or not tactical radio communications will be possible at all in the face of massive professional jamming. If they ultimately turn out not to be, then almost the whole theoretical basis of modern tactics will be swept away at a stroke. The development of an entire generation of 'state-of-the-art' weaponry will suddenly be seen to have been a hideous blind alley – an anachronism far more gigantic and damaging, in its way, than was the widespread training of infantry to form squares against cavalry in the 1920s, not to mention the building of the Maginot Line.

As the world's armies enter the 1990s, they are facing a profound technical military conundrum. Truth to tell, they cannot properly visualise what a future high-technology conventional battlefield will look like, any more than the armies of July 1914 could imagine the battlefield over which they were to fight for the next four years. Whether or not they

Above: A sign of the times? The heads of the US and Soviet armed forces, Admiral Crowe (left) and Marshal of the Soviet Union Akhromeyev

CONVENTIONAL FORCES IN EUROPE

East-West negotiations for mutual and balanced force reductions (MBFR, or MFR for those who do not believe in the concept of 'balance') were held in Vienna between 1973 and 1989 without coming to any firm conclusion. In 1989, however, new talks began that turned out to be much more positive. Also held in Vienna, they concerned reductions in conventional forces in Europe (CFE).

In late 1988 President Gorbachev announced some unilateral cuts in Soviet forces, then, in the course of 1989, specific ceilings were agreed. Still, at the beginning of 1991, the Warsaw Pact had the capacity to put something like 30,000 tanks into what was West

Germany within a month, out of a total of around 51,000 tanks stationed west of the Urals. Western diplomats hope that a CFE agreement will see the number of Warsaw Pact tanks reduced to 20,000 west of the Urals, with NATO retaining up to the same number in Western Europe. Since NATO has around 17,000 tanks, of which perhaps 10,000 would be available for Germany, this would lead to a position not far from parity.

The current proposals also provide for each side to have 28,000 armoured troop carriers, 500 air defence interceptor aircraft, 4700 combat aircraft and 3800 attack helicopters. The Eastern bloc refuses to count its numerous

defensive fighters in the equation, and so would retain numerical superiority in the air. Quite apart from this negotiation, the advent of a unified Germany means that we may see a demilitarized buffer zone at the heart of Europe. This has been suggested by some CFE negotiators, although at the time of writing the military status and alignment of the re-united Germany remains unclear. Nevertheless, should the storm clouds return and Germany become a battleground, even under CFE there would still be very large forces available to fight a war there. After all, Hitler was able to defeat France in his 1940 *blitzkrieg* using a total of just 3000 tanks.

Above: The beginning of the end of the Cold War. Former US President Ronald Reagan (left) greets Soviet leader Mikhail Gorbachev in December, 1987. Almost three years later the Treaty of Paris formally ended 40 years of impasse

consciously know it, therefore, the world's more advanced armies may well be teetering on the brink of a technological abyss very similar to the one into which their counterparts fell on the outbreak of World War I. With the new technologies must come changes in training and tactics as the soldiers struggle to stay abreast of the most advanced military practice.

Modern war: more of the same, or something completely different?

But if weapons, tactics and training are in a state of flux, what of the basic plan, or 'doctrine', that an army embraces to fight its wars? It has generally been believed that the only way in which a war can ultimately be won is through mounting a successful offensive. No matter how effective one's defensive battle may be, it cannot on its own 'bring the war to the enemy', or completely destroy him, unless it is supplemented by some sort of attacking move. Therefore, efficiency in the assault has been seen

as the touchstone of military competence, and it has often been claimed that truly high military morale can be achieved only in the offensive, especially when the attacking army enjoys surprise and has wrested the initiative away from the enemy.

The problem, however, is that reckless assaults tend to result in more casualties than do careful tactical defensives, thereby rather quickly demoralising the attacker and giving correspondingly high reassurance to the defence. Thus it is not good enough just to recommend the offensive on every occasion – as the French came close to doing in 1914, and as, in recent times, both the Soviets and the Israelis have sometimes seemed wont to do. In the October War of 1973, the Israeli tactic of having tanks forge ahead and leaving the infantry behind led to problems in Port Suez, for example. When the Israeli armoured spearhead arrived there, what infantry there was with it dismounted too late from its carriers. In the maze of streets, Egyptian anti-tank teams took a heavy toll of both tanks and infantry as a result.

11

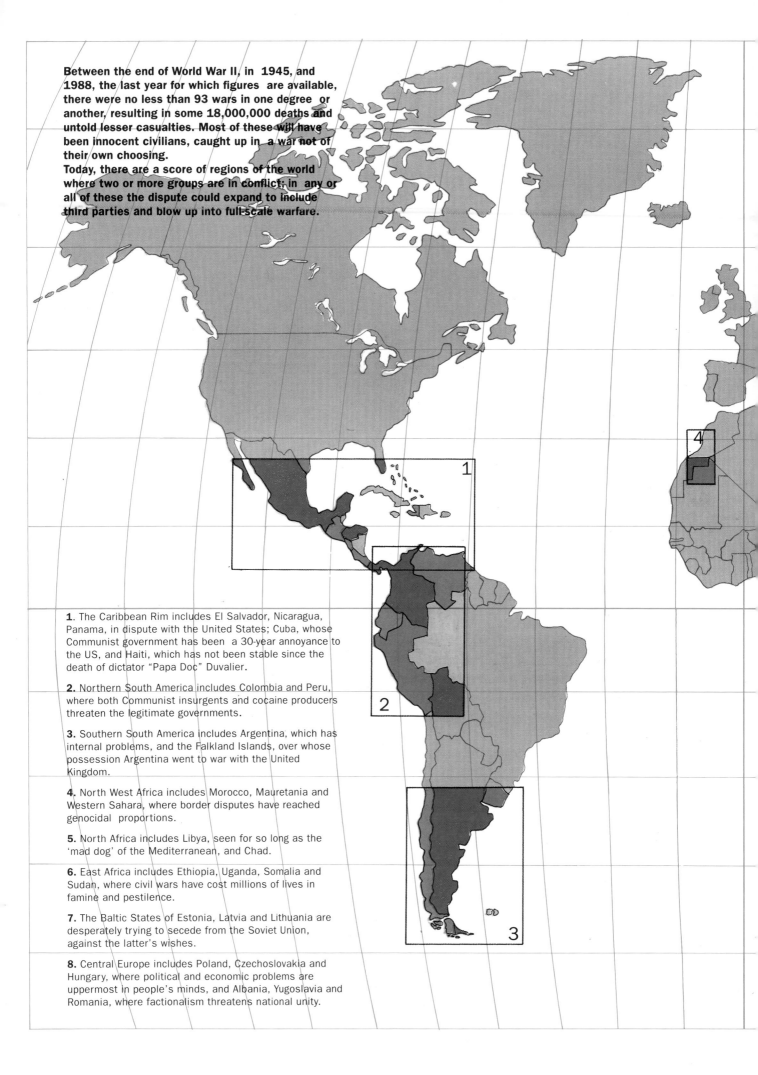

Between the end of World War II, in 1945, and 1988, the last year for which figures are available, there were no less than 93 wars in one degree or another, resulting in some 18,000,000 deaths and untold lesser casualties. Most of these will have been innocent civilians, caught up in a war not of their own choosing.

Today, there are a score of regions of the world where two or more groups are in conflict: in any or all of these the dispute could expand to include third parties and blow up into full-scale warfare.

1. The Caribbean Rim includes El Salvador, Nicaragua, Panama, in dispute with the United States; Cuba, whose Communist government has been a 30-year annoyance to the US, and Haiti, which has not been stable since the death of dictator "Papa Doc" Duvalier.

2. Northern South America includes Colombia and Peru, where both Communist insurgents and cocaine producers threaten the legitimate governments.

3. Southern South America includes Argentina, which has internal problems, and the Falkland Islands, over whose possession Argentina went to war with the United Kingdom.

4. North West Africa includes Morocco, Mauretania and Western Sahara, where border disputes have reached genocidal proportions.

5. North Africa includes Libya, seen for so long as the 'mad dog' of the Mediterranean, and Chad.

6. East Africa includes Ethiopia, Uganda, Somalia and Sudan, where civil wars have cost millions of lives in famine and pestilence.

7. The Baltic States of Estonia, Latvia and Lithuania are desperately trying to secede from the Soviet Union, against the latter's wishes.

8. Central Europe includes Poland, Czechoslovakia and Hungary, where political and economic problems are uppermost in people's minds, and Albania, Yugoslavia and Romania, where factionalism threatens national unity.

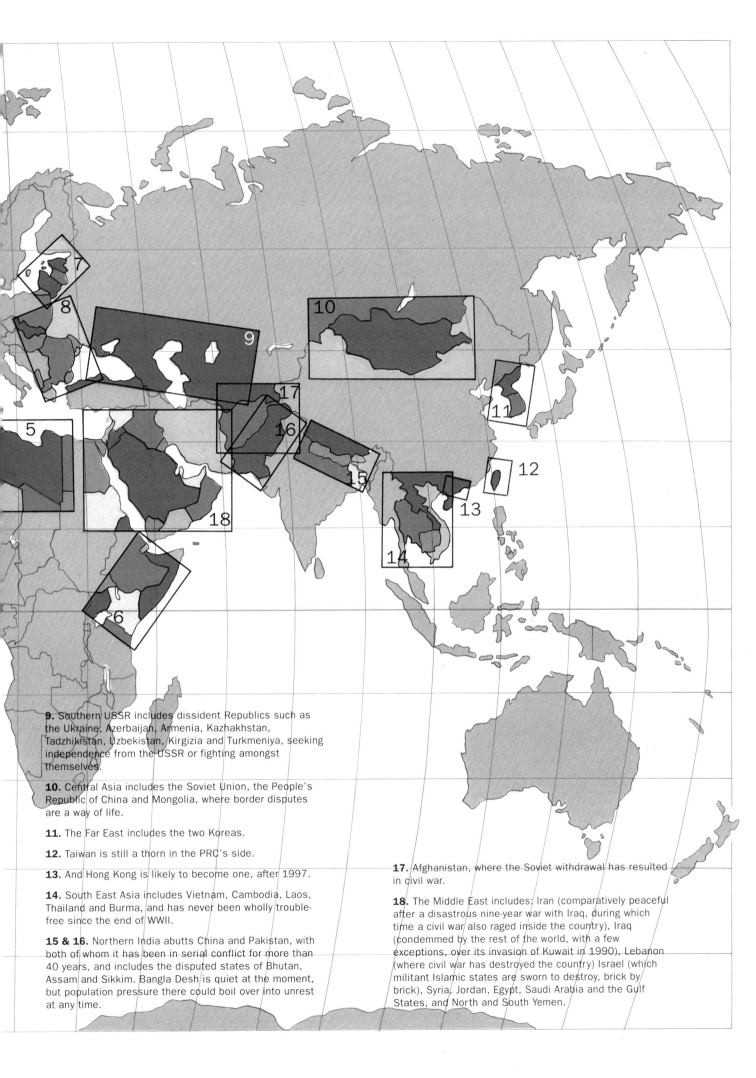

9. Southern USSR includes dissident Republics such as the Ukraine, Azerbaijan, Armenia, Kazhakhstan, Tadzhikistan, Uzbekistan, Kirgizia and Turkmeniya, seeking independence from the USSR or fighting amongst themselves.

10. Central Asia includes the Soviet Union, the People's Republic of China and Mongolia, where border disputes are a way of life.

11. The Far East includes the two Koreas.

12. Taiwan is still a thorn in the PRC's side.

13. And Hong Kong is likely to become one, after 1997.

14. South East Asia includes Vietnam, Cambodia, Laos, Thailand and Burma, and has never been wholly trouble-free since the end of WWII.

15 & 16. Northern India abutts China and Pakistan, with both of whom it has been in serial conflict for more than 40 years, and includes the disputed states of Bhutan, Assam and Sikkim. Bangla Desh is quiet at the moment, but population pressure there could boil over into unrest at any time.

17. Afghanistan, where the Soviet withdrawal has resulted in civil war.

18. The Middle East includes; Iran (comparatively peaceful after a disastrous nine-year war with Iraq, during which time a civil war also raged inside the country), Iraq (condemmed by the rest of the world, with a few exceptions, over its invasion of Kuwait in 1990), Lebanon (where civil war has destroyed the country) Israel (which militant Islamic states are sworn to destroy, brick by brick), Syria, Jordan, Egypt, Saudi Arabia and the Gulf States, and North and South Yemen.

Above: Trench warfare, 1988-style. Irani militiamen killed in an Iraqi offensive in prepared positions close to the disputed Shatt-al-Arab Waterway. Perhaps two million men, women and children died or were seriously injured in one of the longest and most bloody wars of the Twentieth Century

There must also be some stratagem for deceiving the enemy, and some means of limiting the risks to the offensive and of assuring its success by scientific all-arms tactics. In 1939-41, for example, General Heinz Guderian's doctrine for his Panzer divisions included both a belief in all-arms co-operation and – wherever possible – the aim of by-passing identified centres of opposition in order to take them from behind. Indeed, it may not even be too much to claim that the secret of his successful assaults lay mainly in his concept of avoiding enemy positions and pushing hard only through the points that had not yet been properly manned.

His idea followed the classic German belief in encircling the enemy through a strategic offensive, but then fighting a tactical defensive battle on favourable terms to prevent the enemy breaking out of the trap.

In the years since World War II there has certainly been plenty of emphasis on the attack; for example, in the concept that General William C. Westmoreland put into practice in Vietnam, of heliborne 'search and destroy' operations. Soviet offensive doctrine has also described how heavy spearheads, 'supercharged' by agile, flexible operational mobile groups (OMGs), would be helped forward by airborne and other deep penetration forces which unroll a 'carpet' along the road ahead.

Most recently of all, during the 1980s we have seen a re-alignment of Western military doctrine for Germany away from static defence and towards a fluid, offensive scheme of manoeuvre by armoured spearheads. The American Field Manual 100-5 of 1982 is the most important milestone in this development, as it envisages an 'extended' mobile battle by all-arms teams, using armour, helicopters, sophisticated surveillance, deep-attack missiles and air power. It all adds up to a fast-moving battle that is in many respects very similar to the Soviet idea of 'intermingled' combat by OMGs and other deep-striking forces.

If fighting an offensive battle is essential to

TRENCH WARFARE
The Recurrent Nightmare

The Western Front in World War I is seared into the popular mind as the epitome of fruitless, static, attritional warfare. Lines of trenches or strongpoints in depth, protected by barbed wire and covered by powerful artillery, resist every assault, with the attacker suffering devastating casualties. The battlefield is churned into an almost uncrossable landscape of craters and mud. Overloaded soldiers wallow helplessly around it, with no protection from random shelling or snipers. If a trench is captured it is soon recaptured and the line restored. Reinforcements can be fed in quickly to stop any breakthrough – but they cannot make progress through the beaten zone or 'no man's land'.

Unfortunately, this nightmare scenario was not rendered obsolete by the invention of the tank, but has recurred in many phases of wars since 1918 – for example: outside Madrid in 1936; at Cassino and Normandy on the Western Front in 1944, and at Leningrad and in many other places on the Eastern Front between 1941 and 1944; in the Korean War between 1950 and 1953; and, most recently, in the Iran-Iraq War of 1980-88. Admittedly the tank can help an attack to make progress, and in some circumstances it *can* be a decisive weapon that creates a breakthrough – but it has often been as vulnerable to anti-tank guns as the infantry has been to machine guns. The tank's greatest successes have been achieved against defences that have not been well dug in or co-ordinated.

Above: A platoon of British infantrymen in reserve near Ginchy, on September 25, 1916. Trench warfare on the Western Front was a nightmare – the conditions in this picture are not really representative. One million, two hundred thousand men are estimated to have perished, or been seriously wounded, on the Somme alone, between July and mid-November, 1916

victory, a successful defensive strategy is fundamental to survival. Fortunately defence tends to be easier than attack, since it usually needs less organisation, less movement, fewer communications channels and smaller numbers. Moreover, a defending army is usually on familiar ground, where it has been able to take advantage of any natural protection that the terrain can offer.

The main problem for a defending force, perhaps, is to know just how static or mobile it should be. History is full of entirely static defence lines that have been defeated or bypassed relatively easily – the Maginot Line in 1940 and the Bar Lev Line in 1973 spring to mind – although some equally immobile fortresses have on occasion given an attacker a very tough time. In 1916 the Germans had to fight long and hard to reduce Fort Vaux at Verdun, while in South Vietnam in 1967 the Americans found the tunnels of Cu Chi – a different style of fortification – especially troublesome.

WWI battlefields were dominated by barbed wire and machine guns

It is almost axiomatic that a defensive position should incorporate at least some mobile elements to reinforce threatened points; to make counter-penetrations (that is, to block holes that may develop); to make counter-attacks (in other words, to carry out a direct strike on the attacking enemy) or to implement counter-strokes (that is, to manoeuvre to take him in the rear). The classic German defensive doctrines that emerged in the middle of World War I stipulated a dense belt (or 'archipelago') of defensive strongpoints, perhaps 10km in depth, each of which would include a mobile force to react in one or other of the ways mentioned above. The enemy would be not so much 'beaten off' by a front line, as 'enmeshed and smothered' inside an all-enveloping hostile area.

In the battle of Kursk, July 1943, the Russians first halted the German assaults within a very similar 'web' of infantry and anti-tank strongpoints, laid out sometimes more than 100Km in depth and supported by obstacles and minefields. The defending forces ground the attackers down by the depth and complexity of the defences, then mounted a major counter-attack with large, fresh, armoured forces that pushed the Germans far back behind their original start-line. It is this concept which is still at the root of their ideas of 'defensive defence' in the era of *perestroika*.

From 1943 onwards the Germans lacked the resources necessary to lay out defences on the same scale as the Russian positions at Kursk; nor could they launch similarly decisive counter-moves. Nevertheless they did perfect an economical system of mobile defence, under which the front line was relatively fragile but there were concentrated armoured forces manoeuvring behind. The enemy would be lured forward and then struck hard by this armour after the initial impetus of the attack had been lost. In this way generals such as Erich von Manstein made the Soviets pay dearly for their tactical advances, even though the outnumbered Germans could never hope to restore their front line entirely once it had been breached. Just as Russian defensive tactics today are inspired by the Kursk model, von Manstein's 'fire brigade' concept of mobile defence has been carefully studied by many of the NATO armies as a model for their own defensives.

'Doctrine' may be expressed as the ideas and expectations with which soldiers are trained to enter battle and then fight through it, and it should not be underestimated as an element of battle. If troops have poor doctrine and training, even their best weapons will be defeated, but with sound doctrine even badly equipped soldiers may achieve great overall results.

Beyond the doctrines of the offensive and the defensive, success in battle depends on the technical tactical balance between the two sides in that battle. Wars tend to bog down when conditions are such that an initially favourable attack is unable to finish off the enemy with a single blow. Often this is a matter of general strategy: for example, when too weak

SYMBOL	BRITISH NAME	US NAME	SIZE (INFANTRY)
•	Section, detachment	Squad	6-14 men
• •	Section	Section	12-20 men
• • •	Platoon/troop	Platoon	25-40 men 3-4 sections/squads
I	Company/squadron/ battery	Company/troop/ battery	100-200 men 3 platoons
II	Battalion/regiment	Battalion/squadron	500-800 men 3-4 'combat' coys
III	–	Regiment	1500-5000 men 3-4 'combat' btns.
X	Brigade	Brigade	1500-5000 men 3-5 'combat' btns.
X X	Division	Division	7000-25,000 men 2-4 bdes/regts
X X X	Corps	Corps	20,000-150,000 men 1-5 divisions

COLOURS: BLUE – Friendly units, installations and activities
RED – Enemy units, installations and activities (regardless of
political persuasion)
GREEN – Friendly or enemy demolitions, minefields, obstacles
and fortifications
YELLOW – Nuclear, biological and chemical weapons information

1/15
INF (+)

LOCATION & HQs
This II symbol above the size symbol indicates an
all-arms grouping under the command of the HQ or
the unit shown.

DESIGNATION
1/15 inf – Unit designations can be placed to the
right of the symbol (in this case, 1st
Battalion 15th Infantry Regiment)

ATTACHMENTS AND DETACHMENTS
(+) – A unit is substantially reinforced
(–) – A substantial part of the unit is detached
Both these symbols are placed to the right of the main symbol

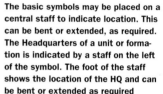

LOCATION & HQs
The basic symbols may be placed on a
central staff to indicate location. This
can be bent or extended, as required.
The Headquarters of a unit or formation is indicated by a staff on the left
of the symbol. The foot of the staff
shows the location of the HQ and can
be bent or extended as required

ARM OF SERVICE SYMBOLS

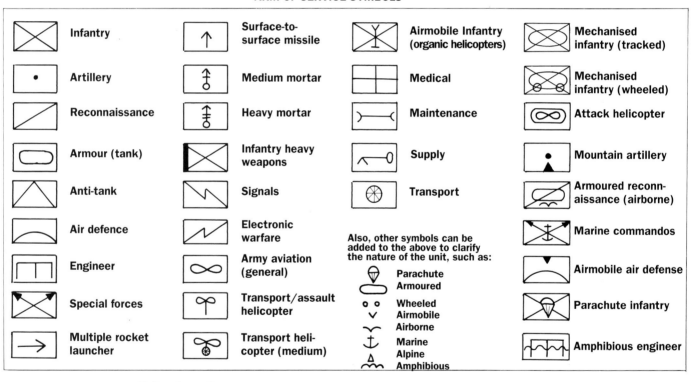

Infantry

Surface-to-surface missile

Airmobile Infantry (organic helicopters)

Mechanised infantry (tracked)

Artillery

Medium mortar

Medical

Mechanised infantry (wheeled)

Reconnaissance

Heavy mortar

Maintenance

Attack helicopter

Armour (tank)

Infantry heavy weapons

Supply

Mountain artillery

Anti-tank

Signals

Transport

Armoured reconn-aissance (airborne)

Air defence

Electronic warfare

Also, other symbols can be added to the above to clarify the nature of the unit, such as:

Marine commandos

Engineer

Army aviation (general)

Parachute
Armoured
Wheeled
Airmobile
Airborne
Marine
Alpine
Amphibious

Airmobile air defense

Special forces

Transport/assault helicopter

Parachute infantry

Multiple rocket launcher

Transport heli-copter (medium)

Amphibious engineer

Unit or formation
boundary (in this
case a division)

Unit or formation
in defensive posi-
tion (in this case,
a mechanised
infantry battalion)

Screen line

Forward edge of the
battle area (behind
which the main defen-
sive battle is fought)

Observation post

o   Anti-tank mine
8   Anti-personnel mine
¤   Booby-trapped anti-tank mine
    Minefield (boundaries drawn
    to scale). In this case, mixed
    anti-tank and anti-personnel
    Weapon slit, foxhole or
    emplacement

 Trench system

Dugout
Pillbox or casemate
Strongpoint

Anti-tank ditch
Anti-tank ditch (covered)

Anti-tank wall or bank
Proposed demolition (eg:
road block, crater, blown
bridge)
Prepared, but passable,
demolition

Completed demolition

NOTE: For all symbols (including units)
a broken outline represents future or
intended locations or activities

a force is deployed to attack too large an enemy. In other cases, however, the failure to win a decisive result will have more to do with the technical tactical balance than with the numerical or strategic one. In both World War I and the more recent Iran-Iraq War, the fighting bogged down because the tactical attacker was unable to sustain his momentum and mobility through the whole depth of the enemy's defences. His forces were too vulnerable when they moved, so they had to dig in and stay put.

The tactical balance between two sides is decided by the relationship of four characteristics: firepower, mobility, protection and the quality of the troops that each side has deployed. If firepower is heavy against poor troops with low mobility and protection, they will be unable to advance, whereas shaky or badly deployed defenders with low firepower will be unable to stop a rapid armoured advance by well-trained soldiers.

An army's ability to fight and win is conditioned by its training

What this in fact says is that victory will go to the side that can make the most intelligent combination of the three arms – infantry, artillery and cavalry (which today includes armoured and air mobile forces). So in circumstances where an unsupported infantry assault is suicidal, success may be achieved if the foot soldiers can be accompanied by tanks and can follow a rolling artillery barrage. Of course in reality matters tend to be more complicated because there are really many more than three arms: for example, engineer preparation of the battlefield is very important, as are the logistic and command and control systems that allow the armies to fight at all. Furthermore, throughout the

Twentieth Century's wars, air power, in all its many forms, has exerted a decisive influence on the tactical results of battle.

As if the tactical and technological mysteries of the future battlefield were not already quite enough to bear, the world's armies must today confront all the uncertainties generated by the huge changes now taking place in the political alignments of Eastern Europe and the world. In his 1978 book, *The Third World War*, General Sir John Hackett drew up a scenario for a battle to take place between NATO and the Warsaw Pact in 1985 that included vast masses of tanks being hurled from East into West Germany. Although his timescale has thankfully proved to be inaccurate by more than six years (and now seems unlikely to pertain), his scenario at least struck a familiar chord in the minds of most commentators, and was also generally agreed to be 'realistic' within the structure of the Cold War. Today, however, only a few years later, the Cold War is over and the old certainties can no longer be sustained.

The Soviet empire is crumbling and the iron curtain that divided Germany has been torn down. East European dictators have been shot, and non-communist parties have made their voices heard in countries that until very recently appeared to contain absolutely no potential for change. Even in South Africa the apartheid regime appears to be in crisis, while for the USA the 50-year habit of massive troop deployment to Europe has been broken. The question in people's minds is no longer 'How long will it be before nuclear war destroys us all?', but 'Where and how will the next war be fought?'

In Europe the two massive armed camps left over from the late 1940s may now wither away altogether. If there is to be a war in Europe at all, it

The British Army's much-vaunted ability to control the Empire with small detachments of troops was earned in equal measure by discipline and equipment. Trained soldiers, armed with breech loading rifles and primitive rapid-fire weapons, could easily defeat men used to more basic forms of weaponry.
Below: The Gatling Gun saw service with the British Army during the 2nd Afghan War (1878-80). It made massed attacks by insurrectionary tribesmen suicidal affairs, just as its successor, the Maxim gun, was to during the Sudanese War, 20 years later. There, Kitchener's troops killed more than ten thousand Mahdists for the loss of less than five hundred of their own.
That this same weapon of mass destruction could also act against them, as it would during World War I, seemed to escape the strategists

FIRE AND MANOEUVRE
Winning The Firefight

The basic principle of tactics is to combine fire and manoeuvre so that the troops first 'win the firefight' – that is, neutralise the enemy – and then go on to overrun the enemy's position. Traditionally the idea has been for the 'base of fire' to be provided by a static force that keeps the enemy's head down while a separate force manoeuvres to exploit a covered line of approach. But often the manoeuvring assault force may have to provide its own massed covering fire as it moves. In General Patton's World War II infantry tactics this was called 'marching fire', and more recently it has sometimes been called 'prophylac-

tic firepower'. It is especially useful in distracting the operators of wire-guided anti-tank weapons, who have to keep the crosshairs aligned on their target throughout the missile's flight.

Until very recently it was technically impossible for tanks themselves to fire on the move with any accuracy at all, and a stationary tank would always have a great advantage over a moving one. With today's technology, however, gyroscopically stabilised guns give a moving tank considerable accuracy potential. Artillery, on the other hand, cannot fire on the move, although it may well change position between fire missions ('shoot and

scoot'), to avoid counter-battery fire.

A variation on 'fire and manoeuvre' is the concept that has sometimes been called 'manoeuvre and fire'. This means that the infantry, rather than overpowering the enemy itself at close quarters, advances cautiously and goes to earth close to the enemy. Then it calls up artillery and support weapons not just to win the firefight, but to destroy the opposition utterly. This tactic is less risky for the assault troops, but may fail to eradicate the enemy unless the balance of firepower is massively in favour of the attack, thus bogging the artillery down in indecisive and expensive attrition.

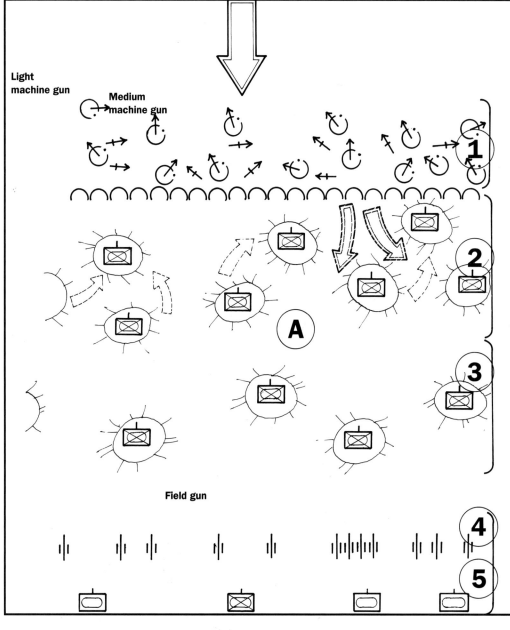

Light machine gun

Medium machine gun

Field gun

ARCHIPELAGO DEFENCE

This system of defence was developed by the German Army during World War I after the First Battle of the Somme in 1916. The linear defensive system used in that battle had caused the Germans to suffer many casualties from the heavy British shelling of the front-line trench. In archipelago defence, the forward defended localities (1) are manned by infantry of about section strength, to give early warning of an enemy attack. Machine-gun posts firing in enfilade (at the flank of the enemy advance) disrupt the enemy attack. Any enemy that penetrate the line of forward defended localities are then engaged by fire from the company strongpoints in the main defensive position (2). Should one of these strongpoints fall, then troops from another company position will launch a counter-attack to retake it (A). Similarly, a company position will launch a counter-attack against enemy between the strongpoints who have been weakened. The depth positions (3) provide a final line of defence in front of the artillery positions (4) and force the enemy to spread his attacking troops and artillery over a much larger area. Between and behind the artillery positions are the mobile counter-attack forces (5). These destroy any enemy units that break through to the artillery positions.

seems most likely to be between the disintegrating USSR and its constituent republics (as witness the peace-keeping operation in Azerbaijan); between the USSR and its centrifugal allies, or between these allies themselves with, for example, Hungary and Romania coming to blows over Transylvania or Romania and the Soviet Union fighting over the region of Moldavia – rather than between the Warsaw Pact and NATO. Moreover, the Romanian revolution vividly demonstrates that there is a potent risk of civil war lying dormant in many Eastern states, not excluding the Russian Federal Soviet Socialist Republic itself.

Small wars have often been used to head off internal unrest

Nevertheless, there is a need for caution. In Hackett's book the *casus belli* was precisely the sort of disintegration in Eastern Europe that we are witnessing today. In his book it was problems within the Soviet empire that made its leaders look for a successful external war, just as the difficulties within Galtieri's Argentina in 1982 made him seek to annex the Falkland Islands. The price of eventual peace may therefore be a period of tension in which every nation must remain on its guard.

If the political future is uncertain within Europe, it remains even less certain elsewhere in the world. In the 1980s we witnessed a number of wars – for example, the Falklands conflict (1982), the Israelis

Left: One of the faces of war. A British casualty – one of the lucky ones – makes his way from the Regimental Aid Post after receiving attention

Below left: Some of the kit and equipment an infantry soldier needs to do his job. A member of a support company, or a specialist of some kind, would be familiar with a much wider range

in Lebanon (1982), the Iran-Iraq War (1980-88), Afghanistan (1979 onwards) and the US invasion of Panama (1989) – in which high technology was deployed by at least one of the protagonists. We must therefore face the unpleasant fact that if such wars could take place during the era of superpower confrontation and the central balance that this provided, in all likelihood they will continue to occur now that the old central balance is breaking down.

Admittedly most of the wars of the 1980s have now largely been fought to a standstill, but there are still plenty of powder kegs waiting to explode in many parts of the world. These potential time-bombs include Korea, where the North may try to impose reunification on a very reluctant South, using military means; Hong Kong, where tension is rising as reunification with China approaches; Ethiopia, where the conflict continues between the Addis Ababa government and rebels in Eritrea, Tigre and the Ogaden; Sri Lanka, where ethnic unrest may lead to full-blown civil war; Kashmir, where the Muslim militant campaign for separation from India continues to cause friction between India

and Pakistan, and the Falklands themselves, where sovereignty is still a bone of contention between Britain and Argentina. Individually these problems (and there are many more worldwide) pose very serious questions in their own right, but if they are all taken together as symptoms of the global inequality between North and South (an inequality that has been especially accentuated by the financial movements of the 1980s), they may even be seen as portents of a more universal explosion.

The West will certainly have to stay alert to the many so-called 'brushfire wars' that will in all likelihood break out around the world – and in the absence of an over-arching global balance it may even be tempted to intervene more frequently than before. In this context the Christmas 1989 invasion of Panama may be seen as something of a model, insofar as the USA was encouraged to take action partly because the USSR was so spectacularly distracted by its own internal concerns in Europe.

Above: Indian Army gunners assist a truck in dragging a 25-pounder field gun up a mountainside in Kashmir during the 1965 Indo-Pakistan war. The 25-pounder entered service in 1940, but was still in service with the Indian Army 50 years later

Since there was no obvious counter-balance to the US military initiative, American decision-makers were doubtless more ready to go ahead with the use of force than they might otherwise have been.

The 'outbreak of peace' in Eastern Europe has certainly created, in the prediction of imminent hostilities elsewhere, a whole new industry. It is possible that current talk about potential 'brushfire wars' is merely a case of 'governments and armies in search of an enemy', or still more so of 'weapon manufacturers in search of a market'.

Yet even without this, most Western states will wish to 'keep their powder dry' by staying abreast of the new weapons technologies. No army can afford to sit back doing nothing while other armies are perfecting new and exotic super-weapons and preparing themselves for future conflict.

It has of course always been notoriously difficult to predict the shape of future battle. Lieutenant Colonel Sir George Chesney discovered this in 1871

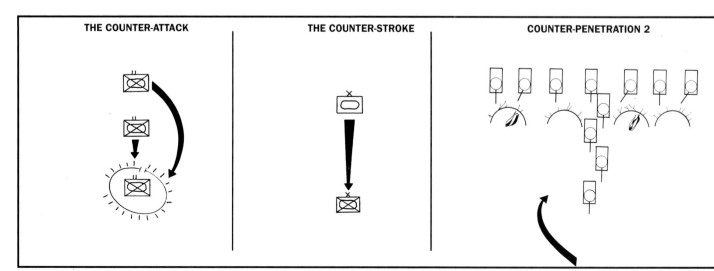

ORGANISATION
Fighting In Teams

Most modern armies are organised along similar lines, although there are local variations among nations and among the formal arrangements in peacetime and *ad hoc* groupings used for specific types of combat.

The basic infantry fighting unit is the platoon, which consists of around 30 to 40 men, commanded by a first or second lieutenant or senior NCO. Within each platoon there are three or four sections, or squads, that may be further divided into fireteams. Each section or squad is normally carried in a single armoured personnel carrier (APC), infantry fighting vehicle (IFV) or helicopter. In tank units a platoon may consist of between three and five vehicles. In the artillery it may be called a section, and consist of two guns with their supporting vehicles.

Three or four platoons, plus an HQ and administrative element, make a company, commanded by a captain or perhaps a major. In tank units it is called a squadron, and in the artillery a battery. Three or four companies – again with an HQ and admin element – make a battalion, commanded by a major or a lieutenant colonel. But, just to confuse matters, some battalion-strength units in the British army are called regiments.

Two or three battalions usually make a regiment, with an HQ element under a lieutenant colonel or full colonel, while two or more regiments make a brigade commanded by a brigadier or one-star general. However, in some armies a brigade may be composed just of three or more individual battalions, without an intervening regimental level of command.

Several brigades make a division, under a major general or two-star general. Several divisions make a corps, under a lieutenant general or three-star general (the Soviet army, however, calls a unit this size an army). Several corps make an army group (or 'front', in Soviet parlance), under a four-star general, while two or more army groups make a theatre under a field marshal or five-star general. A theatre is a TVD for the Soviets; NATO designates each one individually – for example Allied Forces Centre for the Central Front, which means most of western Germany. At divisional level and above there are usually large specialist formations held directly by the commander, outside the normal pyramid of battalions, brigades, and so on. Thus a Soviet combined arms army (a corps in Western parlance) might have several independent tank, helicopter, engineer, signals and artillery battalions on top of four motor rifle and two tank divisions.

In actual combat many armies use mixed groups of all arms right down to company level – where a combat team tailored for a specific task might consist of two platoons of infantry, one of tanks, and one of engineers. At one level higher, a battle group might have two tank squadrons, one infantry company and an engineer squadron, supported by an artillery battery. At the start of a war these groups can be created as an act of deliberate choice, but later on they will often result from the scraping together of whatever remains after complete units have been shattered in hard fighting.

The conventional signs used to represent units on tactical maps try to reflect the rank of the commander – e.g. a brigade, commanded by a one-star general, is signified by one cross at the top. A platoon gets three dots, to represent a sergeant's three stripes, and so on.

The icons designating the unit's type are less self-explanatory, although armour is indicated by a rhomboidal shape vaguely reminiscent of early tanks; engineers get a little bridge, and machine guns and anti-tank guns are roughly sketched in plan view.

In this book we are mainly concerned with the lower level of military action that is usually called 'tactics' – in other words, the way that relatively small units, at divisional level or lower, come into close combat with each other in individual battles.

The level of battle above tactics is called 'operations' (in Soviet terminology, 'operational art'). This includes the actions of corps and army groups, manoeuvring to set up a series of individual tactical battles to achieve a broader overall goal. This process will often mean that some battles will deliberately be conceded to the enemy – and one's own troops sacrificed – in the interests of achieving a higher advantage in other battles elsewhere.

Above operations comes 'theatre strategy' – the combination of all the operations within a given theatre. This in turn will reflect the general political strategy – the war aims – of the nation or alliance that is fighting the war. At this level strictly military considerations will often be secondary to political ones.

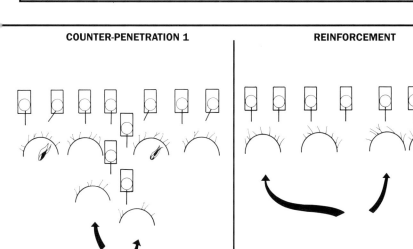

COUNTER-PENETRATION 1

REINFORCEMENT

REINFORCEMENT – Uncommitted elements take up defensive positions alongside those already, or just about to be, engaged.
COUNTER-PENETRATION 1 – Uncommitted elements take up defensive positions to block enemy forces penetrating the defence.
COUNTER-PENETRATION 2 – Uncommitted elements attack an enemy penetration.
THE COUNTER-STROKE – Launched by a brigade or large formation, against an enemy force that is moving or temporarily halted. It aims to destroy the enemy, rather than to capture ground. (Here, an armoured brigade attacks mechanised infantry.)
THE COUNTER-ATTACK – This is launched against an enemy that has stopped with the intention of holding ground. The aim is to recapture the ground. (Here, mechanised infantry battalions are engaged.)

Above: A technician of the 37th Tactical Fighter Wing, at George AFB, California, prepares an F4E Phantom's wing pylon to receive a Sparrow air-to-air missile

when he alarmed the British public with his detailed story of an imminent German invasion that was stopped only in 'The Battle of Dorking'. When the real next battle actually occurred, it did so more than 40 years later and at Mons in Belgium – nowhere near Dorking.

Predicting future weapons and tactics has been no easier and this was borne out during the 30 years before 1914. The problem was not that the generals were stupid or lacked insight, but simply that they were faced with too many new weapons and potential technical innovations for sensible judgments to be made. In fact the allegedly 'unimaginative' cavalry general Douglas Haig was actually a pioneer in military aviation and motor transport before the war, and would later be sympathetic to the claims of the tank corps. He found it difficult, however, to pick and choose between the many new technologies on offer.

For instance: would the Maxim gun, which had caused some 30,000 Dervish casualties at Omdurman in 1898, be capable of repeating the feat on the very different European battlefields? Surely not! But the armoured car, the motor bike and the tricycle-mounted light field-gun would surely maintain the fluidity and mobility of combat (as indeed their tracked descendants would do only too well in 1939-45). Would high explosive

(HE) shelling drive men mad and make battle all but impossible? Would dirigible airships be capable of seeking out artillery positions and bombing them into oblivion? When faced with such radical tactical imponderables, it is scarcely surprising that no-one fully realised just what the future might hold.

Nonetheless in 1931 S. Southwold's book *The Gas War of 1940* got somewhere close to the mark by fairly accurately predicting the time and place of the German tank-air *blitzkriegs* through Poland and France. But it quite wrongly assumed they would use poison gas on a massive scale. There is, incidentally, a probably apocryphal story that tells of one such doom-laden prediction driving a European family to escape from the impending bloodbath by emigrating to a remote Pacific island named Iwo Jima.

General Hackett was in good company when his scenarios for a third world war were overtaken by events. This seems to be the almost inevitable fate of all such 'future histories', and there will be no attempt to produce anything of that type in the present work. This book is a discussion of the types of weaponry that may be used in the next high-technology war, what they might be expected to achieve, and how they could affect the overall shape of the battlefield. As mentioned earlier, these weapons will not only be of the traditional variety; if and when the next war breaks out, the armouries of the modern armies may well bristle with 'emerging technology' (ET) super-weapons.

High-technology equipment, however, often suffers from the disease of 'gold plating' – that is, the designer wants to incorporate several new and desirable features into the new weapon. The result is that the complexity, difficulty and expense of designing the final version become so overwhelming that the basic original requirement is almost lost from view. And then during the work-up phase there will be teething troubles not just with one new technology but with several, and all at once.

In many cases, such as the American attempt to

Above: A Soviet Kresta II class guided missile ASW cruiser. Fitted with four SS-N-14 Silex anti-submarine missile launchers, along with a mass of other weapon systems, the Kresta IIs were the first Soviet ships to carry helicopters

VIETNAM
How Many Wars Was Vietnam ?

As the USA deployed major forces to Vietnam between 1965 and 1967, American politicians and military commanders were inspired by futuristic, space-age visions of how to fight the war. The problem, however, was that these visions often conflicted with each other and became rallying cries for opposing institutional lobbies. The US Army, for example, constantly had to defend its own air power – in the shape of helicopters and unarmed fixed-wing aircraft – against the US Air Force's claims that it could provide all the troop-lift and fire support that was needed. Hence the Army was tempted to make extravagant claims for its transport and gunship helicopters, and even set up an all-helicopter airborne cavalry division.

The Marine Corps, by contrast, did not have this problem, since it possessed its own integral air force of fast jets. It did not need helicopter gunships, simply because it could call up its own Phantoms. Nor did it believe in the small

Huey utility helicopter, preferring the much larger Sea Knights and Jolly Green Giants that were better adapted to operating from ships. The US Navy, meanwhile, feeling that it should take part in the war inland, built an advanced riverine flotilla – the 'brown water navy' – to transport troops and firepower around the Mekong delta.

The story did not end there. The Armor lobby wanted to move and fight on tracks, while the Engineer lobby wanted to solve battlefield problems by defoliation – using such unconventional weapons as the (mechanical) Transphibian Tactical Crusher or the (chemical) Agent Orange. Others wanted one-man personalised flying machines, while yet others looked to the hovercraft. Finally, and in some ways most portentous for the future, a whole new lobby emerged for electronic warfare. Its vision was to avoid moving around the battlefield entirely, wiring it up 'like a pin table' with electronic sensors that would activate artillery or air strikes.

produce an armoured divisional air defence system (DIVADS), or the British TSR-2 fighter-bomber, finding solutions to the technical problems involved become so expensive that the whole project has to be cancelled (in TSR-2's case this happened just as the problems were close to solution).

There are two alternatives to gold plating. The first is to follow Soviet practice and build slowly but carefully on existing designs that have already been

combat-proven. This approach shows clearly in the unbroken line of development from the World War II series of JS tanks through the T54/55, T62, T64, T72 right up to the latest T80s. The Red Army has thus had a plentiful supply of reasonably up-to-date tanks that were also reliable and cheap, and did not pursue technological dead-ends or follow utopian dreams.

The second alternative to gold plating is to be

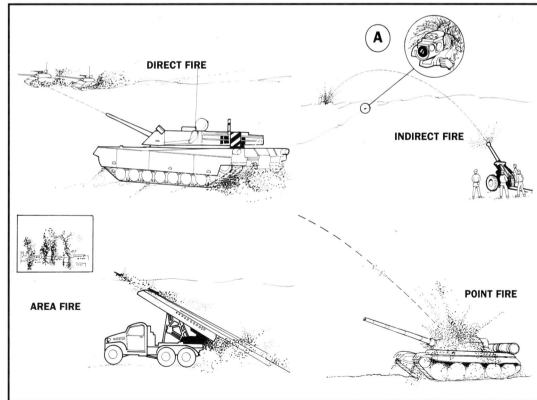

DIRECT FIRE

A

INDIRECT FIRE

AREA FIRE

POINT FIRE

TYPES OF FIRE

In DIRECT FIRE the firer can see the target, even if someone else (such as a tank commander) is helping to adjust his fire.

In INDIRECT FIRE the firer cannot see the target, and must either fire using information from the map, or rely on a forward observer, who can see the target (A), to adjust the fire for him.

AREA FIRE aims to achieve its objective by filling an area with sufficient lethal particles (eg: bullets or shrapnel) or damaging effects (eg: blast or chemicals) that the target is neutralised or destroyed. It does not rely on pin-pointing the target.

POINT FIRE fires a given projectile or missile at a specific target and can be either direct or indirect.

thoroughly adventurous with new technologies but to take them one at a time, fitting them to existing vehicles that may not be perfect but that do at least work to minimum standards. The Israelis are past masters of this art, bolting 1970s guns onto 1940s tank chassis, or clipping the latest American ET electronics into World War II half-tracks. This is the quickest and cheapest way to deploy the latest kit, and many observers have noted that the Israelis have often put brand new American hardware into the field many years before Uncle Sam himself has managed to do so.

The emerging technology that has so far made the biggest impact links advanced real-time target surveillance to long-range missiles that dispense terminally guided sub-munitions. Such a package lets an operator accurately and systematically track and engage moving enemy vehicles at ranges up to 100km, and possibly beyond. In the past, moving targets could only be attacked by using the line of sight from a direct-fire weapon such as an anti-tank gun, or by relying on the fleeting opportunities given to roaming fighter-bomber pilots. But with ET weapons in play, such engagements become much less dependent on chance and, in addition, the front line of battle will become far deeper than ever before.

The microchip allows even shells to make decisions

Supporting the full-blown deep-strike weapons that can hit moving targets at hitherto unthinkable ranges, there will be many lesser weapons that can each do a part of the same job. The range of conventional tube artillery will be increased and several types of guided anti-tank shell will be developed. Phases 1 and 2 of the multiple-launch rocket system (MLRS) are designed to fire various types of munition to varying ranges up to 30km; phase 3 of the system has a range of 70km and can also launch discriminating terminally guided warheads, which would be used against moving targets or radiation sources. At longer ranges, minefields or specialised anti-airfield munitions can be scattered on static positions from aircraft or from larger missiles – for example, the joint tactical missile system (JTACMS) or the long-range stand-off missile (LRSOM). Another possibility is that the advanced real-time surveillance systems – including 'super drones' or remotely-piloted vehicles (RPVs) as pioneered by Israel in the Lebanon in 1982 – may be used independently of deep-strike weapons, simply to help a commander 'read the battle' as he would have done in the past from a helicopter or light spotter aircraft.

Beyond all this, there are several new weapons coming forward which call on quite different physical principles from those used in 'traditional' computers, cannons, rockets, or chemical-energy, shaped-charge warheads. Weather warfare has already been used in American cloud-seeding operations in Indochina, and there have even been rumours that the USSR has been able to provoke earthquakes. At a more tactical level, the magnetic-

rail gun promises to fire small hypervelocity kinetic energy (KE) bolts, capable of penetrating any conceivable armour – and to fire them at a terrific rate. (Kinetic energy weapons are those firing solid, tangible projectiles. With the advent of DEW, see below, it has become necessary to define the term. It never was, before.)

Death rays are a practical proposition, if we can find the power

Even more futuristic is the family of directed-energy weapons (DEW) based on lasers, high powered microwaves, or subatomic particle beams travelling at the speed of light. These 'death rays' would dispose of the need to take account of the target's movement and make even worrying about the effectiveness of its armour protection a thing of the past. Nor would these weapons require a logistic tail to keep them supplied with ammunition, since each 'round' would consist merely of the energy itself. The firing vehicle or emplacement could thus be largely self-sufficient, provided of course that it could generate the levels of power these weapons require.

The Americans seem to enjoy a clear lead in the development of ET weapons, some of which are spin-offs from the still more ambitious strategic

Above: The most advanced helicopter yet, the AH-64 Apache, is just as capable at night as it is by day. The bulge on the nose is a multi-sensor navigation and weapons system

WAR OR PEACE
How Likely Is War Between The Superpowers ?

It can be argued that a major world conflict is now more likely than ever. The reasons why:

• The USSR is in the midst of an internal crisis, which may degenerate into an internal war that drags outsiders in on one side or the other

• The USSR's leadership may try to avert or defuse an internal crisis by starting an *external* war. This might begin, and be intended, as a minor affair that degenerates into a much wider conflict

• Tensions between individual members of the Eastern bloc may turn into a shooting war that brings the USSR in on one side and Western nations in on the other

• Conflicts of interest in the Middle East remain unresolved, and the area remains a potential flashpoint for political confrontation between the superpowers that could lead to a shooting war. Another war between individual states or groups of states in the region could also draw in nations from outside

• The revolution in weaponry that emerging technology has brought about is in itself a destabilising factor. The first nation in an unstable area, such as the Middle East or SE Asia, to field an effective 'superweapon' may be tempted to use it before the opposition can either match it or develop effective counter-measures

• Emerging-technology weapons encourage aggression because they give an attacker huge advantages in surprise, mobility, and the ability to suppress a defender

• The more the military refine their doctrines, the easier it seems to predict the outcome of a particular strategy. If these calculations imply an easy victory, there will be a temptation for an aggressor to make a pre-emptive strike

It can also be argued that war is *less* likely than ever. The reasons for this view:

• NATO and the Warsaw Pact are dissolving as opposed military alliances. If this trend reaches its logical conclusion – so that NATO loses the integration of its members' armed forces and the American presence in Europe is drastically reduced, while the USSR withdraws its troops within its own borders – a major European war will be less easily triggered

• Potential flashpoints will be less likely to inspire a global war if the USA and the USSR continue to find ways to work together

• The current revolution in weaponry actually makes the battlefield *less* predictable, and thus more dangerous to a would-be aggressor.

• The current revolution in weaponry favours a defender, since it vastly increases the capacity for surveillance to give warning against surprise attack, and for reducing an enemy's ability to move, either through firepower or by creating impassable obstacles

• An armed force that improves performance by developing and applying a military doctrine at all levels may become more efficient, but it may be difficult to persuade politicians that these improvements can increase the chance of victory as effectively as new hardware

Below: The US Airforce's ALL – Airborne Laser Laboratory. This KC-135 is equipped with a high-energy laser and a target acquisition system that enables it to destroy Sidewinder missiles in flight

defense initiative (SDI) space defence programme, otherwise known as 'Star Wars'. There is plentiful evidence that this has worried Soviet planners to the point where they have recently been forced to re-think their whole military doctrine. Indeed, according to one school of thought the Red Army has accepted Gorbachev's plans for conventional disarmament only because greatly increased research and development of ET weapons, sufficient to match Western advances in this field, has been promised. It could be argued that such a theory exposes *perestroika* as merely a blind to cover an increased programme of qualitative hyper-rearmament. There are rumours that the USSR is not nearly as far behind the USA in this sphere as is often suggested, and that it has, for example, already experimented with radiation weapons in the Sino-Vietnamese proxy war of 1979.

Whatever truth there may or may not be in the 'military technological conspiracy' theory of *perestroika*, it is clear that a wide range of ET weapons will gradually be introduced into the armouries of the more advanced nations during the next 10 or 20 years. Intensified efforts will also be made to find antidotes – which may well turn out to be easily and cheaply available. It may even be the case that the present 'revolution' in tactics is no more than an expensive *cul de sac* that leads to an essentially unchanged balance between attack and defence on the future battlefield. But we should by no means discount the possibility that at least one (and it need be no more than one) of the new technologies will turn out to be entirely decisive – the little bit of grit in the works that throws the whole machine hopelessly off balance, and into catastrophe.

ALL OVER BY CHRISTMAS

In World War I, it was sometimes said that officers of the rank of Major and upwards were effectively 'non combatants', since they ran the battle from protected shelters set back behind the front line, leaving the everyday leadership of the men in the trenches to Captains and Lieutenants. In future warfare, we can expect this trend to continue still further, with the vital combat decisions made still further down the chain of command.

Below: A platoon from 2nd Battalion, the Light Infantry, supported by a Chieftain tank, moves up for the attack during an exercise on Salisbury Plain

HELIBORNE ASSAULT

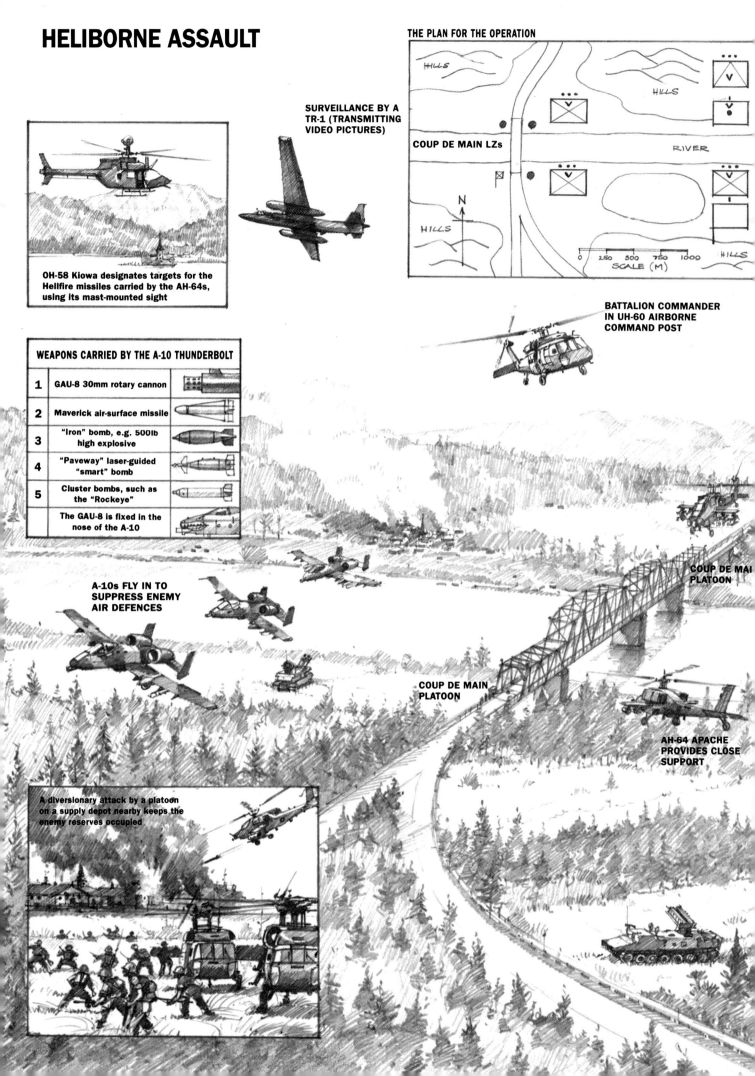

OH-58 Kiowa designates targets for the Hellfire missiles carried by the AH-64s, using its mast-mounted sight

SURVEILLANCE BY A TR-1 (TRANSMITTING VIDEO PICTURES)

THE PLAN FOR THE OPERATION

HILLS
HILLS
HILLS

COUP DE MAIN LZs

RIVER

N

HILLS

HILLS

SCALE (M)
0 250 500 750 1000

BATTALION COMMANDER IN UH-60 AIRBORNE COMMAND POST

	WEAPONS CARRIED BY THE A-10 THUNDERBOLT	
1	GAU-8 30mm rotary cannon	
2	Maverick air-surface missile	
3	"Iron" bomb, e.g. 500lb high explosive	
4	"Paveway" laser-guided "smart" bomb	
5	Cluster bombs, such as the "Rockeye"	
	The GAU-8 is fixed in the nose of the A-10	

A-10s FLY IN TO SUPPRESS ENEMY AIR DEFENCES

COUP DE MAI PLATOON

COUP DE MAIN PLATOON

AH-64 APACHE PROVIDES CLOSE SUPPORT

A diversionary attack by a platoon on a supply depot nearby keeps the enemy reserves occupied

OH-58 and AH-64
THE ANTI-ARMOUR
TEAM

LASER BEAM

HELLFIRE MISSILE

ENEMY TANK

1. Rises above trees to fire missile
2. Drops back down after firing
3. Moves to new fire position
OH-58 spots target and designates it
with laser designator

The 2nd lift, with
artillery, vehicles and
casevac choppers,
comes in 10 minutes after
the initial assault

ESCORTING
AH-64 APACHE

Artillery, aircraft and helicopters 'sanitize' a
corridor to the objective

ASSAULT TROOPS IN
UH-60 BLACKHAWK

Forty minutes before the attack, the assault helicopters
pick up the infantry from a secure hide deep behind
the friendly FEBA (Forward Edge of the Battle Area)

ASSAULT TROOPS IN
UH-60 BLACKHAWK

ESCORTING AH-64 APACHE

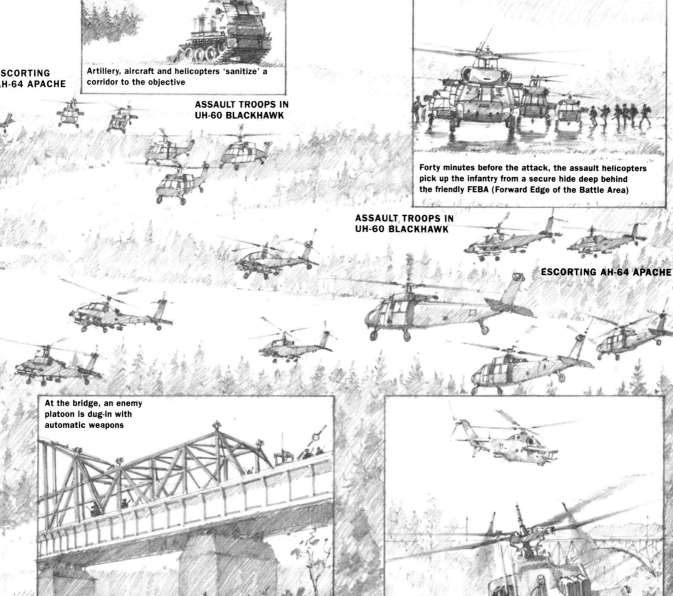

At the bridge, an enemy
platoon is dug-in with
automatic weapons

Escort AH-64 Apache
helicopters engage any
enemy helicopters which
try to intercept the assault force

The responsibility resting on the shoulders of a senior commander on the battlefield is possibly more onerous today than at any other stage in history. For although the strategic plan for any war is made by the national government of a particular country and its top military staff, the plan for any one specific battle, including the battle that starts the war, will in all likelihood begin much lower down the chain of command – perhaps even down as far as divisional level – and be drawn up with the minimum of reference to higher authorities. This much perhaps has not changed over the years; what is new, however, is the battery of technological wizardry that the commander has both ranged against him and at his disposal. Therefore, when planning the battle, a modern-day general must take into account the problems that this causes and the possibilities that it opens up.

The battle commander makes his plans with the help of a group of specialist staff officers, each heading one particular command department. In order to assist and standardise this planning process, most armies demand that their military doctrine – that is, their particular tactical approach to fighting wars – become a habit of thought for all members of the high command. Every general's headquarters staff will then be able to tackle each tactical problem, starting with a similar set of assumptions, with the result that major formations will be able to work

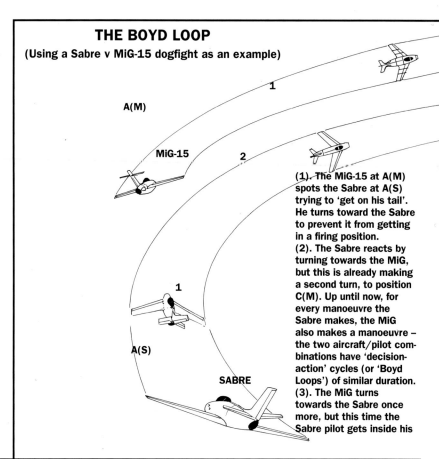

THE BOYD LOOP
(Using a Sabre v MiG-15 dogfight as an example)

A(M)

MiG-15

1

2

1

A(S)

SABRE

(1). The MiG-15 at A(M) spots the Sabre at A(S) trying to 'get on his tail'. He turns toward the Sabre to prevent it from getting in a firing position.
(2). The Sabre reacts by turning towards the MiG, but this is already making a second turn, to position C(M). Up until now, for every manoeuvre the Sabre makes, the MiG also makes a manoeuvre – the two aircraft/pilot combinations have 'decision-action' cycles (or 'Boyd Loops') of similar duration.
(3). The MiG turns towards the Sabre once more, but this time the Sabre pilot gets inside his

THE BOYD LOOP

To achieve surprise, an attacker must attempt to get inside the 'Boyd Loop' of his opponent. This concept derives from Boyd's study of air-to-air combat in the Korean War, in which he analysed the importance of reaction times in the two opposing pilots. In 'normal' manoeuvres a MiG pilot seeing a Sabre appear on his tail would turn towards the threat, forcing the Sabre pilot to turn behind the MiG to give chase once more, thereby completing the Boyd Loop. However, Boyd reasoned that if the Sabre pilot could take two actions within the time in which he had previously taken only one, then the MiG could be caught out reacting to the first American manoeu-

vre – turning behind to follow – while the second move – lining up and firing – was about to blow him out of the sky.

In terms of army manoeuvres, 'getting inside the Boyd Loop' means exactly the same thing as it does in aerial combat: achieving surprise by getting inside the enemy's surveillance and decision-making cycle through carrying out a sequence of manoeuvres faster than the defender can cope with them. Thus a defender's surveillance network may pick up an enemy advance towards the border and report this information back; the commanders will analyse it, make battle preparations and order troops forward to man the front line at the fron-

tier. In the time that it has taken the defending army to reach this stage, however, the attacker will have already completed the first manoeuvre and crossed the border. Moreover, he will be taking decisions on his second move – that of pushing his advanced spearheads tens of kilometres behind the defender's front line – based on information on the defender's actions received through his own surveillance network.

By the time the defender hears of this second move and reacts, the attacker will have completed it and be on to a further manoeuvre, and so on. Armies take longer to react than fighter pilots, but the principle is the same.

more easily together, with greater mutual understanding, and with less time spent on detailed explanations. For example, at the battle of Gravelotte in 1870, the Prussian commanders all knew that doctrine demanded that they should march towards the sound of cannon fire, regardless of what other orders they may have received – and without waiting for new orders. This helped them win the battle, just as the French, who were without doctrine, lost it partly because they would not move until they had received long and detailed orders – which were usually out of date by the time they arrived.

Today armies based on the Soviet model apply

doctrine even more extensively and systematically than did the 19th-century Prussians, while the German, French and Israeli armies are also fully committed to their own particular doctrinal mixes. The Americans – for all their stress on individual initiative and originality – have laid increasing emphasis on doctrine during the past two decades, and much more recently even the British – whose colonial tradition of personal (not to say eccentric) command is more deep-seated than anyone else's – have accepted the need for such a framework. An alliance-wide NATO version is also today under active discussion; if finally adopted, it would mark

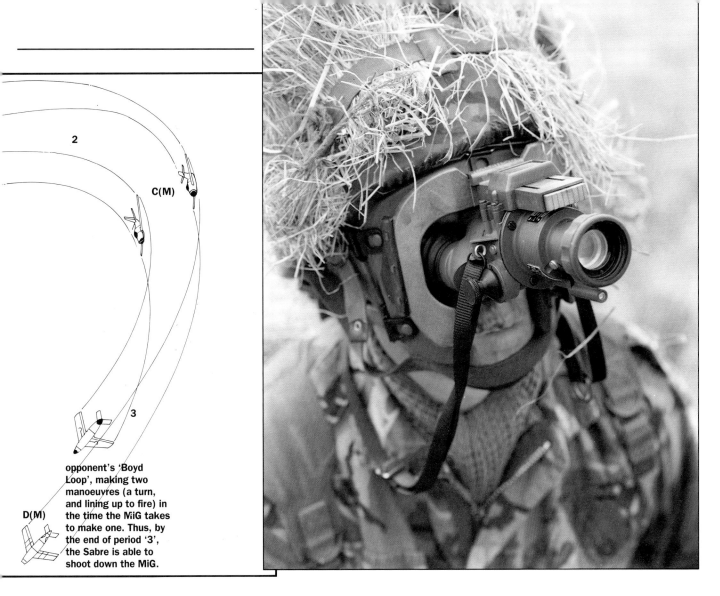

2

C(M)

3

opponent's 'Boyd Loop', making two manoeuvres (a turn, and lining up to fire) in the time the MiG takes to make one. Thus, by the end of period '3', the Sabre is able to shoot down the MiG.

D(M)

a major step towards the unification of that notoriously disparate and individualistic group of armies – some time after the main threat has disappeared!

A standardised military doctrine of the type being discussed is usually the result of many years' deep thought and debate by a general staff, helped by specialist experts. It cannot be improvised or disseminated quickly, which means that armies cannot change their fundamental attitudes overnight. This in turn means that the doctrines must be constantly updated and adapted in line with changing political needs and technical challenges, otherwise a situation may be reached whereby a country expects to fight the next war using the doctrine that was already obsolete in the last, as Poland, Britain and France all did in 1939-40. Nevertheless, even though a nation's doctrine may be brought up to date in terms of the available technologies, this will not alter the underlying national attitudes towards manoeuvre, attack and defence. The result is a deep-rooted military culture which is spread throughout the high command, and gives it much of its characteristic shape. The commander's plans will thus be guided by national military doctrine and by the type of battle he is about to undertake.

The climate and the topography of the area in which an army expects to fight also conditions both its doctrinal approach and its equipment fit. The United States – and, to a lesser degree, both NATO

Above: A British infantryman equipped with a Pilkington Nova passive night vision device. The unit incorporates a single image intensifier which amplifies ambient light, allowing the user to see clearly in low light conditions. It may be hand-held, or harness-mounted, leaving the user free to operate a vehicle

and the Warsaw Pact forces – work on the understanding that they may have to fight anywhere from the tropics to the Polar regions, and this disparity inevitably leads to weaknesses. Defensive wars are generally easier to plan for – at least, one has a very clear picture of the territory one would be willing to defend to the death. The necessity for sudden aggressive action, on the other hand, can often take one by surprise to an even greater extent than a sudden attack, as the British Government found in 1982, when it sent a Task Force to the Falklands.

A decisive fast-moving surprise attack is every commander's dream

The 'ideal battle', for all military men, regardless of nationality, would surely be an attack in which the enemy is caught so completely off guard that he is almost powerless to resist. Attacking columns burst through the defending line at many points, splitting it into small fractions that can each be quickly surrounded and then destroyed piecemeal. Simultaneously, strikes using firepower or commandos neutralise depth installations, such as nuclear launch sites, command centres, airfields, supply dumps and mobilisation depots. The enemy is disarmed and deprived of central direction almost before he knows the battle has started, and tactical combat is reduced to a series of clashes

DEGREES OF SUPRISE

An attacker can achieve military surprise in varying degrees. A defender is completely surprised if he does not foresee that he is about to be attacked or does nothing to guard against it. On the other hand, he may suspect or even know that an attack is imminent, but be powerless to take measures against it; in such a case he is said to be militarily surprised.

For example, in October 1973, the Israeli forces had military intelligence that the Arabs were massing troops for an attack, but for some time were unable to convince their government that such an attack was politically conceivable. At the same time the Arab *maskirovka* was very effective in diverting political attention away from the Middle East towards other matters, such as the seizure by Palestinian terrorists of a train containing recently released Soviet Jews at Marchegg on the Austro-Czech border on 28/29 September. The result was that the Israeli order for mobilisation was delayed until just before the Arab attack was unleashed. And in April 1940, the Norwegian government had several warn-

ings of an impending German invasion, but was persuaded to order mobilisation only after being formally notified of the attack by the German ambassador himself – and even then the orders had to be sent out through the cumbersome hand-delivered postal system!

An attacker seeking to achieve surprise is, however, most unlikely to win such a clear run. He must aim to maximise the degree to which he can pre-empt defensive counter-measures. Indeed in most military operations, the best that can be achieved is partial surprise – that is, some parts of the defence remain unprepared, while others are manned and ready. This was in fact what the Arabs in 1973 and the Germans in 1940 achieved, since some of the defenders did manage to fight back effectively even though the defence as a whole was unready. In the event, in 1973 the Arabs failed to achieve enough surprise to capture all of their initial objectives, whereas in 1940 the Germans did so – and went on to conquer the whole of Norway.

A good example of complete strate-

gic surprise is the Japanese attack on Pearl Harbor in December 1941, in which they smashed the US fleet without warning and when the two nations were not technically at war.

Then there can be military strategic surprise – which, for example, the Argentines gained in the Falklands in April 1982: Britain knew they were coming, but could not get a task force there quick enough to prevent invasion. All other combinations of degrees of surprise are possible at the operational level (that is, starting a battle within a war) and tactical level (that is, starting an action within a battle). Military operational surprise was gained by the Germans in the Michael Offensive of March 1918. Although the Allies knew they were coming, there were no reinforcements available to withstand attack; and an instance of complete tactical surprise was the SAS attack on Jebel Akhdar in 1959, in which the rebels were taken unawares by SAS troops scaling a seemingly impossible rock face while diversionary engagements were fought elsewhere.

---

between fast-moving small units. Generally speaking, in a battle of this type – exemplified by the Israeli assault on Egypt in 1967 – there is far more movement than fighting, and each individual episode of combat is improvised as an 'encounter battle' by local leaders on the spur of the moment.

In order to put into effect an all-conquering assault that finishes the war at a single blow (*Sieg ohne Morgen* as the Germans put it – 'victory without a tomorrow'), the commander needs to achieve a high level of surprise. To help him in this, he will need a comprehensive deception and concealment plan. Soviet doctrine especially places great emphasis on the concept of *maskirovka* – which includes all aspects of hiding one's own forces and intentions, while feeding the enemy with false ideas of what is actually going on. *Maskirovka*, as a vital part of achieving surprise, is central to every planning process right from the very start, including deliberations at the political level.

One effective technique for achieving surprise at the strategic level is to play the game of mobilisation followed quickly by demobilisation, thereby making the enemy mobilise his own forces, only to stand them down once again. Having thus been caught out and forced to 'cry wolf', the enemy will afterwards be more reluctant to take seriously a second or third mobilisation – and fail to react to the real one. This technique was used successfully by the Arabs in the run-up to the October War of 1973.

Other deception techniques which may be used at strategic or operational levels include the leaking of false plans to the enemy, the broadcast of

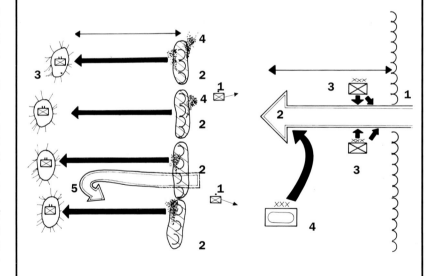

HEINRICI METHOD
Heinrici's method relied on fighting patrols (1) capturing prisoners, from whom the timing of the next Soviet attack could be extracted. Thirty minutes before the Soviet artillery bombardment was due to start, the Germans evacuated their forward positions (2), moving into strongpoints at the rear (3). The Soviet artillery was therefore wasted on empty trenches (4), and once the main attack had got beyond its artillery fire, it met the untouched German strongpoints, and was repulsed (5). The Germans could often then return to their forward positions.

'FIRE BRIGADE' or MANSTEIN METHOD
Manstein's method induced the Soviets to penetrate the weakly-held German positions (1), encouraging the armour at the spearhead of the enemy thrust (2) to become separated from its supporting infantry. German infantry corps would then counter-attack the flanks of the penetration (3), hitting the Soviet infantry and sealing off the gap in the defences. Meanwhile, a German panzer corps would strike the Soviet armour at the head of the thrust, attacking it from the flank and rear, and destroy the Soviet tanks and eliminate the penetration (4).

Although no strategic or operational surprise is possible under these circumstances, a commander may still attempt to achieve 'tactical surprise' – for example, by using multiple feints to confuse the enemy's intelligence picture, or by driving obviously towards one objective but then veering off sideways at the last minute to strike at another unsuspecting position. A classic Soviet technique is to assault over terrain that the enemy has assessed as impassable or almost so. In its whirlwind advance into Manchuria in August 1945 the Red Army completely surprised and outflanked the Japanese by pushing a major armoured spearhead through the Great Hingan mountains, using petroleum, oil and lubricants (POL) replenishment by air on the far side. The Japanese had expected none of this, imagining the mountains to be impassable to armour, rather as the French and Americans had imagined the Ardennes to be in 1940 and 1944 respectively.

In his memoirs of the great Soviet offensives into Poland and Germany in 1944-45, Marshal Chuikov assures his readership that a search for near-impassable terrain was standard practice in the planning of any offensive. There is much truth in the argument that 'the only bad terrain is terrain held by the enemy', and the Russians, more than anyone, have equipped their armoured forces to traverse the most unforgiving of hills, forests and rivers. These forces are lavishly provided with mine- and obstacle-clearing equipment, and have an impressive range of advanced bridges.

misleading signal traffic and the establishment of dummy units – complete with skeleton HQ staffs, dummy vehicles, new roads, pipelines and the like – combined with careful concealment and radio silence by the real spearheads that are preparing to strike from an unexpected direction. All of these techniques were widely used by both sides during World War II, and they have since been refined further– especially in the field of electronic warfare.

Yet an attack must also possess the flexibility to tackle prepared defences head on, on those occasions when something goes wrong with plans to avoid, encircle or pre-emptively smash through enemy strongpoints. For this type of operation the troops must be ready to mount a more formal and careful style of action – the 'set-piece assault'. This must be the 'worst-case scenario' for an attacker: a battle in which no strategic or operational surprise is achieved but where the defender must still be prised out of strongly fortified positions.

Deception techniques are a cheap way to buy time for an attack

In this type of operation the high command will have a much greater voice in tactical affairs than it does for encounter battles. In the former type of operation, the attackers' command staff must complete extensive and meticulous long-term preparation; must pre-brief and co-ordinate the spearheads and depth operations, so that they fully understand their own particular place in the overall picture but will hope to intervene relatively little on the day of the battle itself, leaving the tactical footwork to more junior commanders. For set-piece assaults, on the other hand, there must be meticulous planning of every detail – and especially generous logistic support – since this is potentially the most costly type of combat of all. Staff work must here reach down into the lowest levels of command, in order to maximise the chances of success, since brilliantly improvised manoeuvres will no longer be adequate on their own.

Above: Tanks of Rommel's 7th Panzer Division prepare to advance on the River Somme, in northern France, in June, 1940. A month earlier, the Germans had achieved complete operational surprise over the French by sending a solid phalanx of seven armoured divisions through the mountainous forests of the Ardennes – a region thought impenetrable to armour

Right: A German infantry commander from WWII signals his men to advance. One of the reasons for the Wehrmacht's success during that war was the high degree of initiative shown by even quite junior officers

At the end of the day, however, the formal set-piece assault will have to tackle enemy strong-points head on. This means that, as an opener, the strongest possible barrage of high explosive must be laid down from bombers, rockets and artillery. At the start of their Reichswald battle in early 1945 the British employed large numbers of all these, supplemented by almost everything else that could shoot, including Bofors anti-aircraft artillery (AAA) and Vickers medium machine guns. This was called a 'pepperpot' barrage, and it was entirely success-ful. The enemy troops in the front line were numbed and quickly surrendered. The only prob-lem was that the bombardment had been so intense that fallen trees obstructed forward movement through the forest, while the town of Cleve was so badly cratered by bombing that it was impassable to the attackers' vehicles; a mighty traffic jam ensued, preventing the planned pursuit.

Today's artillery is capable of putting down even more terrible barrages. The Israelis working in the massive stone and concrete bunkers of their Bar Lev Line took a fearful pounding from the Egyptian guns during the shelling along the Suez Canal between 1970 and 1973. Although they were deeply dug in and not directly hit, the soldiers suffered badly from the shock waves and concussion of the shelling. In future wars it may be possible to kill defenders even in very deep bunkers by using fuel-air explosives (FAE) – clouds of explosive droplets that can pene-trate concrete and masonry bunkers through ventila-tion systems and gun apertures before they ignite.

Developments in technology have not only enhanced the effectiveness of artillery fire, but also the distances at which it can be effective. The greatly increased range of modern artillery and rocket weapons means that the whole of even a very deep defensive layout can now be within the reach of an attacker's fire. Already in their 1972 Easter Offensive, the North Vietnamese were laying down intense barrages at ranges up to 27km, using the relatively lightweight Russian M46 130mm gun. Today the world's advanced armies regard such an outreach as routine, and can more than double it with specialised weapons.

The degree of surprise a force can achieve is conditioned by its reach

Achieving surprise is perhaps more important than ever on the modern battlefield, since the potential costs of a frontal slugging-match – which would take place were surprise not achieved – have risen in proportion to the rise in firepower and improve-ments in defensive capabilities. Mobile counter-moves can be very fast indeed, so an attacker must win the initiative especially quickly if he is to com-pletely disarm them.

Yet as surprise has become more important, its achievement has become increasingly difficult. Major obstacles include the array of greatly enhanced surveillance technologies, which promise to give warning of impending threats well before they are launched. All advanced nations maintain

Right: The Battle of Kursk and (far right) the Israeli campaign to conquer Sinai. The Israelis were faced only with light oppo-sition, and cut through it within four days. The Germans, on the other hand, were faced with a defensive force twice as strong as itself, where orthodox doctrine sug-gests at least a three-to-one superiority is neces-sary. They barely reached the third of the soviet forces' seven defen-sive belts

Right: German tanks would by-pass and seal off a strongpoint, leaving the infantry to deal with the besieged defenders. Few Wehrmacht infantry units were motorised, which meant that the infantry 'Landsers' walked – first across Poland, then across France, and later across Russia, almost as far as Moscow. Those that were left walked back

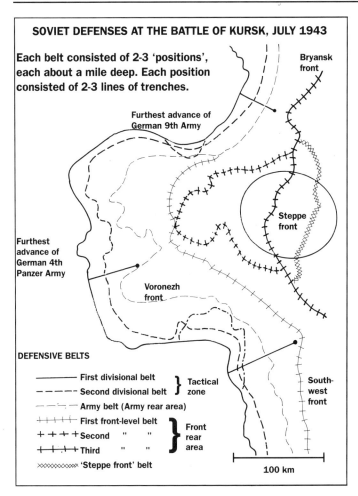

SOVIET DEFENSES AT THE BATTLE OF KURSK, JULY 1943

Each belt consisted of 2-3 'positions', each about a mile deep. Each position consisted of 2-3 lines of trenches.

Bryansk front

Furthest advance of German 9th Army

Steppe front

Furthest advance of German 4th Panzer Army

Voronezh front

Southwest front

DEFENSIVE BELTS

First divisional belt } Tactical zone
Second divisional belt
Army belt (Army rear area)
First front-level belt } Front rear area
Second " "
Third " "
'Steppe front' belt

100 km

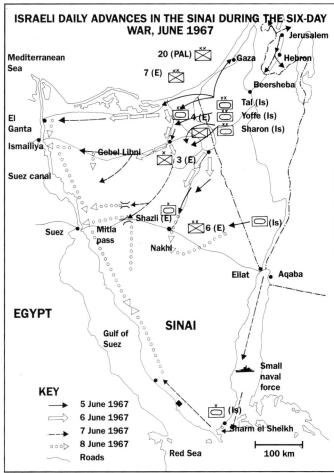

ISRAELI DAILY ADVANCES IN THE SINAI DURING THE SIX-DAY WAR, JUNE 1967

Mediterranean Sea

Jerusalem

20 (PAL)
7 (E)
Gaza
Hebron
Beersheba
Tal (Is)
Yoffe (Is)
Sharon (Is)
4 (E)
El Ganta
Ismailiya
Gebel Libni
3 (E)
Suez canal
Shazli (E)
Shazli (E)
(Is)
Suez
Mitla pass
6 (E)
Nakhl

EGYPT

SINAI

Gulf of Suez

Eilat
Aqaba

Small naval force

KEY

→ 5 June 1967
⇨ 6 June 1967
--→ 7 June 1967
ooo▷ 8 June 1967
— Roads

Sharm el Sheikh

Red Sea

100 km

vast electronic monitoring services (for example, GCHQ in Britain) that search the air waves for telltale signs of hostile plans or troop concentrations. Surveillance from satellites has made great strides forward in recent times, with increased speed, sophistication and reliability of reports, and improved mobility for receiving-stations. The days are gone when it took at least 24 hours to analyse the 'take' and then disseminate it to relevant tactical commanders.

Below the satellites, aircraft such as the American TR-1 tactical reconnaissance aircraft at high altitudes and drones lower down carry advanced multi-sensor imagers. TR-1s (the successors to the famous high-altitude U-2 'spy planes') form part of the precision location strike system (PLSS), under which they would fly in threes at high altitudes in pre-set 'race track' patterns. As soon as one aircraft latches on to a radar emission, which TR1s can monitor up to a distance of 320km, the other two will follow suit, thus providing a very precise 'fix' through triangulation. This result will be relayed instantly to the ground, theoretically allowing ET rockets to engage specific targets in less than 15 minutes. Equally the airborne warning and command system (AWACS) can monitor aircraft movements at very great ranges, although attempts to produce comparable airborne radars to identify ground movements at these distances have not been successful. At shorter ranges, however, the side-looking airborne radar (SLAR) and forward-looking infra-red (FLIR) is fully effective.

On the ground, there are many types of sensor that make the previously 'empty' battlefield appear very full indeed. Infra-red, passive thermal, acoustic, radar and other instruments – many of which may be unmanned and monitored at a distance – can shed light on the enemy's whereabouts and activities even in storms or on moonless nights. In Vietnam there was even a 'people sniffer' helicopter, equipped with sensors to detect human body odours...although apparently it had difficulty in distinguishing them from the smell of water buffalo!

Modern technology makes hide-and-seek a dangerous game

All this means that a surprise attack is harder to mount than ever before; and batteries of surveillance and monitoring equipment may be complemented by other conditions or devices which reduce the opportunities still further. For instance, where a defender has good surveillance methods and a wide 'no-man's-land' or 'buffer zone' that an attacker must cross before making contact, he can be reasonably confident that he will receive adequate warning. This is doubly true when there is a relatively stable political relationship between two possible antagonists. For example, a Chinese invasion of Russia would today be unlikely, and if launched, would probably fail to achieve surprise. The same is the case for an Egyptian invasion of Israel, though here there is an added safeguard. In very sensitive areas of the world, diplomatic

Above: Keeping front-line vehicles supplied with fuel will be one of the most difficult tasks facing a modern army

On the other hand, a country's surveillance cover might be incomplete; take, for example, the Ugandan air defences facing Israel's Entebbe raid of 1976, or the PLO in Lebanon facing Operation Peace for Galilee in 1982. Or the defending army may be deployed well forward in a linear formation that may be quickly penetrated by attacking spearheads. In this way Syria was able to reach Israel's Golan Heights defences quickly in 1973, and the Germans rapidly smashed through Russian lines along their border in 1941, while in the past 30 years NATO's potentially fragile 'forward defence' has always had to be covered by an exceptionally high level of surveillance. Then, there is the political scene to be considered. Stable political relations between countries lessen the likelihood of a surprise attack being successful, whereas volatile political conditions have the opposite effect. It is no coincidence that most surprise attacks in recent times have been in the Middle East. In future there may be a similarly volatile political scene in Eastern Europe and elsewhere.

Yet the fact remains that surprise can seldom be 100 per cent complete, and the best the attacker can realistically hope for is to allow the enemy to find out as little as possible about what his true objectives are – by reinforcing a false picture in the enemy's mind; by reducing the number of tell-tale signatures that are revealed to him, and by delaying the moment at which such signatures can be detected.

supervision may be set up to monitor a particular situation. Such machinery has existed to watch the Sinai desert since the Camp David agreement of September 1978 between Israel and Egypt, and a similar watchdog has, to a lesser extent, been keeping an eye on central Europe since the Helsinki accords of 1975 between NATO and the Warsaw Pact.

SOVIET DOCTRINE
The Continuity of Soviet Doctrine

Soviet doctrine for deep-striking, offensive armoured warfare was first outlined in the works of Triandafilov and Tukhachevskii during the 1930s, and was incorporated in the 1936 Field Regulations (known as PU36). Their ideas were shelved throughout Stalin's purges, the 1939 Winter War against Finland, and the initial German assault in 1941, but by the end of 1943 they had been rehabilitated in the light of battlefield experience. From then Soviet armoured offensives were designed to a set pattern that was practical, robust and highly successful.

Specific mathematical norms were established for each phase of battle. For example, Soviet practice in set-piece assaults was to select a sector for the breakthrough and there amass a ratio over the enemy of, on average, 5:1 in men, 8:1 in artillery, and 6:1 in tanks and assault guns. Each assaulting rifle division would be allocated a frontage of around two kilometres, and some 225 gun and mortar tubes (besides multiple rocket launchers) plus 19 tanks would be assigned to each kilometre of this breakthrough sector. On top of this an average of 64 tanks per kilometre were available to be committed

within 36 hours as mobile tank armies or other exploitation forces.

An instance of this system in practice was the Vistula-Oder operation of January and February 1945. On average 278 artillery tubes were lined up on each kilometre of front – which would have put them wheel-hub to wheel-hub had they been placed in a single line, rather than in the 'archipelago' layout that 20th-century artillery is able to use. There were also 22 tanks and self-propelled (SP) guns allocated to each kilometre in the initial tactical phase, with some 98 more per kilometre lined up in depth for the operational exploitation. This made a superiority over the enemy of 11.25:1 in artillery and 6:1 in tanks plus 7.25:1 in men; and the operation was supported by 4772 air sorties overall.

Using these norms the Soviet armour smashed through the German defences of the Vistula Line almost instantly, destroying its entire infantry garrison and most of the four Panzer divisions allocated for mobile defence. The front troops penetrated nearly 500km to the Oder Line – a breakthrough of record depth, in an area that had previously been thought

exceptionally well-defended. However, the Vistula-Oder operation actually failed to achieve its objective. Although the Soviet forces overran western Poland and eastern parts of the German Reich, it could still not punch through to Berlin itself. In 1945, therefore, even the Soviets' exceptionally high estimates of the basic forces needed to achieve breakthrough turned out to be somewhat less than a total recipe for victory.

Nevertheless, these doctrines have survived right up to the present day. In the 1950s they were adapted to cope with a nuclear battlefield, including a chequerboard of echelons in depth; then in the late 1970s they were converted back to provide a framework for purely conventional combat in the form of a 'single echelon' surprise assault.

Currently there is a new round of revisions under way that is intended to accommodate both ET weapons and the newly altered political map of Eastern Europe. Although Soviet doctrine is thus being taken in the direction of Kursk-style 'defensive defence', it will still retain a strong emphasis on fast armoured counter-attacks.

The problem is that there are so many different parts of the enemy's military and political machine to be taken unawares that at least some of these will almost inevitably find out at least a little of what is going on, and attempt to alert other departments.

Success in combat operations calls for more than just surprise and effective firepower. Warfare has always imposed great demands on wakefulness. Night has never stopped the artillery from firing, and darkness used to be an invitation to infantry to move because of the protection it provided. Indeed, the Israeli infantry, drawing partly on the British example in two world wars, particularly prided itself on its night-fighting skills, as the Israelis explained after their 1967 victory, and admirably illustrated in many a commando raid. Today the problem of sleep deprivation among troops is spreading to tank crews as high-tempo offensive moves, envisaged in both Soviet and US doctrines, call for a round-the-clock 'continuous battle' in which not only infantry and artillery but also armour participate.

The stamina of the men behind the equipment will be a ruling factor

In past wars armour often made night marches out of contact with the enemy in order to win positional advantage for a dawn attack; to that extent the continuous battle is no novelty for tank crews. However, in those days, when they were close to the enemy, being blind and vulnerable to infantry tank-killer teams armed with satchel charges, bazookas or RPGs, they would laager during the hours of darkness.

Admittedly, much of the night might well have been occupied in mechanical repairs and maintenance, but this was a very different level of activity from combat itself. The introduction of the infra-red sight (as used, for example, by the Syrians on the

Golan Heights in the 1973 Arab-Israeli War) and more recently of the extremely efficient passive thermal imager changed all that by giving tank crews greatly enhanced night visibility.

It is ironic that the very technology – the passive thermal imager – that has made tanks able to fight at night has placed a large question mark over the place of the tank in modern war, by striking at its very mobility. At rest and waiting in ambush the thermal signature of a tank can be damped down by modern multi-sensor camouflage nets, such as the Diab-barracuda.

But these nets must be dismantled when the tank moves and the thermal image from its exhausts can once again be picked up. This means that tanks are more visible when mobile than when at rest, which in turn means that it is much more dangerous for

Right: Polish combat engineers assist in ferrying a T-72 tank across a river

Below: The higher the echelon, the further in front the commander must plan. Really fast-moving actions will tax both the intelligence-gathering and the decision-making processes

PLANNING AHEAD

The Corps commander, who is running the entire battlefield, can be expected to place his headquarters anything up to 100km behind the FEBA, for security reasons and to be sure of seeing the widest possible picture of events. He will have to plan for contingencies perhaps 36 or 48 hours ahead. The assets under his control range from air strikes, perhaps launched from a continent away, to *coup de main* attacks by Special Forces squads or infantry platoons. Tying all the information together into a cohesive whole is the most difficult job of all.

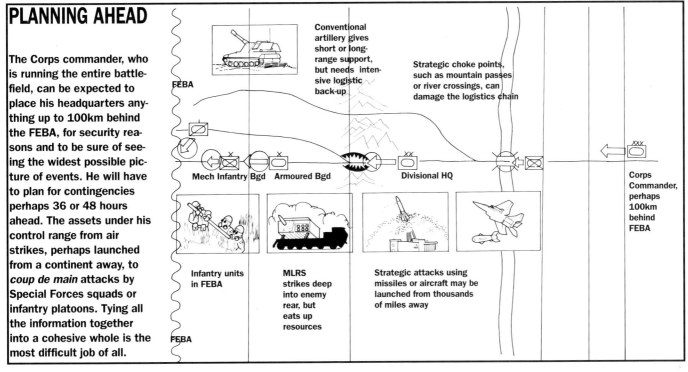

THE PASSAGE OF LINES

To keep up the momentum of a battle, commanders have to replace exhausted troops with fresh ones without losing any of the impetus of their attack. This operation is called 'the passage of the lines', and its success or failure will obviously have a critical effect on the outcome of the battle as a whole.

During World War I, problems of command, control, communications and terrain made the passage of lines very difficult, and many attacks failed as a result. At Cambrai in 1917, for example, the British cavalry could not get through the initial wave of tanks and infantry to complete what should have been a victorious breakout. As a result the Germans were able to consolidate their resistance in the final line of their defences. The lesson was not lost on the British commanders. At Amiens the following year the cavalry was properly fed through the

initial assault and did great damage to the German rear. Unfortunately there was not enough cavalry to turn the battle decisively in favour of the British forces.

In World War II, the passage of the lines was a key part of Soviet doctrine. Each unit was allocated enough ammunition and fuel to fight a particular type of battle for a set time. When that time was up, the unit was regarded as exhausted, and a fresh one was sent through to replace it. Great care went into the timing, planning and execution of these manoeuvres: police were deployed to prevent traffic jams, and the troops' proficiency in march discipline and flag signalling was crucial.

Today, successful passage of the lines is vital. The relative efficiency of the two sides in carrying out the manoeuvre will go a long way to deciding the outcome.

tanks to move than to halt – by day no less than at night – even though they can now fire accurately on the move, as they could never do before.

Although nocturnal fighting now seems to be technically as possible as day fighting for all three main arms, there is still the considerable question of whether the soldiers have the physical stamina to fight this sort of 24-hour battle. In the 1973 October War, for example, sheer fatigue often persuaded the two sides to agree – tacitly but mutually – to 'switch off' each night. On the other hand, against this, there is scientific evidence that most

troops can in fact keep going for a few days with only an hour or two of sleep per day. Guderian's spearheads at the Meuse crossing in early May 1940 went for six nights without much sleep in the decisive battle of the French campaign, but had to slow down for a few days thereafter.

But even if troops and machines can theoretically keep going 24 hours a day, can sufficient supplies to maintain men, artillery and now tanks be transported around the battlefield? Wars end quickly if the initial thrust can be pushed through to a successful conclusion, but if an attack runs out of fuel at a key moment, it will be stopped just as effectively as if it had met unexpectedly strong enemy resistance – as the Germans discovered in their Ardennes offensive of Christmas 1944.

A US armoured division requires 17,300 gallons of fuel per hour

The logistics departments of the advanced armies are today run in a scientific fashion and backed by the same computerised and mechanised technology as any major warehousing and distribution system. Nevertheless in mobile operations immense strain is placed on the transport services, both by the sheer weight of supplies that must be carried and by the unpredictable moves called for in a fluid situation. With modern long-range firepower, moreover, unarmoured transport vehicles are desperately vulnerable, especially the large 40-ton 'juggernauts' that armies are increasingly using.

The fact is, however, that there is at present no substitute for these soft-skinned road vehicles. Ammunition can be transferred quickly to lorries on special pallets by the use of purpose-built lifting devices, and offloaded just as fast at gun positions, but trucks are still required to convey it to the gun line. Advances have been made, however, in the field of fuel transport, with advanced extendable pipelines for POL now in service that can bring

Below Left: A British Skynet 4 satellite in the course of testing. Three such satellites, in geo-synchronous orbit, provide secure and reliable strategic and tactical communications for the British armed services worldwide

The strategic HQ (A) receives information from Special Forces (1), via communications satellites (1A), from surveillance satellites (2), and from high-speed, high-altitude 'spyplanes' (3). The army group, or theatre, HQ (B), receives information from aircraft listening to enemy communications and radar emissions (4), and from 'AWACS' radar-surveillance aircraft (5). It can also task low-flying photo-recce aircraft (6), as can the corps HQ (C). This also receives information from dedicated jamming-detection (7) and stand-off radar aircraft (8), together with drogues and RPVs (Remotely Piloted Vehicles) (9), corps-level reconnaissance units – often including helicopters (10) – and the artillery's counter-battery radars. Signals units monitoring enemy radar traffic (12) report back to corps HQ, or divisional HQ (D). This will also receive information from its own recce units and maybe artillery RPVs, but its main source is from front-line units and observers (13), (14) and (15), using the assets shown in the accompanying box

Above: A Grumman E-2C Hawkeye Airborne Early Warning aircraft taxis towards the catapult prior to taking off from the *USS John F Kennedy*. The Hawkeye can detect aircraft 500km away. The Israelis used them to good effect in their battles with the Syrian Air Force over the Lebanon in 1982

to require between 1375 and 3100 tons of artillery ammunition alone; and in the Vistula-Oder operation of early 1945 the Russians expended no less than 315,000 projectiles in only the first 25 minutes of fire preparation. Unfortunately in almost every 20th-century war the logistic requirement has turned out to be much greater than predicted, especially for ammunition. In the October War of 1973, both sides had planned for at least three weeks' fighting, but were already running low after just 10 days, while for much of the 1980-88 Gulf War, Iran and Iraq were making do with very inadequate scales of ammunition, in scenes reminiscent of the general European shell shortage of 1915.

Thus the successful prosecution of a battle requires not only that supplies be efficiently moved about the battlefield, but also that adequate supplies be set aside in the first place. However, a barrier to the latter is that the manufacture and resupply of advanced modern munitions is enormously expensive, which gives rise to the temptation to stockpile unrealistically small quantities. Once again the 1973 War may be cited as an example: in that conflict there was an especially acute shortage of advanced anti-tank and surface-to-air missiles.

truly prodigious volumes up to divisional rear areas. And this is just as well, for an American armoured division would need some 173,000 gallons of fuel for every 10 hours of tactical advance, with each of its M1 Abrams MBTs consuming a full load of 508 gallons within that time, while Soviet norms for an operation by a Front allow for the consumption of some 25,000 tonnes per day.

This assumes of course that the enormous quantities of supplies required by a fighting army are available. For example, a single deep attack by a modern US armoured division has been calculated

Defence in depth is more effective than packing a front

So far the emphasis has been on the problems faced by an attacking commander; the defending general has his problems too, and his plans to make. When faced with the possibility of massive deliberate bombardment, for example, a defending general must choose carefully how he will deploy his forces. In such a situation he seems to have several options open to him. On the one hand, he may rely on digging in his troops as deeply as possible, in something like the Bar Lev Line – although as outlined above, increased artillery firepower makes this a far from ideal solution. An alternative is to arrange defences in great depth, as the Russians did at Kursk – the 1943 battle that has undoubtedly made most impact on recent Soviet doctrine. However, the increased range of artillery has also called this option into question.

In the summer of 1943, the Germans wanted to pinch out the Kursk salient by mounting a twin offensive through its two shoulders, from Orel and Belgorod respectively. However, the operation was delayed for some three months while Hitler insisted on bringing up additional forces and the new Panther and Tiger tanks. By the time the attack actually started on 5 July, the Russians had long known of its details and had carefully prepared their defences, with strongpoints and minefields arranged up to 120km in depth. These were so arranged that the attacker's short-range artillery could tackle only a small part at any one time. Once he had dealt with each section of defence and made a 'bound' forward, the enemy would have to redeploy his guns to engage the next section. Although this entails the sacrifice of the front line by the defenders, the constant halts that the enemy is compelled to make fixes him and renders him ripe for a counter-attack, in this case in crushing style by massed armour.

THE SURVEILLANCE ARRAY IN MODERN WAR

A
1A
2
3
5
4
6
B
8
7
9
1
D
10
HQ (xxx)
C
HQ (xx)
13
14
12
15
11

Seismic sensors

Radar

Thermal imager
Image intensifier
Binoculars/optical weapons sights

When it began, the German assault force contained over 1000 tanks, but it made heavy weather of the enemy infantry positions. It advanced less than 30Km during the first week – scarcely a *blitzkrieg* rate of advance – and was then halted in a massive armoured battle, principally around the village of Prokhorovka, as the Russians committed their reserve of over 3000 tanks. Three weeks after the battle had started the Germans were in full retreat towards the west, while the Red Army finally realised that it possessed both the numbers and the operational skills needed to defeat the Nazi invader.

The events of 1943 on the Eastern Front illustrate a third style of mobile defence. For between the surrounding of the German Sixth Army at Stalingrad at the end of 1942 right up to and beyond Kursk, the Germans fought a series of desperate thrust and parry defensive combats all along the front, giving an idea of what 'mobile defence' with armoured forces should be about. These actions, put into effect by the German generals Erich von Manstein and Hermann von Balck, have been carefully studied by both NATO and Warsaw Pact armies ever since.

In November 1942 the Soviet army perfected the successful operational doctrine that they have followed in general ever since. At Stalingrad, it used *maskirovka* to conceal the build-up of huge out-flanking forces which smashed through the weak allied armies on either side of the German Sixth Army, thus putting it in a 'cauldron' from which there was no escape. Manstein took command of the relief attempts but at the same time, the Russians threatened a second and greater encirclement of the German Army Group A in the Caucasus.

It was during the successful fighting to extricate this army group that General von Balck's 11th Panzer Division used Manstein's technique of 'mobile defence', performing a sequence of illuminating defensive 'fire brigade' actions on the River Chir, in which the formation marched under cover of darkness each night to strike a Soviet spearhead at dawn. Often Balck would pin the enemy down with infantry, artillery and anti-tank guns in front, then manoeuvre armour to the rear. The Soviet forces would be shot up from behind, by what they had imagined was their own rear echelon. Without support, however, von Balck could not reverse the tide and the German forces at Stalingrad could not be relieved; they surrendered on 2 February 1943.

Above: Tactical mobility at the lowest level. An Australian trooper crawling under barbed wire during basic training. Stamina and fieldcraft skills often go hand in hand

Below: Soldiers also need stamina of a different kind. An American M60A3 crewman awaiting an order to move out

Manstein's use of a very mobile and hard-hitting 'fire brigade' defence was to be repeated many times during 1943 – sometimes at the level of battlegroups and divisions, sometimes at the level of Panzer corps or above. The technique should be set alongside several other German expedients that were also being used around this time, as Soviet assaults built up to a crescendo after their victory at Kursk. Around Orsha, for example, the German Fourth Army used a system in which enemy offensives were carefully predicted by intelligence, then troops were rushed across from quiet sectors to reinforce the threatened point, exploiting reserve positions dug to a depth of some 50km behind the front line. In the 1970s the US Army was to adopt a very similar doctrine under the name of 'active defense'.

Creative defense is often as mobile as attack

A daring World War II variant of active defense was demonstrated in Russia, East Prussia and finally outside Berlin by the German general Gotthard Heinrici. His technique, based on a German World War I model, was to work out as far as possible from intelligence reports when the Russian assault would start and then, a few hours before it began, evacuate his front-line positions apart from a few sentries and machine-gun crews. The main enemy artillery barrage, often the best and most carefully prepared blow in an assault, would thus fall harmlessly on the evacuated positions and the infantry attack that followed would be left denuded of artillery support when it finally came up against the real German position a few kilometres to the rear. Heinrici was using 'tactical agility' rather than

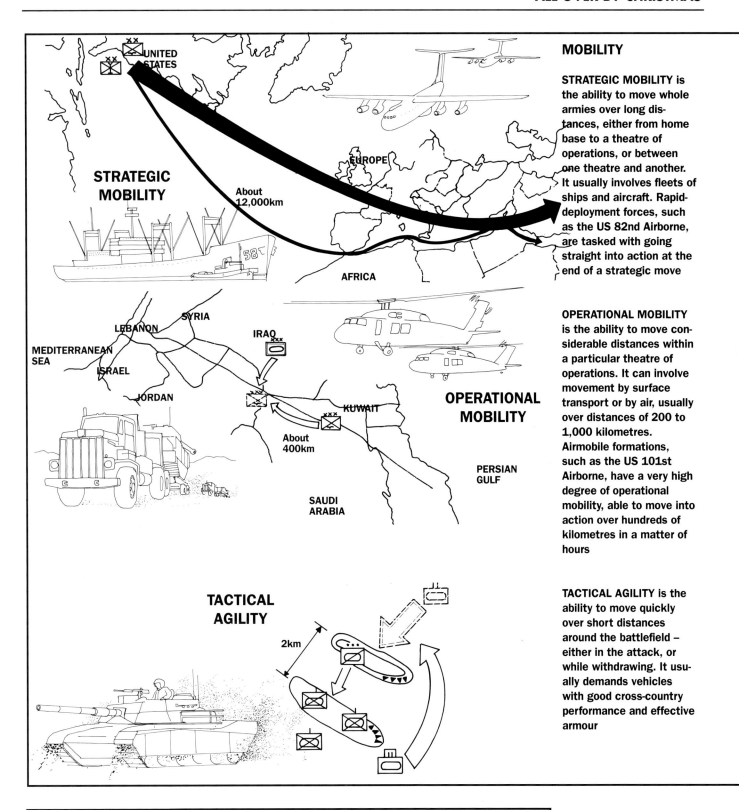

MOBILITY

STRATEGIC MOBILITY is the ability to move whole armies over long distances, either from home base to a theatre of operations, or between one theatre and another. It usually involves fleets of ships and aircraft. Rapid-deployment forces, such as the US 82nd Airborne, are tasked with going straight into action at the end of a strategic move

OPERATIONAL MOBILITY is the ability to move considerable distances within a particular theatre of operations. It can involve movement by surface transport or by air, usually over distances of 200 to 1,000 kilometres. Airmobile formations, such as the US 101st Airborne, have a very high degree of operational mobility, able to move into action over hundreds of kilometres in a matter of hours

TACTICAL AGILITY is the ability to move quickly over short distances around the battlefield – either in the attack, or while withdrawing. It usually demands vehicles with good cross-country performance and effective armour

STRATEGIC MOBILITY

About 12,000km

EUROPE

AFRICA

SYRIA

LEBANON

MEDITERRANEAN SEA

ISRAEL

JORDAN

IRAQ

About 400km

KUWAIT

PERSIAN GULF

SAUDI ARABIA

OPERATIONAL MOBILITY

TACTICAL AGILITY

2km

UNITED STATES

SUPPLY
The Concepts for Supplying Armies

Most armies organise their logistics 'from the bottom up' – front line units hold the transport resources and send back to rear depots when they need supplies. In Soviet-model armies, however, it is the HQs in the rear that hold the transport, and release it only to units judged to be of particular importance to the tactical plan.

This system allows senior commanders to concentrate resources at key points, and reinforce success in a fluid situation. It is less wasteful in supplies than systems where everyone has an equal right to top up – but it effectively denudes and abandons the units that are not considered worth replenishing.

the 'operational mobility' that Manstein and Balck had been able to employ. It may be that in future 'tactical agility' will be the only defence against a crushing deliberate attack.

In any event, on the modern battlefield, a large military formation, such as an army group, which is awaiting attack will have certain priorities built into its national or alliance-wide doctrines and plans. Such a formation would have its territory arranged in zones, each of which will be designated for a particular task or phase of the battle, and accorded a certain priority.

First, the most advanced zone is the 'deep surveillance zone', which extends into the enemy's territory and is intended to give early warning, thereby eliminating surprise. Once the battle has started, at least the forward parts of this zone will remain under surveillance to identify oncoming reinforcement echelons and developing thrusts.

Second, the enemy's territory will also be used for the 'interdiction battle' – that is, attempts to destroy or delay the second attack wave and support units coming forward behind the enemy's advancing front. The idea is to isolate the battlefield from outside help, in the same way that Montgomery's desert air force cut off Rommel's army from its fuel supply during the second battle of Alamein in late 1942. Today this could be achieved by modern ET weapons, which could launch devastating anti-armour strikes from as much as 300km behind the defenders' front line.

Third, along this front line itself there will be a zone for 'covering forces' – mobile armoured forces deployed to challenge and delay the initial enemy spearheads. Besides winning time for the main defences further to the rear, their job is to identify the precise size, direction and intentions of these enemy spearheads. In some cases this initial zone

Right: The Space Shuttle *Discovery* lifts off from Cape Canaveral. Though expensive, the Shuttle allows satellites to be put into precise orbit at short notice, like that placed to observe and report on the Persian Gulf in November 1990, following Iraq's invasion of Kuwait

Below Left: Aircraft such as the U-2 and the now-withdrawn SR-71 can obtain pictures like this within hours of the need arising. Flying at altitudes of up to 100,000 feet, they are invulnerable to normal air defences

may be fortified with strongpoints, anti-tank obstacles, and such like, although in the case of a surprise attack the problem will be how to man these positions quickly enough – and with sufficient troops. The USA has tried to solve this through 'graduated mobilisation response' (GMR). This is a phased mobilisation concept that allows partial local mobilisations to take place ahead of the general national decision to mobilise, thereby enhancing tactical readiness in the front line even before a suspected crisis has reached the President's desk.

Interleaved defense in depth requires careful planning

Fourth, behind the covering forces will be a 'main line of resistance' which – once again, if there is time to man it – should be held in force by major formations, including infantry and some of the less mobile armour, covered by extensive engineer work, such as minefields and demolitions. The task of these troops is to crush each oncoming spearhead in a set-piece battle. If the attacker has achieved a high level of surprise, however, this line may be full of holes, and a formless 'intermingled' battle will ensue, in which the attacker enjoys many advantages.

Fifth, integrated with, or held behind, the main line of resistance will be counterattack formations – reserves that will aid the defence at identified weak points, and destroy the attacker's shattered remnants where he has been halted. These forces may operate at a local level or at higher levels, all the way up to multi-corps counter-moves reaching far into the enemy's territory; they should be especially mobile and able to support themselves during a long move.

Sixth, and behind everything else, is the 'logistic rear' – the zone from which supplies and reinforcements are drawn to feed the fighting line. This zone will be pounded by the enemy's interdiction attacks and so must be defended: in modern war it will be more of an active fighting zone than was normal in the past. And its importance cannot be overstated: a well-sited defence that runs out of food before it runs out of men and weapons will be unable to sustain fighting morale. The Argentines found this out in the Falklands campaign of 1982, in which the efficiency of their food distribution to the defending troops left much to be desired.

The important questions for defensive war planning are: just how much of the available resources will be allocated to each of these zones? and how deep will each of them be? For example, in NATO there are certain assumptions that arise from the operational concepts accepted within the alliance. Thus, the concept of Forward Defence means that NATO would have wanted to fight the battle to defend West Germany in a strip of territory running along the border with the East – not deep inside West Germany. This might have helped to preserve German cities, but it brings some military disadvantages, such as a lack of room for manoeuvre, acceptance of war on German soil and a commitment to linear defence in an age of depth warfare.

It also places a relatively high priority on surveillance, and there will be a longer logistic chain to defend. But this may well be at the expense of the main line of resistance and – especially – of the counter-attacking reserves. Furthermore, the area of defence would be very narrow (50km deep at the most), and the forces to man it would have to move a long way to get into position; something that could prove fatal if an opponent did in fact achieve surprise. The American air-land battle (ALB) doctrine of the 1980s and the follow-on forces attack (FOFA) planning guideline for the 1990s both take forward defence even further, stressing the need to strike deep against Warsaw Pact second echelons, delaying and destroying them before they reach the main battle. Once again the main line of resistance might have to make sacrifices, but the hope is that by destroying the second wave, the US troops in the front line would not have too many enemy units to tackle at once and could fight to win against an isolated first-echelon force.

Modern reconnaissance techniques make surprise difficult to achieve

A future war will be finished off quickly only if the attacker can achieve a high degree of initial surprise, and follow that with extremely efficient logistics to keep his forces supplied with all they need through the full depth of the enemy's position. Careful *maskirovka* will have to go into the initial planning, after which junior commanders must operate loyally according to doctrine. Troops will have to make great efforts to maintain the momentum of the 'continuous battle', and they will need far greater provisions of fuel and ammunition than has been customary in the past.

DOES VICTORY DEPEND ON SURPRISE ?

The argument that a future war can be won only if the attacker achieves a very high degree of surprise is based on these suppositions:

• Emerging technology has helped make defensive warfare so effective that an attacker will commit his forces only if he is sure that he will catch his enemy off his guard, unable to bring his own arms to bear in time to defeat the assault

• Fashionable, peacetime military and political theories may cause a country to get its defensive priorities wrong – in which case he runs out of supplies, reserves or operational depth before he can blunt a surprise attack

• Sophisticated deception measures and *maskirovka* make surprise easier,

and launching an attack correspondingly more effective

• Surprise is an especially important ingredient of an attack against inexperienced armies who are unfamiliar with a real battlefield. The first battle of a war may then be its last

• New long-range emerging-technology weapons are ideal for making a mass pre-emptive strike against the full depth of the enemy's positions, crippling him almost before he is aware that he is at war

Arguing against the crucial importance of surprise are these arguments:

• Improved techniques of defensive warfare may make it harder to exploit surprise even if it can be attained

• A defending army with the correct doctrine will be able to sustain, supply and prolong the battle for a long time after the initial surprise has worn off

• All-weather, long-range battlefield surveillance technology is now so sophisticated that surprise is virtually impossible to achieve in the first place

• Potential defenders now understand the importance of surprise to an attacker so well that they are now taking comprehensive diplomatic, doctrinal, organisational and tactical measures to make it all but impossible

• Surprise can never be 100 per cent complete, and modern mobile armies can very quickly switch units from 'unsurprised' sectors to surprised ones

COMMAND AND CONTROL

Managing a battlefield is much like managing any place of work, if rather more stressful than most. Without management information, the task is hopeless. In military circles, the management process goes by a different name: Command, Control, Communications and Information – C^{3}I. It breaks down into the reception and analysis of data, the decision-making process and the dissemination of the resulting orders.

At tactical levels of command, such as brigade or division (that is, below the higher operational planning echelons), the requirement for mobility demands that command be exercised from armoured vehicles, from helicopters or from improvised bunkers that can be re-dug hastily at another site, when a move becomes necessary. There will be no elaborate, hardened command bunkers such as may be enjoyed – if 'enjoyed' is the right word – by army group commanders, though the tactical HQ is probably more immediately vulnerable. Where a prefabricated structure is available, even that is likely to be rudimentary – a length of steel tube, eight or ten feet in diameter, for example, equipped and ready for use, to be placed in a deep trench and then buried.

The first priority is to combat the obvious threat of direct attack. For most armies, enemy HQs are high-priority targets: a single shot to the 'brain' is cheaper and quicker than laboriously chopping off each of the 'limbs' in turn. And due to their commu-

Left: The commander (left) of an American M60A3 Main Battle Tank briefs his driver during an exercise in Germany. The picture shows very clearly just how concentrated a target a tank unit can present. This formation would be vulnerable to a single aircraft's load of cluster bombs

nications requirements, HQs always sign themselves large, and in ways that any competent surveillance and intelligence system will be able to detect: they use particular types of command vehicle and particular patterns of electronic emission, for example. Having located an enemy HQ, an attacker may send in commandos to destroy it, or he may use aerial bombardment of one sort or the other. The possibility of destroying a command base is taken very seriously indeed, and special weapons have been developed for the task – missiles with target acquisition systems specifically designed to seek out HQ radio arrays, for example. Even if such an attack fails to kill the commander and his staff, the blast may incapacitate them, or destroy antennae,

Below: The commander of a British infantry company scans the ground ahead through binoculars. At the tactical level, commanders still try to obtain a personal view of the battle

Bottom: The Company Commander's view of an attack going in. This one was during an exercise in Korea

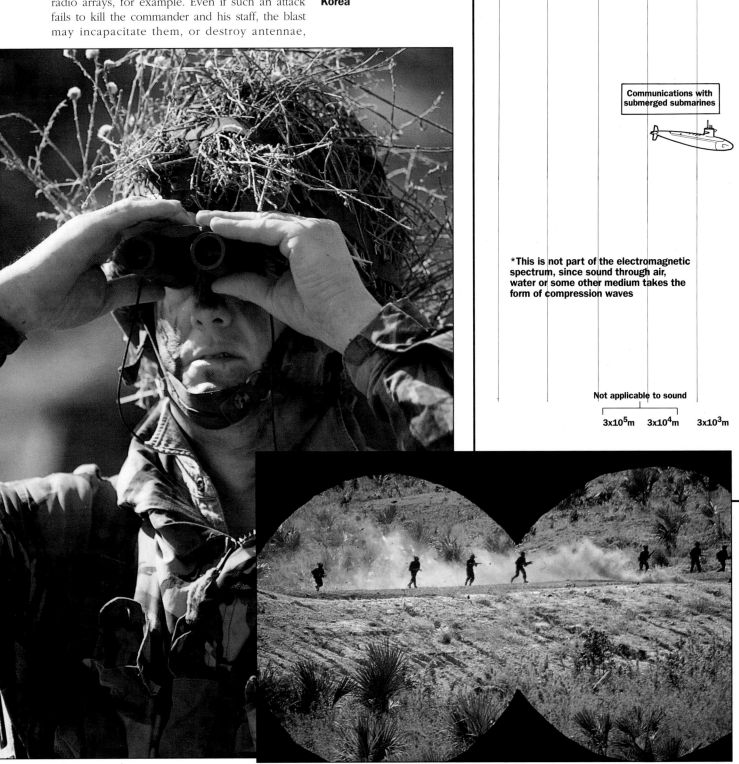

10Hz	100Hz	1kHz	10kHz	100kHz

AUDIO BAND*
(The frequencies of sound)

Used for voice communications, sonar and artillery sound-ranging (sonar also operates above this frequency)

V L F	LF (low frequency)	MF (medi freque

Communications with submerged submarines

*This is not part of the electromagnetic spectrum, since sound through air, water or some other medium takes the form of compression waves

Not applicable to sound

$3x10^5$m $3x10^4$m $3x10^3$m

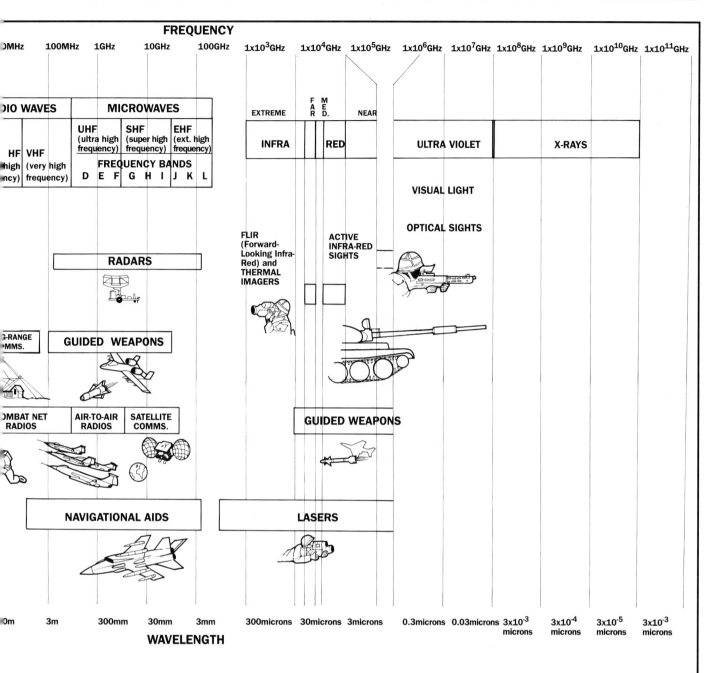

MILITARY USES OF THE ELECTROMAGNETIC SPECTRUM

THE INTELLIGENCE CYCLE

The overall commander's 'decision/action cycle' brings together all the separate 'cycles' of his various staff branches. The work of an intelligence officer is a good illustration of how every staff function can be broken down into a cycle of actions.

First of all, the intelligence officer must understand his commander's general plan and picture of the enemy. Then he must see how that picture needs to be modified or amplified in the light of the plan – for example, if a left-flanking counter-stroke is

envisaged, special care must be taken to analyse the enemy's flank protection on that side. The intelligence officer breaks down this requirement into specific questions and starts to issue appropriate orders to his various surveillance forces – for example, RPVs, helicopters, stay-behind troops and signals intelligence (SIGINT). Other intelligence sources – for example, from interrogated prisoners of war – may not be appropriate to any one particular operation, and would not be exploited.

Once the intelligence sources have been briefed, the intelligence officer must set a time limit for gathering in replies, so that he can assess the incoming 'raw' intelligence and update his appreciation of the situation. Once he has 'got his story straight' in his own mind, he must then tell all relevant agencies what he has found, starting with his commander, who can then commence a new round of his own decision-making and give a new briefing to the intelligence officer!

exposed vehicles and the like, thereby considerably reducing the HQ's effectiveness.

To guard against direct attack, the HQ must be properly camouflaged and hardened as much as is possible. This means, for instance, radio antennas 'remoted' – set up at a distance from the command site itself. Decoys and modern multi-frequency camouflage nets that will screen the site from a variety of sensors are essential. Movement into and out of the HQ will be kept to the absolute minimum.

Effective command relies on personal qualities

Security procedures always limit the freedom of that which they seek to protect. A commander has to choose between the safety of his HQ, and his own convenience and capacity to respond to circumstances – for example, by putting his command post (CP) in a vulnerable and obvious place such as on a hilltop or in a village.

Then there is the danger that peacetime habits will ruin the effectiveness of wartime command. Command and control call for intangible qualities of leadership as much as for the hardware of communications, surveillance and data processing. Many generals who can master the technical art of command in peacetime have found that they lack the resilience to take the intense strain and loneliness of command in war, and cannot maintain the charisma necessary to carry their subordinates along with them.

An army can win an important combat edge if it shrugs off its peacetime habits and appoints true warriors to high command alongside the bureaucrats and politicians. Modern methods of psychological screening bring a measure of precision to the selection of suitable individuals. The main obstacle to be overcome is that such a programme would mean a break with the accepted career patterns of a peacetime army, slaughtering the most sacred of all military sacred cows – the tacit, even unconscious understanding that toeing the line will, more or less automatically, ensure a leisurely but inexorable rise to high rank. Modern personnel management methods don't sit happily beside such assumptions.

Too much aggression clouds a commander's judgement

But whatever a peacetime army demands, the qualities needed for successful battle leadership have changed little down the ages, regardless of what particular C^3I technologies are being employed. The world's officer classes have always tried to find self-confident men, apparently untroubled by inner doubts, who would be quick to see into an enemy's intentions and understand a rapidly unfolding situation. On the one hand, they wanted hard men, who could make rapid decisions regardless of the cost – either in incompetent subordinates or in troops asked to make sacrifices for the good of the greater whole – and who are apparently unafraid of telling their seniors just what is possi-

ELECTROMAGNETISM GOES TO WAR

For simplicity, let us divide up the electromagnetic spectrum into its constituent parts, and consider each band in turn. Confusingly, electromagnetic radiation can be measured – and is classified – both by its wavelength (expressed in metres) and by its frequency of oscillation (expressed in Hertz – one Hertz is one cycle per second). As the wavelength becomes longer, the frequency lessens, and vice versa.

The names given to radiation groupings reflect their position in the spectrum, so have very little variation, one from the other. It's worth spelling them out, though, as the groups are more frequently referred to by their initial acronym. Starting from the low-frequency, long-wavelength end of the spectrum, first come Extremely Low Frequency (ELF) and Very Low Frequency (VLF), between 3Hz and 30KHz, with a wavelength of between 100,000km and 10km. They are used for radio communications with submarines worldwide, although only very simple messages can be transmitted or received, and then slowly. Considerable modern research is being devoted to these frequencies, and they may in future be harnessed for the land battlefield, if suitable uses can be found. ULF can be transmitted through the ground and may even have an effect on soil movements. They may also work in tandem with biological rhythms.

Between 30 and 300KHz (10km and 1km) lies the Low Frequency (LF) band. Very similar to VLF, it is used for familiar 'long wave' civilian radio channels. Medium Frequency (MF) – 300KHz-3MHz (1km-100m) – is the civilian 'medium wave', and is no longer important for military use.

High Frequency (HF) signals – 3-30MHz (100-10m) – travel by both a ground wave and a sky wave, with the latter bouncing off the ionosphere more reliably than MF – and not just at night. On HF, when the sky wave returns to earth it bounces back to the ionosphere, and so on around the world. It can be received wherever it comes to earth, but not in the areas between. HF is widely used by civilian 'short wave' stations, and until quite recently was the chief means of long-range radio. However, the HF wavebands are now too crowded and jammable for military use, and many alternative systems have become available.

Very High Frequency (VHF) – 30-300MHz (10-1m) – is the mainstay of television, civilian local radio and military tactical radio at the lower levels of command. It is limited almost to 'line of sight' and hence to short ranges. It includes a wider band of possible frequencies than HF, in practice made still wider by its restricted range cutting out competition from distant transmitters. However, VHF is interruptable across the whole range of its frequencies either by massive barrage jamming across the appropriate part of the spectrum – likely in a major high-tech war – or more selectively, if the enemy has detected the exact frequencies in use. Electronic warfare is already a very mature science indeed, and the location of enemy frequencies is central to it. Modern tactical radio systems attempt to overcome the problem by automatically (and synchronously) changing frequency many times in each second ('frequency hopping'). The way in which hops are synchronised provides a would-be jammer with the means to predict the next 'destination'. Just like any other coding system, they are either the product of a repeat, or of an algorithm, or they must be set and determined by a master list. In any event, they are susceptible.

From 300MHz to 3GHz (1m-10cm) lies the Ultra High Frequency (UHF) band, which is becoming increasingly important on the battlefield, as the potential problems inherent with VHF become more realistic. Despite a greater power requirement, it offers advantages both in its narrower, more directional – and therefore less jammable – beam, and because its range can be increased by bouncing the signal off the troposphere: a phenomenon known as 'tropospheric scatter'.

Operational command trunk networks such as the French Rita or the British Ptarmigan operate in the UHF band, and allow operators to dial a specific user rather than broadcasting indiscriminately throughout the net. These systems can also relay facsimile and computerised data, which makes them ideal for handling high volumes of the more mundane C^3I statistics of battle on a minute-by-minute basis.

Above UHF comes Super High Frequency (SHF), with a band of 3 to 30GHz (10-1cm). This is sometimes known as the 'microwave' or 'centimetric band' and is dominated by satellite radio communications and radar. Certainly the majority of combat radars operate in the SHF and upper UHF bands, although these frequencies have become somewhat overcrowded, especially in NATO. But even more than overcrowding, the vulnerability of the frequency band to jamming and interference means its life is limited. It's worth noting that these self-same frequencies are used in the home to heat and cook soft foods with a high liquid content, such as meat. High Power Microwaves (HPM) use this effect, in directed beams, to destroy the electronics in enemy munitions.

Microwave radio depends on a fine beam that needs a completely clear, unobstructed line of sight. Because its operational range is very high indeed, the band is perfect for transmissions that can be relayed by satellite. Signals are largely unjammable, and secure apart from minor leaks through 'side lobes' in the transmitter. A lightweight, easy to carry dish forms the antenna, and setting it up in the right direction is the only complicated part of the operational procedure. However, the difficulties of re-orienting the antenna each time the installations moves probably means that only fixed installations are likely to get microwave transmitters for tactical use.

Next comes the 'millimetric band': Extremely High Frequency (EHF), which lies between 30 and 300GHz (1cm-1mm). The future of tactical radio and radar probably lie in this area it has been in the past, since it combines many of the qualities of SHF with smaller antennae and side lobes, and a broader bandwidth. Some guided weapons already use EHF band sensors, while its close proximity to infra red is likely to increase its application to surveillance in future. It has two disadvantages. Its signal cannot be carried by conventional cable, and at longer ranges many of its bands are attenuated by the atmosphere, so specific high-performance 'windows' must be found.

By the time we get into the infra red (IR) frequencies – 300GHz-3×10^4GHz – we finally leave the world of radio and radar altogether, and enter that of 'electro-optics'; heat generates electromagnetic radiation in the infra red band, which can easily be detected and turned into a 'heat picture'.

Most existing applications of IR are in surveillance or weapon guidance sensors – for example, thermal imagery, IR seeker heads incorporated into SAMs or top-attack anti-armour submunitions – rather than in communications. However, in the special case of lasers we encounter a versatile instrument that does include communications among its many potential function. Battlefield lasers can accurately read ranges, illuminate targets to guide in missiles, strip the retina from an enemy gunner's eyes and perhaps eventually develop enough power, as a Directed-Energy Weapon (DEW) to immobilise vehicles and missiles themselves.

A laser can also function as a line-of-sight signalling system, similar in some ways to the morse code-transmitting directed searchlights of the late 19th century, some of which had a range of 100 miles – but with enormously more rapid and reliable results. Lasers fed through optical fibre cable can mean a whole new lease of life for traditional hard-wired land-line systems.

Electro-Optical Counter Measures (EOCM), which operate chiefly in this band, have become very important, ranging from flares and heat strobes to distract IR weapons, through smokes against thermal imagers and lasers, to decoys for all three.

Passing quickly through the optical spectrum (1×10^6GHz), and pausing to mention optical sights, image intensifiers and night driving aids, we arrive at the ultra violet (UV), X-ray and gamma ray bands (above 1×10^6GHz). They all have military applications in several fields, of which the most dramatic is perhaps the Electro-Magnetic Pulse (EMP) of gamma rays released by a nuclear explosion. This is destructive to all electronic equipment – especially computers – within a considerable distance from the explosion and would wipe out, for example, the guidance systems in missiles otherwise unharmed by the blast. Attempts are being made both to 'harden' electronic equipment against EMPs, and to harness EMPs themselves into directed beams or DEWs that could fire particles several kilometres through the atmosphere (and much further in space) at the speed of light.

Below: Signallers setting up the radio antennae on an FV436 Headquarters Vehicle – a standard FV432 with a mapboard and extra radios fitted. The VHF radios used for tactical command and control at lower echelon level operate in line-of-sight only, so the antennae need as much elevation as possible to increase their range

5

4

3b

A

C

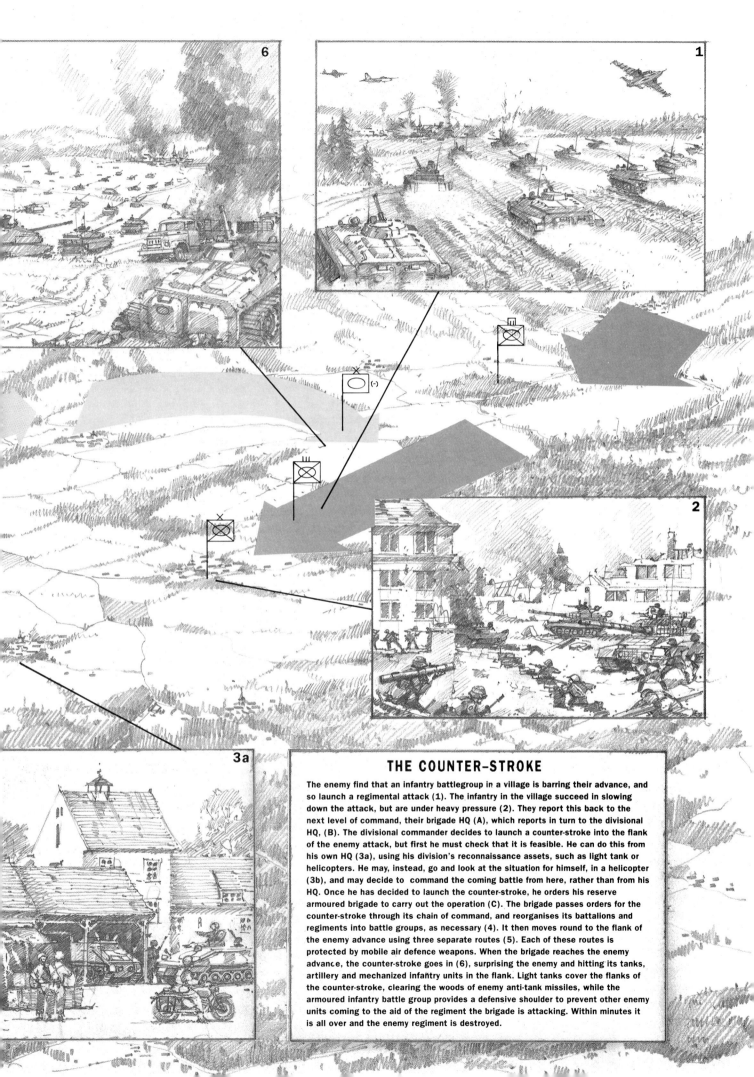

THE COUNTER-STROKE

The enemy find that an infantry battlegroup in a village is barring their advance, and so launch a regimental attack (1). The infantry in the village succeed in slowing down the attack, but are under heavy pressure (2). They report this back to the next level of command, their brigade HQ (A), which reports in turn to the divisional HQ, (B). The divisional commander decides to launch a counter-stroke into the flank of the enemy attack, but first he must check that it is feasible. He can do this from his own HQ (3a), using his division's reconnaissance assets, such as light tank or helicopters. He may, instead, go and look at the situation for himself, in a helicopter (3b), and may decide to command the coming battle from here, rather than from his HQ. Once he has decided to launch the counter-stroke, he orders his reserve armoured brigade to carry out the operation (C). The brigade passes orders for the counter-stroke through its chain of command, and reorganises its battalions and regiments into battle groups, as necessary (4). It then moves round to the flank of the enemy advance using three separate routes (5). Each of these routes is protected by mobile air defence weapons. When the brigade reaches the enemy advance, the counter-stroke goes in (6), surprising the enemy and hitting its tanks, artillery and mechanized infantry units in the flank. Light tanks cover the flanks of the counter-stroke, clearing the woods of enemy anti-tank missiles, while the armoured infantry battle group provides a defensive shoulder to prevent other enemy units coming to the aid of the regiment the brigade is attacking. Within minutes it is all over and the enemy regiment is destroyed.

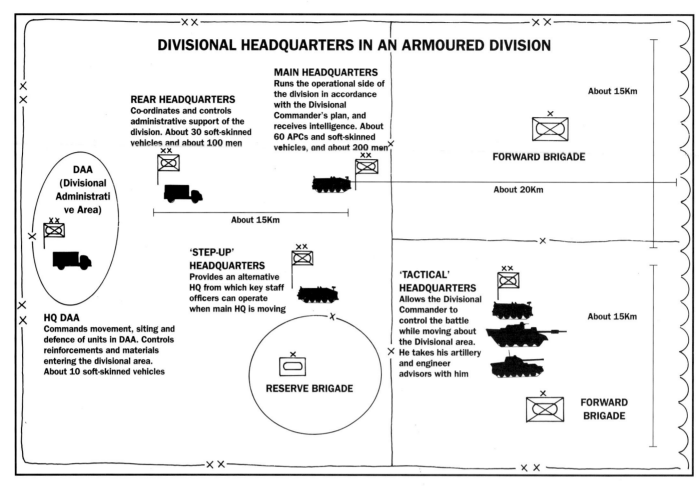

DIVISIONAL HEADQUARTERS IN AN ARMOURED DIVISION

MAIN HEADQUARTERS
Runs the operational side of the division in accordance with the Divisional Commander's plan, and receives intelligence. About 60 APCs and soft-skinned vehicles, and about 200 men

REAR HEADQUARTERS
Co-ordinates and controls administrative support of the division. About 30 soft-skinned vehicles and about 100 men

About 15Km

FORWARD BRIGADE

About 20Km

DAA
(Divisional Administrative Area)

About 15Km

'STEP-UP' HEADQUARTERS
Provides an alternative HQ from which key staff officers can operate when main HQ is moving

HQ DAA
Commands movement, siting and defence of units in DAA. Controls reinforcements and materials entering the divisional area. About 10 soft-skinned vehicles

'TACTICAL' HEADQUARTERS
Allows the Divisional Commander to control the battle while moving about the Divisional area. He takes his artillery and engineer advisors with him

About 15Km

RESERVE BRIGADE

FORWARD BRIGADE

ble and what is not. And at the same time they also wanted soft men who understand the inner nature of the human animal with humour and warmth; who know how to fit into a big organisation, yet also how to harness their men's loyalty through affection as well as fear.

A blend of the hard and soft is required: too much aggression towards the enemy may also be expressed as aggression towards seniors and subordinates; social affability in the mess may lead to pliability when it comes to the crunch. The problem is that in peacetime, armies tend to prefer officers who are unaggressive and conventional, simply because they 'fit in' better. In his important book, *The Psychology of Military Incompetence*, Norman Dixon points out that this process may attract men with authoritarian personalities who are obsessional about the outward appearance of drill and dress – but who in combat are unable to cope with situations which apparently do not obey the rules.

Even the right man for the job is only human, however, and can make only so many decisions per hour of combat – even when not distracted by enemy attack or by the physical needs of eating, sleeping or moving from one HQ site to another. In modern warfare the demands upon his limited capacity for decision-making will be greater than ever, because the battle will move faster than ever, and in more dimensions. Thus instead of controlling three brigades of foot infantry and one brigade of artillery, together mounting just one or two one-dimensional attacks per day within one small area –

Right: A British Army Wireless Communications Centre in World War I. At the time, radios were large, cumbersome and unreliable, so the telephone was preferred for strategic communications. Neither were at all suited to infantry warfare, however, so there was little effective real-time communication between commanders and their troops

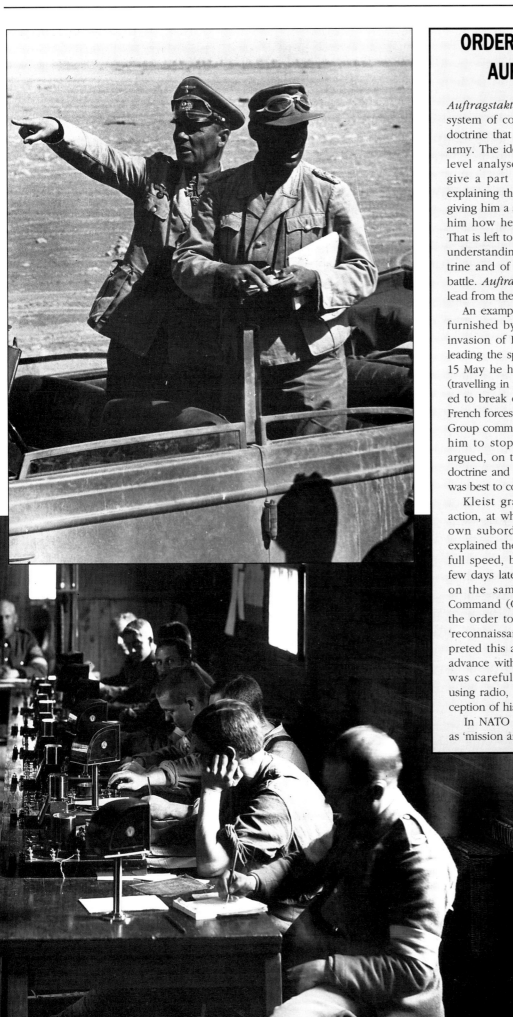

ORDERS AND INITIATIVE: AUFTRAGSTAKTIK

Auftragstaktik is the German name for a system of command based on a common doctrine that is understood throughout the army. The idea is that commanders at each level analyse their general mission then give a part of it to each subordinate – explaining the general situation to him and giving him a specific mission; but not telling him how he is supposed to carry it out. That is left to his own initiative based on his understanding of the army's military doctrine and of his own closeup view of the battle. *Auftragstaktik* allows commanders to lead from the front.

An example of *auftragstaktik* in action is furnished by Heinz Guderian during the invasion of France in 1940, when he was leading the spearhead XIX Panzer Corps. By 15 May he had already crossed the Meuse (travelling in the first assault boat) and wanted to break out in pursuit of the retreating French forces. His superior officer, the Panzer Group commander Ewold von Kleist, wanted him to stop and consolidate. Guderian argued, on the basis of accepted German doctrine and the situation at the front, that it was best to continue the advance.

Kleist granted Guderian freedom of action, at which point the latter visited his own subordinates in the front line and explained the importance of pressing on at full speed, but left the details to them. A few days later Kleist himself was overruled on the same issue by the Army High Command (OKH) and was forced to give the order to stand fast and conduct only 'reconnaissance in force'. Guderian interpreted this as effectively allowing him to advance with his whole force, although he was careful to order the move without using radio, thereby preventing OKH interception of his message.

In NATO today *auftragstaktik* is known as 'mission analysis'.

Above Left: Field Marshal Erwin Rommel (left), and his Chief of Staff, Lt General Fritz Bayerlin. Rommel always believed in leading from the front, and used any available vehicle to move around the battlefield, leaving Bayerlin to run the detail of the battle from Headquarters

mand anything, or he may be tempted to step in and run low-level engagements in person. Well-documented examples of the latter occurred frequently during the Vietnam War, when a US infantry battalion commander's helicopter carried as many radios as had a whole battalion in World War II, the nets being monitored by his brigade commander, and also by the divisional commander.

Improved communications can be an invitation to intervention

Since Vietnam was often a 'low intensity' war, with relatively infrequent combats, it was quite likely that if a company firefight broke out within the battalion's area, all three of these commanders would hear of it almost immediately, and rush to the scene to supervise it. Thus the company commander might find himself talking directly to the division commander – a case, perhaps, of a lieutenant being manoeuvred by a major general! An instantaneous command pyramid along these lines was set up during Operation Cedar Falls in the 'Iron Triangle', north of Saigon, in January 1967. In extreme cases during the Vietnam War, the available communications were so sophisticated that the tactical net was even patched in to the White House itself!

There has always been debate as to whether this 'top heavy' command structure is really effective, or whether junior officers should be left to their own

as he might have done in World War I – the modern division commander may have to manage up to a dozen widely dispersed armoured, mechanised or heli-borne battlegroups, each fighting one or two multi-dimensional combats per day. With sophisticated radio links to the front line and automated data processing (ADP), he may even be presented with details of what is happening within each platoon.

Unless a commander is very careful indeed, this can lead to a bad attack of 'information overload', a disease that can take two forms: either he will be completely immersed in detail, and unable to com-

Top Left: A 101st Airborne Division platoon commander calling in an artillery fire mission, somewhere in Vietnam. Simple codes and pre-planning made impromptu artillery barrage a useful option

Left: What happens when the radios give out. The new generation of lightweight, high-performance motorcycles has brought the despatch rider back into favour

54

initiative. In the German Army the latter system has held sway for at least a century, and every officer is trained to give and receive 'mission orders'. This means that a commander may brief his subordinates about only his broad aims and intentions, then leave the details of execution to the subordinates' own initiative. They will do the same with their own subordinates, and so on down the chain.

This practice encourages tactical leaders to make their own decisions in the light of local circumstances, provided they stay within the broad outline of their superior's plan. It also encourages them to 'lead from the front', even if this means an increase in their personal risk and isolation from the good radio links and staff advice to be found in a rearward HQ. Another advantage is that if the higher commander tries to fuss too much about details, he may find the radio is switched off on him with 'technical problems' cited as the reason for the interruption. Such switching off was not an infrequent occurrence in the German armies of World War II,

Above: The communications consoles of a Boeing E-3A AWACS 'Sentry'. The NATO airborne warning and control aircraft have multinational crews (the man in the forefront is American, and his colleague is Italian), which sometimes complicates command and control

and an extreme example took place in Sinai on 7/8 October 1973, when Major General Ariel Sharon turned off his radios as a protest against the Sinai Front commander, Schmuel Gonen.

Against the advantage of allowing a commander to read the battle at close range and react instantly, leading from the front tends to encourage tunnel vision. This happened to Rommel in North Africa in November 1941. Believing, wrongly, that British armour was now ineffective after battles that he had not personally supervised, he made his 'race for the wire' – an attempt to regroup his armour on the Egyptian border; while so engaged, he had to fight off a New Zealand infantry attack, and in so doing, lost touch with events around Tobruk, which was both his ultimate objective and that of the British. Due to this distraction, Rommel had eventually to abandon the attempt to take Tobruk, and within a month was forced into a long retreat before he could counter-attack.

It is also true that if the centre of tactical deci-

COMBAT SIGNALS IN AN INFANTRY BATTALION GROUP
(Much simplified)

Military radios are divided into networks known as 'nets'. Each net is on a different frequency, so that when someone talks on the radio, those on the same net can hear him, but no-one else. Radios linked by lightning flashes with the same letter next to them are on the same net. This is just a simplified example, for a mechanised battalion has radios with the vehicles as well as with the men, and the battalion logistics net is not shown.

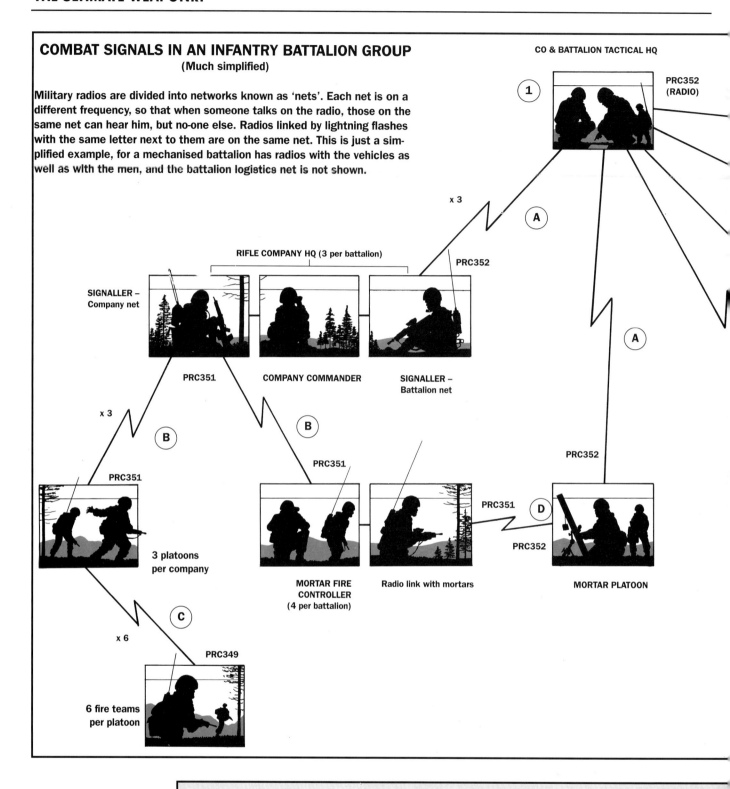

CO & BATTALION TACTICAL HQ

PRC352 (RADIO)

x 3

A

RIFLE COMPANY HQ (3 per battalion)

PRC352

SIGNALLER – Company net

PRC351

COMPANY COMMANDER

SIGNALLER – Battalion net

A

x 3

B

PRC351

B

PRC351

PRC352

PRC351

D

PRC352

PRC352

3 platoons per company

MORTAR FIRE CONTROLLER (4 per battalion)

Radio link with mortars

MORTAR PLATOON

C

x 6

PRC349

6 fire teams per platoon

Above: A simplified schematic diagram of radio communications within a British Infantry Battalion. Where the unit is equipped with Infantry Fighting Vehicles (IFVs), there is and even greater proliferation. A rifle company in an Armoured Infantry Battalion, with its 14 Warrior IFVs, has 60 radios between its 160 officers and men

WHEN THE RADIOS DIE

If tactical radio is blown off the air, we may yet have to revert to messages relayed orally by couriers, or by other essentially non-mechanical means.

AFV crews regularly use hand signals, and flag signals would be entirely appropriate, for instance, among vehicles during high-density road movements, as long as point-to-point visibility was good. A corps of motorcycle couriers, mounted on lightweight off-road machines would also effective.

And there is always the civilian communications networks. In August 1914, British patrols used the public telephone to report intelligence from points far in advance of the main spearhead units. In the 1982 Falklands War, the commander of 2 Para telephoned from Goose Green to Bluff Cove, heard from a civilian that no enemy forces were in evidence, and promptly helicoptered in a force of his own.

To a defender in a static position, the 'phone

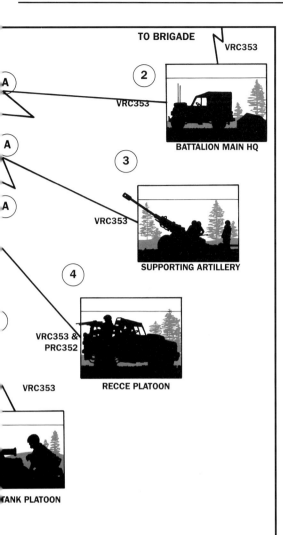

TO BRIGADE

VRC353

②

VRC353

BATTALION MAIN HQ

A

A

A

③

VRC353

SUPPORTING ARTILLERY

④

VRC353 &
PRC352

RECCE PLATOON

VRC353

TANK PLATOON

NOTES:
(1) The Commanding Officer (CO) of the Battalion fights the battle from his small, mobile 'Tactical' HQ.
(2) The Battalion 'Main' HQ co-ordinates fire support, collates information and keeps the battalion running smoothly.
(3) Artillery 'in close support' of a battalion is usually one battery (6-8 guns).
(4) 'Recce' (reconnaissance), mortar and anti-tank platoons all have their own platoon nets.

sion-making moves too far away from the front line towards a more remote level of command somewhere in the rear, decisions may be made without proper understanding of the true situation in the firing line. Yet if communications are really first class and the rearward commanders are truly imaginative, this situation can be avoided, as was the case in von Manstein's mobile defence in South Russia in 1943.

Command is impossible without effective communications

Any system that relies too heavily on its centre may find itself in difficulties should communications fail. A good illustration of this comes from the trench warfare of World War I, when command was heavily centralised but the available communications channels were quite inadequate to maintain any sort of control over battles fought beyond the commander's line of sight. News of changes in the situation always arrived too late for sensible countermeasures to be taken, and to compensate for their isolation, commanders made plans that were very cumbersome and detailed. 'Chateau generalship' was thus shown to be a dangerous game.

As will be clear from the options outlined above, the common requirement is first class (or at least reliable) communications, whatever style of command is chosen. Yet there is no reason to believe that in a future war communications will be any more able to cope than they were during World War I, not by reason of any intrinsic inefficiency but rather through the modern spectre of electronic warfare (EW). This is the third of the major threats to the commander and his HQ – an HQ whose communications are degraded by enemy jamming or interception can no longer do its job properly.

Modern EW and jamming techniques are so efficient that secure communications may be impossible on anything other than line-of-sight links. Were it possible for tactical operations always to be resolved 'from the front' by brigadiers using such links and line-of-sight intelligence, there would be little problem. However, while communications may revert to World War I conditions, the rest of warfare will not. Even if command is properly decentralised and mission orders properly exploited,

network would be even more useful. A defending army would certainly requisition and occupy key exchanges and secure the power supply, and could then maintain widespread secure communications on the friendly side of the front line. The network would sustain a lot of damage, but the density of the system in any advanced country provides a high degree of redundancy, which means it can take an enormous amount of punishment before it finally fails. Soldiers would

need to carry a combat ration of small change, though, to feed into coin boxes!

The motorcycle despatch rider looks set to make a comeback, too. The new generation of lightweight motorcycles makes it possible to cross difficult country quickly, relying on speed for protection. Where stealth is required, Morse Code, transmitted by mirror or lamp, offers a quick and easy way of passing a message over surprisingly long distances.

Above: A British radio operator in full NBC suit. The standard microphone is useless in this situation, so he must use a special microphone fitted to the front of his respirator

there will still be a greater need for rapid communication beyond the line of vision than in any previous conflict, simply because of the mobility of modern warfare.

The flow of battle will probably be such that a tank platoon commander will not be able to keep his small group of widely dispersed vehicles in sight, so what is the likelihood of a battlegroup or brigade commander maintaining direct watch on a whole formation? Equally, there will be a far greater need for complex target data for the guns, and supply status updates for the logisticians. And, in any set-piece assault, there must also be a temporary suspension of mission orders, so that everyone can be fully briefed on the way his role fits into the overall strategy.

Remote control is quite impossible without adequate feedback

The prospect of having to do all this without radio is appalling. Two hundred years ago, before remote signalling in real time was even thought of, signallers relied on their virtually unaided eyes and ears to see or hear signals and messages passed by flag or semaphore. Then came telegraphs, telephones and radios, until the whole electro-magnetic spectrum was exploited; not merely to provide inter-personal communications but also to guide weapons to their targets. Thus the electro-magnetic spectrum has itself become a major battleground, and it has often been said that the winner in the modern war will be the side that can best master it.

The EW threat to VHF tactical radios will be acute during a major war. Of course, the enemy will want to listen in to certain channels, perhaps inserting spurious information into messages or making subtle changes to them, while he will want to jam others completely. Modern encryption methods, burst broadcasts and such like reduce the chances of listening in, so jamming will become a more attractive option. Indeed, if this same army has prepared its troops to communicate without radio, it may use blanket jamming right across the board, with EW assets especially concentrated on its main axes of advance.

Even though the performance of ground-based radio systems will be seriously degraded by jamming, that will be as nothing when compared to the degree of interference experienced by aircrew, who are totally reliant on radio. And because their battlefield will also be the ground forces' battlefield, if slightly elevated, the ground forces will be affected by their collateral activities even more than by those directed at themselves. The aircraft overhead, whether friend or foe, is likely to just blanket everything in its attempts to become a black hole in the sky.

The main hope for tactical security without jamming seems to lie in a line-of-sight beam of high energy radiation, (either radio or light), which could be tampered with only by physical obstructed somewhere along its path. The beam can operate either directly from one user to another – which

would restrict the possible siting of transmitters and receivers, especially on the move – or via a satellite link. Congestion at the 36,000km orbital level used by geo-stationary satellites – and modern space weapons – is threatening the usefulness of military satellites, and in addition, both the USA and the USSR have effective anti-satellite weapons. Though secure beam communications are available, they are currently deployed only for very specialised purposes, and are certainly not yet available to front-line commanders. They will have to live with the uncertainties of VHF for some time to come.

The importance of secure, reliable communications on the battlefield cannot be overstressed. Command is exercised through the co-ordination and interaction of the various staff branches within

Above: A Soviet Kapusta class intelligence-gathering vessel. He (all Russian ships are male) was designed to collect data on Western strategic missiles, including orbital vehicles and operations to do with the Strategic Defense Initiative. Nuclear-powered, this 35,000 ton warship would be used as a floating battle-management centre during time of war

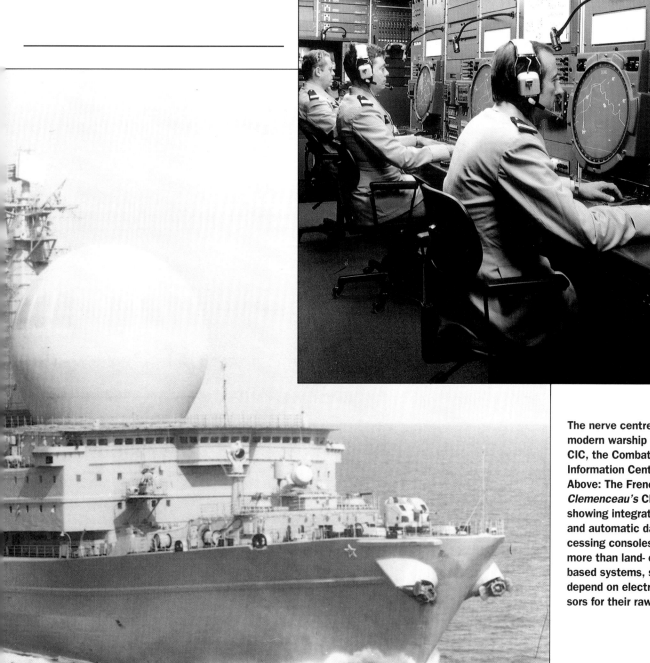

The nerve centre of a modern warship is the CIC, the Combat Information Centre. Above: The French carrier *Clemenceau's* CIC, showing integrated radar and automatic data-processing consoles. Even more than land- or air-based systems, ships depend on electronic sensors for their raw data

a headquarters. A commander cannot make meaningful decisions without knowing his superiors' intentions and the location and status of his own troops, together with their supporting arms and logistics, not to mention intelligence of the enemy, the weather and the terrain. His staff works assiduously to learn as much as possible of all these factors from the massive flow of information between the HQ and the subordinate units. But communications, vital as they are, cannot do the commander's job for him. The protean nature of battle dictates that he has no chance of ever learning all he needs to know – no matter how efficient the signals and intelligence network. At some point, he will be forced to cut short his deliberations and make decisions long before the picture is complete, and the gaps in his knowledge – the 'fog of war' must be made good by plain old-fashioned intuition and guesswork.

Information lights a path through the fog of war

Once the commander has understood as much of the general picture as he can, he must decide what he can do to change it in his favour. For instance: intelligence has confirmed that an enemy motor-rifle regiment is rapidly approaching a division's forward defended localities down a narrow valley. The divisional commander may opt to wait and see what develops, thereby giving himself extra time for intelligence gathering and decision-making.

Alternatively he may act pre-emptively to reinforce the threatened localities directly, to counter-attack, or to manoeuvre for a counter-stroke. Whichever course of action he chooses, he must give his own forces adequate warning, so that they are informed of the situation and the plan and not just overtaken by events. That in itself is a tall order, requiring still more communications traffic within a short timescale. And if additional units are to be committed to the battle, they must be given time to organise themselves into appropriate tactical groupings, top up with POL and ammunition in a leaguer area, and for their line of march to be reconnoitred and protected against both enemy surveillance and attack on the ground or from the air.

The higher the command level, the better the juggling act

This in itself is a massive task for an HQ staff that may be under attack, and it is only the beginning. If anything goes seriously wrong at any point along the way – for example, if a vital bridge is destroyed – a whole new command/decision cycle will have to initiated.

To cope with the demands of the modern battle, the commander must be both cool headed and far thinking. He must simultaneously remember what his subordinate units are doing and be able to give each one of them sound, clear orders at short

notice. If there is some unforeseen development in one sector, he must instantly analyse what it may mean for other sectors and pass on appropriate orders in good time. A commander may wish to improve his chances of controlling the battle by going forward to see for himself – in a jeep, a tank or a helicopter. There is a strong case to be made for this type of personal reconnaissance, if only because it gives the commander the opportunity to talk personally to the men on the ground, though doing so will cut him off from his HQ and staff, and effectively prevent him from exercising all his command functions.

It is perhaps an agressive commander's natural instinct, in any event, and there is plenty of historical precedent. Guderian led the *blitzkrieg* through France from the front; Rommel did the same in North Africa, and even Montgomery, the most conservative of men when it came to committing troops to battle, placed himself firmly in the forefront of the action. Often, the presence of the Commander in Chief boosts the men's morale considerably, even though it may actually degrade his own command ability – Wellington's performance at Waterloo springs to mind – and there will be times when engendering the will to fight and win is more important than retaining control of the battle. Colonel 'H' Jones, VC, realised this at Goose Green during the Falklands War, and pressed on with a personal attack that cost him his life.

IS COMMAND AND CONTROL STILL POSSIBLE ?

Modern weaponry and electronic counter-measures pose such a threat to modern armies' intelligence and communications that battlefield command and control may simply break down. Backing up this argument are these salient points:

• Tactical radio, especially VHF, may well be blown off the air from very early in the battle, leaving only cumbersome line-of-sight communications or satellite links – which themselves may be shot down

• HQs are much more vulnerable than in past wars. They will be targeted by smart weapons launched at very long ranges

• The modern battle will be faster and more complex than ever before. It will demand an exponential improvement in analysing data and automatic data processing may backfire on itself, as increasingly complex systems are inevitably more prone to failure, while commanders as well as computers may suffer from information overload

• Few of today's high-ranking officers have fought a real war. The habits of peacetime generalship are well-known enemies of wartime generalship

• Leadership 'from the front' is particularly dangerous, and puts the leader out of touch with the rest of the battle besides

But command and control may be easier and more effective than ever, for these reasons:

• New areas of the of the electromagnetic spectrum will be exploited for tactical communications, and new ways will be found to make them easier to use

• Remote antennae, better protective techniques and more mobile command vehicles may allow HQs to stay one jump ahead of the enemy's weapons

• Improved data processing leads to a better analysis of complex information, and commanders get an instantaneous ('real time') picture of the battle as it develops

• Modern methods of personnel selection and vetting give us a better chance than ever before to appoint leaders who will perform well under stress of war

• Leading from the front is probably the best way to lead, especially within the doctrine of *auftragstatik* or 'mission analysis'

Right: Forward Observation Officers (FOOs) practising their skills on the range. The laser rangefinder/designator, seen on the right, has revolutionised the FOO's working methods and has given him the capacity to make far more accurate judgments than were possible in the past. One of the keys to success on future battlefields will be the speed and efficiency with which the information supplied by the FOOs can be acted upon by senior commanders. Given the weight of artillery fire available, especially from systems such as MLRS, then a well-timed artillery strike, say on a mechanised infantry brigade on the move, could very well destroy an entire formation within a matter of minutes

THE AIR WAR

Aircraft play a part in the land battle primarily through directly attacking enemy forces. They may operate in immediate support of friendly ground forces (close air support, or CAS), or in the rear areas of the battlefield (battlefield air interdiction, or BAI), or deeper within enemy territory (interdiction). In the last instance, strategic bombers may supplement the efforts of tactical attack aircraft, as happened in Vietnam and throughout the Southeast Asia conflict, and as is envisaged by the current United States Air Force doctrine and plans.

Below: The ominous shapes of two F-117A Stealth Fighters of the USAF. This was the first aircraft in the world whose chief design consideration was to reduce radar detectability – hence the unusual shape. The F-117A first saw action in Panama in 1989

Flexibility and speed of reaction have long been cornerstones of air power theory. In the doctrines and forces needed to deal with the variable and multiple threats that will, no doubt, succeed the Soviet menace, the vaunted flexibility, long reach and fast reaction of air power should count for a great deal. Threats other than that of a massive Soviet land campaign against Western Europe have naturally been evaluated by the NATO air forces, and plans laid to counter them. Indeed there was for much of its history a general agreement within NATO that the uncertainties of international politics could lead to a shooting war in virtually any area of the world with little advance warning. Consequently NATO planning took account of potential out-of-area operations and even the remote possibility of direct intervention in local crises.

The mission distances in modern war will be tremendous

The United Kingdom's dispute with Argentina over the Falkland Islands demonstrated just this premise, as did the United States' operations in Grenada in 1983 and in Panama in 1989. Air transport played an intrinsically important role in these operations, and the Falklands campaign of 1982 offers an especially instructive illustration of the value of in-flight refuelling. The distances involved in the Falklands campaign were tremendous. Some 6250km separated Ascension Island from the Falklands; a Victor reconnaissance mission to

Right: The LOS-F-H (Line-Of Sight/Forward/Heavy) anti-aircraft system. Based on the hull of the M2 Bradley, it combines ADATS (Air Defence/Anti-Tank System) missiles with a 30mm cannon on the same chassis. This combines the accuracy and range of missiles with the quick reaction time and lack of a minimum range of a gun. Today's aircraft and helicopters are so deadly that such complex and expensive mobile anti-aircraft systems are a vital part of any armoured battlegroup

Below: A pilot training on a simulator. Simulators are an effective, and comparatively cheap, means of learning and practising the skills required of aircrew, but they cannot reproduce the adrenalin flow generated by low-level operations

South Georgia on 20 April 1982 involved a round trip of over 11,000km.

The contribution of attack aircraft to these operations is more controversial, although the operational philosophy underpinning the RAF's Harrier vertical/short take-off and landing (VSTOL) fighter-bomber was certainly vindicated by the demands of the South Atlantic campaign, since no other aeroplane (with the possible exception of the Soviet Yak-38) could have provided CAS and BAI sorties in the circumstances from a fleet equipped with nothing more than cruiser-sized aircraft carriers, with no nearby land base that could accommodate fixed-wing aircraft.

There may be no nearby land bases to accomodate fixed-wing aircraft

The ability of air power to strike quickly and effectively against multiple targets at long ranges, over wide areas, and with a large measure of surprise was largely proved by its performance in these three conflicts. Even the defeated Argentine air force played its own part effectively, even if it did rely on individuals' bravery more than effective technology. But then, it's unlikely that the FAAA ever thought it would have to fight the RAF.

The Soviet view of air superiority differs from Western notions, regarding command of the air as being an unattainable ideal. Air superiority is, rather, a temporary state achieved in a particular

area for a finite period of time. This view is very much a result of historical experience, deriving from the Great Patriotic War of 1941-45, in which German air power was never completely defeated. There's another idiosyncrasy in Soviet theory, too – gaining air superiority is not a job for the fighter pilot alone. Ground-based air defences have an equally important part to play. In the Western air forces, although some concessions may be made to the contribution of surface-to-air missiles and anti-aircraft artillery, any view which did not accord the fighter pilot primacy in this mission would certainly be condemned as heresy – especially by flyers.

The clearing of safe corridors through air defences is vital

Two concepts govern the Soviet approach to the direct support of ground forces from the air: Aerial Preparation and Air Accompaniment. The relatively small number of strategic bomber aircraft in the Soviet Air Force means that both these operations will absorb a very high proportion of all their available air assets.

Aerial Preparation has as its initial objective the clearing of safe corridors through the Western air defences. Not only will SAM sites be destroyed to create gaps in missile belts, but interceptor and air superiority fighters will be attacked both on the ground and in the air.

Aerial Preparation will use electronic counter-measures (ECM) against air defence radars and direct attacks on the vital C³I centres will be made

AIRCREW

Perhaps the air commander's most precious asset is his highly trained personnel. The selection and training of air force pilots and navigators is an expensive process, one estimate putting the cost of training an RAF fast-jet pilot as high as £3 million (over $5 million). Standards are high, and RAF wastage rates, probably typical of most flying services, give some idea of how rigorous selection and training is. Of some 1500 applicants each year, about 270 are selected for training and of these only 75 or so will emerge as qualified fast-jet aircrew.

Even on joining their first front-line squadrons, having negotiated the pitfalls of basic and advanced flying training, a tactical weapons course and final operational conversion on to the aircraft type that they will fly in the front line, the new pilots are not yet considered fully proficient. It will take something like a year's work on the squadron before the newly qualified pilot (often teamed with a navigator) will be considered combat ready. Once at that stage, proficiency must be maintained, which as far as NATO is concerned involves a minimum of 240 flying hours per year.

Once individual skills have been mastered,

the aircrew officer (by then usually a flight lieutenant in the RAF, or a captain in the US Air Force) will begin to master the skills of tactical leadership, which will take the most successful to the command of squadrons and perhaps on to more senior appointments. By that stage in their careers, the officers will have gained knowledge and experience in areas outside the professional skills of the airman, such as staff work and general administration.

Yet, by no means all aircrew are suited (or aspire to) senior command positions. Indeed, many will take their skills and hard-won experience outside the service, just when their performance is at its peak, usually into the lucrative field of commercial aviation. This wastage is a problem faced by all Western air forces. Some, accepting that a degree of disillusionment with service life is inevitable, seek to make the best of the situation by creating opportunities for part-time involvement in the reserves. The US Air Force, with numerous flying units in the Air National Guard and Air Force Reserves offers an excellent illustration of what can be done. There are signs that other air forces may in future follow their example.

Above: Some of today's cockpit technology seems more akin to science-fiction than deployed technology. This pilot has a helmet-mounted sight so that merely by looking at an enemy aircraft he can lock his short-range air-to-air missiles on to it

Below: A Panavia Tornado GR1A fitted with a combat load of nine British Aerospace ALARMs (Air-Launched Anti-Radiation Missiles) missiles and carrying ECM and chaff-dispensing pods. The ALARM is one of the world's most advanced ARMs (Anti-Radiation Missiles) and can even cope with mobile radars. ARMs home in on the electromagnetic signals sent out by a radar. If the radar is switched off, most ARMs will then just fly into the ground, but ALARM deploys a small parachute and hangs in the air until the target radar is turned back on again, whereupon it jettisons the parachute and homes in for the kill

with anti-radiation missiles and other conventional weapons. Those attack aircraft which successfully penetrate NATO defences will be directed to NATO tactical nuclear weapons systems (most probably as an overriding priority), airfields, headquarters, C^3I centres, and – more directly related to the land battle – armour and artillery concentrations, defensive strongpoints, river crossings and centres of resistance.

Soviet air doctrine has been exported, along with its aircraft

Air Accompaniment, on the other hand, is operations in support of ground forces (which embrace more than the much-publicised operational manoeuvre groups) that have penetrated deep into enemy territory. Support will either take the form of pre-planned sorties, or specially requested air attacks on stubborn defensive positions, and developing enemy counter-attacks.

With the rapidly changing situation in Eastern Europe and the Russian homeland, it is tempting to dismiss Soviet concepts of air war as an irrelevance in any future conflict. This would surely be a mistake, not only because the Soviet Union retains

powerful air forces itself, but also because Soviet air doctrine had been exported along with aircraft and armament to many of the world's potential trouble spots. Soviet doctrine emphasises action by all arms directed towards a common objective and as such represents an exceptionally well-integrated view of the aircraft's contribution to the land battle. Many sceptics, however, have questioned whether the practical implementation will match the theory.

Just how dangerous a place have ground-based air defence weapons made the modern battlefield? Again, the Soviet example is instructive. Soviet ground-based air defences create the most lethal aerial environment that the attack aircraft is likely to encounter. The ZSU 23/4 self-propelled AAA system, for example, has a rate of fire of 3400 rounds per minute and is effective out to 3000m. Each vehicle carries an ammunition load of 2000 rounds and accompanying supply trucks will provide a further 3000 (One minute and 28 seconds' worth of sustained fire). The SA-10B mobile SAM has a maximum speed of Mach 6, can engage targets flying as low as 30m above ground level and can acquire its target, lock on and fire, all within 10 seconds.

In theory, the Soviet air defence systems provide their ground forces with an umbrella of interlocking

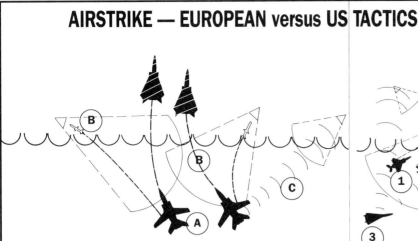

AIRSTRIKE — EUROPEAN versus US TACTICS

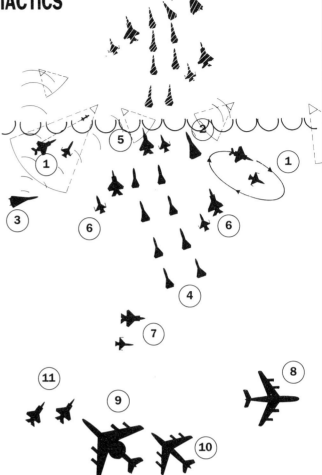

▽ **ENEMY RADARS**

◁ **ENEMY RADAR BEAMS**

))) **JAMMING SIGNAL**

⊬ **ANTI-RADIATION MISSILE**

'European' – particularly British – strike tactics (above) involve sending groups of only two or four aircraft at low level under the enemy radar (A). If enemy radars do pose a threat, they will be dealt with by resources carried by the strike aircraft themselves. These include anti-radiation missiles (B) and jamming equipment (C).

'US'-style strike tactics (right) stress the use of a large grouping of many specialist types of aircraft. 'Wild Weasel' pairs of one F-4G and one F-16C patrol in front of the enemy defences (1). They fly racetrack patterns and destroy enemy radars when they are switched on. Other enemy radars will be jammed by EF-111s – both accompanying the strike force (2), and providing stand-off jamming (3) to confuse the enemy as to where the attack is entering his defences. Ahead of the strike force itself (4) fly fighters – F-15s and F-16s (5) – to sweep the sky ahead of enemy aircraft. Such fighters also provide close-in escort (6) and top cover (7) for the strike force. ELINT and SIGINT (ELectronics and SIGnals INTelligence) aircraft – such as the RC-135 – monitor enemy radio and radar signals and jam enemy communications (8). Providing radar surveillance of the strike is an AEW (Airborne Early Warning) aircraft (9), such as the E-3 AWACS, and this also acts as master of ceremonies. Sometimes, an EC-135 will act as an airborne command post (10). Because both the E-3 and the EC-135 are so important and yet vulnerable, they have heavy fighter protection (11).

sub-systems with a high enough degree of mobility to keep up with an armoured advance. In manoeuvre warfare, however, it is doubtful whether this umbrella's integrity can be maintained at all times. Delays to unit movements, through casualties, congestion, natural obstacles and lack of a complete amphibious capability will create gaps in the air defence coverage. To the rear of the battlefield, air defence will stretch its cover back to the Soviet homeland, presenting NATO interdictor aircraft with a series of threats of varying magnitude. Although rear echelon defences will be less dense than those covering the battlefield, high value targets are certain to be heavily protected.

Air defences will be less dense towards the rear of the battlefield

Any interdictor aircraft must also run the gauntlet of the enemy's interceptor force. Taking the Soviet example once again, these interceptors will include up-to-date fighters, such as the MiG-29 Fulcrum and Su-27 Flanker, equipped with pulse-doppler radar and air-to-air missiles with capability. The total force dedicated to air defence, which also includes older and less capable interceptors, numbers some 1250 aircraft. CFE treaties may reduce these numbers, but they are most unlikely to affect the deployment of the most modern interceptors in the inventory.

4. ELINT and SIGINT (ELectronics and SIGnals INTelligence) support is provided by an EA-3B Skywarrior, which monitors the enemy's radar and radio transmissions, acquiring data and jamming his communications to disrupt the ground control of enemy interceptors.

5. F-14s fly BARCAP (BARrier Combat Air Patrols) between the strike force and the area from which enemy interception is most likely. They also fly CAP (Combat Air Patrols) to protect the carrier force, and deck-launched intercepts for close-in defence.

3. The six SH-3H Sea King helicopters carried aboard most US aircraft carriers carry out "plane guard" duties, during flying operations on and off the flat top. On station to port and just aft of the carrier, the Sea King rescues airmen who have had to ditch.

AIRPOWER AT SEA

The offensive warship's eventual task is to bombard enemy ships and shore installations into defeat or submission. The carrier achieves this end by means of its aircraft, rather than by the missiles and guns of a battleship or a cruiser.

Only the United States of America has been able to afford the huge cost of building, equipping and operating carrier groups in the post-WWII period, though many other nations maintain a limited capacity for marine aviation.

In addition to the carrier's strike aircraft - the offensive arm itself - the rest of the group is made up of a wide variety of defensive and supportive ships and aircraft. The ships - anti-submarine and anti-aircraft frigates, in the main, together with logistical supply ships - provide a defensive screen around the carrier, but can also provide the same service in support of land operations. The carrier's defensive aircraft, in turn, protect both the carrier itself, its offensive aircraft, and the fleet as a whole.

2. The SH-3H Sea King provides short range anti-submarine defence for the carrier force (up to 16km from the flat top), together with the cruisers and destroyers of the carrier group and their embarked helicopters. The Sea King's wide range of sensors includes a "dipping sonar".

1. The S-3 Viking provides long-range anti-submarine defence for the carrier force, with a maximum range of 3700km, and a maximum endurance of 7.5 hours. It has both anti-submarine sensors and a surface radar, and can also act as an anti-ship picquet.

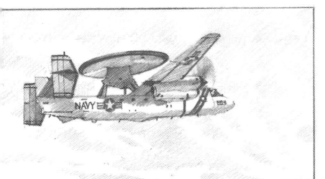

6. The E-2C Hawkeye provides AEW (Airborne Early Warning) cover, on station about 370km from the flat top. The E-2C can detect targets 450km away and assign them to F-14s via a data link. It also coordinates the strike force and provides air traffic control.

7. The F/A-18 Hornet is a true multi-role aircraft. As a fighter, it performs close escort for the strike force, and TARCAP (TARget Combat Air Patrol). This involves maintaining station over or near the target and preventing any enemy aircraft from interfering with the airstrike.

The current US Navy inventory includes:

1. S-3 Vikings, to protect the group against attack from submarines
2. Sea King ASW helicopters, which provide the same service close in, and
3. Sea King rescue helicopters, to look after downed aircrew
4. EA-3B Skywarriors, to intercept enemy radar and signals traffic
5. F-14 Tomcats, to deter would-be airborne attackers
6. E-2C Hawkeyes, to act as airborne sentries and air traffic controllers
7 & 9. F/A-18 Hornets, which double in both offensive and defensive roles
8 & 10. A-6Ds, which form the main arm of the strike force, refuelling each other from "buddy stores" pods as they go

8. Two variants of the A-6 perform important specialist jobs. The four KA-6Ds of a carrier air wing serve as tankers, while the four EA-6B Prowlers provide electronic warfare support for the strike force, either with stand-off jamming and ESM or penetrating with the strike waves.

9. Before the main strike wave attacks, F/A-18 Hornets suppress the enemy defences by destroying radars with HARMs (High Speed Anti-Radiation Missiles). They are also used for normal attack missions and for BDA (Battle Damage Assessment) after the strike has gone in.

10. The A-6 Intruders of the carrier air wing are the main striking force of the flat top. Highly sophisticated, with the latest navigation and bombing technology, they can drop 8000Kg of ordnance 750km from the carrier with pin-point accuracy in all weathers, day and night.

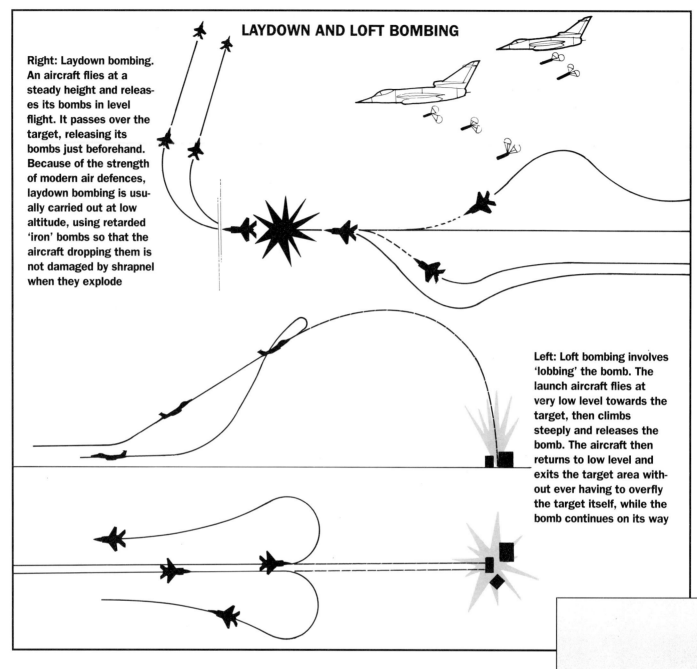

LAYDOWN AND LOFT BOMBING

Right: Laydown bombing. An aircraft flies at a steady height and releases its bombs in level flight. It passes over the target, releasing its bombs just beforehand. Because of the strength of modern air defences, laydown bombing is usually carried out at low altitude, using retarded 'iron' bombs so that the aircraft dropping them is not damaged by shrapnel when they explode

Left: Loft bombing involves 'lobbing' the bomb. The launch aircraft flies at very low level towards the target, then climbs steeply and releases the bomb. The aircraft then returns to low level and exits the target area without ever having to overfly the target itself, while the bomb continues on its way

The aircraft are backed up by an extensive network of ground radars and command centres, together with a small airborne early warning (AEW) element. The presence of AEW assets is extremely significant, since AEW aircraft have closed the low level gap where ground radars are blind, which penetrating attack aircraft have long sought to exploit. Consequently, attacking aircraft must be prepared to fight their way into and out from the target. This means adding yet another capability to an already overloaded aircraft: the ability to execute effective defensive manoeuvres while carrying a full warload.

Clearly, the defender's mission is successful if the attack aircraft is forced to jettison its warload in order to gain superiority of performance. In conditions where an air defence interceptor with a limited load of air-to-air missiles (AAMs) and gun ammunition may have to deal with multiple threats, this could be a decisive factor operating in favour of the defence. Aircraft like the RAF's Jaguar, for example, could find it extremely difficult to carry out an interdiction mission if it was forced to take on the air defence on its own.

AEW aircraft have closed the gap in which ground radars were blind

These active defences will present the most effective threat to interdiction aircraft, but passive defences may also rob an attacker of success just as effectively, even though they do not present a direct threat. Hardened targets, for example, will call for high accuracy in weapons delivery; they may also mean that interdictors will have to carry heavier stores and will have fewer options in their style of attack, if pilots are to be sure their bombs will penetrate the target. A low-level bomb laydown, for example, would not be effective against a hardened target. Only fixed, high-value targets, such as command centres, aircraft shelters and nuclear-weapons storage facilities are likely to be protected by hardening. However, most potential targets will seek a measure of protection through camouflage and dispersal, both of which can make the job of target acquisition and weapons aiming more difficult.

Electronic counter-measures will add to the attacker's difficulties, both through jamming and by forcing him to keep EM emissions to a minimum. The danger that an enemy may black out communications by jamming has especially worrying implications for close air support, where good ground-air communications are essential if aircraft are to react in time to be effective.

Pre-sortie briefings can help to overcome comm. system shortfalls, but they rob the attack aircraft of much of its valuable flexibility of action. The RAF's Harrier force, which will operate from dispersal sites much nearer to the front line than conventional airfields, has an advantage in this respect. Laser designation by forward air controllers (FACs) reduces the need for voice communication, and the crews of air-

craft operating in close formation can of course signal orders and intentions visually to each other.

ECM will place very similar restrictions on radar emission. Crews will use attack radar only sparingly for position-fixing, and even then only in short bursts. Thus, for much of the flight the attack radar, which shows an animated map of the terrain and is such an aid to navigation, will perforce remain on standby. Even so, such aircraft types as the Tornado, F-111 and Su-24 Fencer flying low-level penetration sorties still require continuous transmissions from both terrain-following radars and radar altimeters.

An enemy may block out communications by jamming

The nature of air defences will, of course, affect the tactics of target penetration. The intensity of the threat depends on such variables as visibility, day or night operation and weather conditions, as well as the capability of the defences themselves. For example, the RAF's Tornado crews will positively

Below: A Panavia Tornado of the German Naval Air Force fires its MW-1 dispenser. The MW-1 can be loaded with a wide range of stores from anti-tank bomblets to a runway cratering device which fires a charge that explodes underneath the concrete to make repair much more difficult. Dispensers such as the MW-1 allow the carrying aircraft to fly very low over the target, reducing their vulnerability to enemy air defences

CLOSE AIR SUPPORT VERSUS BATTLEFIELD AIR INTERDICTION

The usefulness of the fixed-wing aircraft in close air support (CAS) of ground forces has more than once been called into question. At one level the arguments are purely technical: they centre on the capability of the present generation of CAS aircraft to survive – let alone operate effectively – over the modern battlefield. The most recent developments in Soviet ground-based air defence will undoubtedly make the front line a very dangerous place indeed for aircraft as slow as

the USAF's A-10A Thunderbolt II, which is otherwise very well matched to the CAS role; and there is always the possibility that Western-developed SAMs and AAA will face Western fliers in future conflicts involving smaller states. The USAF therefore wants to replace its A-10As with an attack version of the F-16 Fighting Falcon (the so-called A-16) in a combined CAS and battlefield air interdiction (BAI) role.

The fact that the two elements of this

combination are quite distinct opens another area of dispute. For army commanders argue that when it comes to a choice between allocating forces to CAS or BAI, air force doctrine will tend to accord the latter higher priority. Quite apart from any inter-service differences in doctrine, there may be sound practical reasons for such a decision. The army commander will have under his direct control a variety of weapons able to deal with the traditional CAS targets. They will include conventional tube artillery, MLRS, attack helicopters and perhaps, in the none-too-distant future, attack drones. In many instances it will therefore make little sense to risk an expensive combat aircraft and its pilot on a mission into the area of greatest danger, when alternative means of dealing with the target are readily available.

The ground commander will also tend to employ the means nearest to hand, especially in those cases when the reaction time of his own forces will be very much quicker than that of a CAS aircraft. Therefore, the aircraft is increasingly becoming a weapon of last resort in the traditional CAS role, although one can envisage occasions on which the army commander will be only too pleased to use it. As a rule, though, the land commander will regard attack aircraft as the means of dealing with targets beyond the range of the resources under his direct command.

welcome a dark, stormy night on which to carry out an attack mission, since the problems that such conditions will pose for the defenders will far outweigh the difficulties that they will create for the attackers. The US Air Force's F-111 crews operating during the December 1972 Linebacker II campaign against Hanoi and Haiphong could fly alone over any part of enemy territory at will, whereas the Linebacker B-52s flew only in close formation, in order to maintain the integrity of their EW protection. Thus the technical capabilities of the various attack aircraft will also affect their penetration tactics.

The lower an interdictor flies, the safer he will be

Terrain, too, will influence penetration tactics, since the masking effect of hills on defensive radar coverage is relatively easy to exploit in planning approach routes, though it is negated by AEW radar. Operations over desert or steppe will have to rely on other means of masking the presence of the aircraft, too. Evasive routing is a valuable way of avoiding enemy defensive concentrations, but its usefulness depends on the range of the attacking aircraft.

Limited-range interdiction aircraft, such as the Tornado, will have to follow a direct route to their targets and the predictability of their arc of approach will make life a little easier for the defence. The longer-legged strategic bombers, such as the Rockwell B-1B and the Tupolev Blackjack, can make good use of their range by bypassing heavily defended areas such as missile belts, and exploiting such weakly-defended points of entry as the Soviet Union's long Arctic littoral.

Although small formations of strike/attack aircraft may be able to rely on evasive flying to get through the enemy's air defences, such tactics are not likely to work for larger formations, who must be prepared – and equipped – to fight their way through to their targets. To stand any chance of success, they must rely on an accompanying force of specialised escort aircraft; not only fighter escorts, but also defence suppression aircraft to deal with SAM and AAA threats, and electronic warfare aircraft to provide assistance, through

Right: Modern bomber aircraft tend not to have the bomb bays of their WWII predecessors. Instead, they carry a variable weapons load on pylons slung beneath the wings and the fuselage, with the centre point normally reserved for the heaviest weapons. This French air force Mirage is carrying a full load of 'slick' bombs

Far right: Rockets, too, are an effective, if risky way of getting ordnance on to an area target. They are notoriously prone to scatter, and require the pilot to make his approach in an attitude that invites ground fire

TYPES OF AIR-TO-SURFACE MUNITION

ANTI-RADIATION MISSILE

The aircraft programmes the Anti-Radiation Missile (ARM) before launch (1), using data from the aircraft's own ESM devices or from another source. The ARM (2A) then flies down the target's radar beam until impact (3), where a fragmentation bomb destroys the antenna. Modern ARMs can home in on the radar even after it has been turned off, provided it has been on long enough to allow the ARM to get a fix on its position. Even if the radar has not been on long enough, the BAe ALARM (Air-Launched Anti-Radiation Missile) dispenses a parachute when the radar is turned off (2B). This slows the missile's descent, and when the radar is turned on again, the missile can home in again on the antenna.

TV-GUIDED (LOCK-ON) & INFRA-RED LOCK-ON

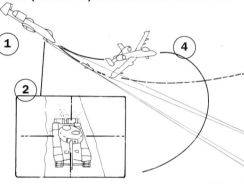

The pilot of the launch aircraft (1) locks the missile on to the target, using a small video screen in his cockpit (2), which repeats the image as seen through the missile's seeker head. Once launched, the missile homes in on the centre of the image, and thus the target (3). The pilot does not have to control the missile

RETARDED BOMBS

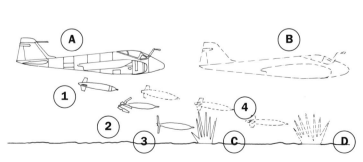

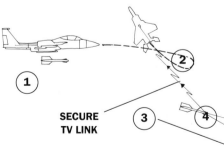

SECURE TV LINK

The bomb (1) is launched when the aircraft is at A and flying at low level. The bomb flies at approximately the same speed as the aircraft until the retarder fins start to deploy (2). These slow down the bomb through drag, so that when the bomb explodes at C, the aircraft (at B), is clear of the explosion. If the bomb was dropped at a very low level (4), it would keep moving at approximately the same speed as the aircraft and, exploding directly beneath it, damage it.

The aircraft launches the TV-guided missile (1), then turns away, keeping out of range of enemy close-range anti-air defences (2). As the missile flies down on to the target (3), a TV camera in the missile's nose relays a picture of the flight path back to a controller in the launch aircraft via a secure TV link. The controller then 'flies' the missile down on to the target (4).

these support functions themselves. Virtually all are now armed with short-range infra-red guided AAMs for self-defence against interceptors. By the end of the 1990s, anti-radiation missiles will have become as common a secondary armament as the AAM and, of course, all interdiction aircraft carry electronic countermeasures equipment of varying sophistication. Yet all this extra capability tends to divert the attack aircraft from its primary mission.

For example, formations of older generation attack aircraft such as the Harrier GR Mk 3 may have to include AAM-armed aircraft as well as bomb carriers, since they lack sufficient payload and range to carry both bombs and AAMs on the same mission. Even a more modern attack aircraft will not be able to engage an interceptor in a manoeuvring fight without first jettisoning its warload. The RAF may be

jamming and 'spoof' techniques directed against the enemy's C³I systems.

A planned airstrike will use a dozen different aircraft types

The USAF and US Navy used such combined 'strike forces' during Operation Linebacker in May 1972, which was designed to interrupt North Vietnam's import of essential war supplies from China and the USSR. A typical mission might involve a basic unit of F-4 Phantoms carrying both laser-guided and conventional 'dumb' bombs to hit the designated target (often a bridge). Preceding them came F-105G 'Wild Weasel' Thunderchiefs carrying Shrike anti-radiation missiles and Phantoms carrying cluster bombs to deal with North Vietnamese surface-to-air (SAM) missile sites before the bombers arrived. Alongside the bombers would fly USAF EB-66s or USN EA-6As carrying chaff and ECM jamming equipment to confuse enemy radar. Yet more F-4s would act as fighter escorts to counter North Vietnamese MiG fighters, and the whole force would be both preceded and followed up by Phantom RF-4s, to take 'before and after' photographs. Linebacker was one of the most effective bombing operations of the Vietnam War, but it was also expensive: if 80 aircraft took part in a strike force, as few as 12 might actually be bombers, the rest flying in protective or supportive roles of one kind or another.

To some extent, attack aircraft can perform all

forced to assign a number of its Tornado strike/attack aircraft as dedicated defence-suppression aircraft, carrying ALARM missiles. The service has resisted the idea of forming specialised units for this task and instead will give the job to particular aircraft within existing squadrons.

Recent developments tend to make the combination of strike aircraft plus escort a more attractive attack force than individual aircraft or small formations. The US Air Force, for example, has continuously improved its aircraft's ability to evade air defences (most notably through its Stealth technology programmes), yet it has simultaneously developed and refined the escorted attack force.

Dedicated defense-suppression aircraft will join the escort force

Both the US Air Force and the US Navy used such strike forces not only against heavily defended major targets in Southeast Asia during the Vietnam War, but also more recently, when they struck at Colonel Gaddaffi's Libya in 1986, so demonstrating their continuing value as an alternative to target penetration by evasion and Stealth. The move towards escorted attack forces doesn't have many supporters in the smaller air forces, which simply do not have the resources to realise the concept. Yet only the most sophisticated aircraft – for example, the A-12/Advanced Attack Aircraft and the B-2 strategic bomber – have a high chance of penetrating modern, dense air defences successfully, and

during its flight, and so can concentrate on flying away from the enemy defences (4). This system can use either a standard TV or a thermal image camera.

TV-GUIDED MISSILES (COMMAND GUIDANCE)

TV PICTURE

VULNERABILITY AND V/STOL

It is easy to overlook the fact that the enemy's tactical air power (and possibly ET weapons also) can destroy one's own airbases and their supporting infrastructure, and so put paid to one's own air power before it has even left the ground. NATO countries have seen their long concrete runways, associated hardstandings and taxiways as potential hostages to fortune ever since the coincidence of the successful Israeli air strikes at the outset of the 1967 Six Day War and a fast-developing Soviet interdiction capability in the late 1960s alerted them to their own vulnerabilities.

An extreme point of view in the debate over the tenability of the traditional airbase in wartime holds that as a matter of course all peacetime airfields will be eliminated by pre-targeted tactical missiles at the outset of hostilities. The corollary of this is that the future of tactical air power can lie only with VSTOL. Besides the apocalyptic powers that proponents of this view accord to tactical missiles, there are flaws in the argument.

In terms of performance, V/STOL aircraft are mid-1950s warplanes incapable of supersonic speeds and have a restricted payload and range in comparison with conventional aircraft of the same generation. Moreover, although VSTOL aircraft might be able to operate independently of long concrete runways, they are certainly not freed from the logistical demands of other tactical aircraft. Consequently, their need for fuel and ammunition resupply, maintenance and spares and numerous other supporting services, create a logistical tail that turns VSTOL aircraft's dispersed sites into a very complex problem indeed.

Not that the weight of attack that a fixed air base will undoubtedly attract should be in any way trivialised. It is highly probable that main runways will be cratered and that much of the airfield's operating surfaces will be made unusable. Personnel must be prepared to operate under air and ground attack and to accept all of the limitations that incoming NBC weapons will impose. Hardened aircraft shelters should ensure that most aircraft survive, since only a direct hit by a heavy bomb will eliminate them. Similar hardened accommodation for people and essential support services should likewise guarantee a fair measure of survivability.

However, all these precautions will go for nothing if the aircraft are effectively grounded. Rapid runway repair techniques can be used to make damaged surfaces usable again, although the presence of delayed-action anti-personnel weapons will undoubtedly hamper this work, as will follow-up air attacks.

In the meantime, it is likely that a reduced level of air operation can be maintained from the base by making use of those strips of runway and other operating surfaces that have escaped cratering. In that case, warload and/or fuel load may well have to be limited to match the aircraft's take-off weight to the available ground run.

Right: In 1982, the Israelis invaded the Lebanon, part of which was already occupied by Syrian forces. To try to negate Israeli aerial strength, the Syrians had set up 19 SAM batteries in the Beqaa Valley. The Israeli response was devastating: on 9 June, 17 of these batteries were taken out in a brilliantly co-ordinated strike, using Boeing 707s and EC-2 Hawkeyes (protected by F-15 and F-16 interceptors) to control pilotless drones (RPVs) that locked onto the Syrian radar frequencies and then to direct ground-attack aircraft and missiles to destroy the radars and the SAMs

these are enormously expensive projects, equally out of reach of those self-same air forces.

Only the most advanced air-superiority fighter can successfully escort a strike force into enemy territory. Not only must its range match that of the attack aircraft it accompanies, but its performance must allow it to deal with more lightly loaded – and therefore potentially more agile – air defence interceptors. The present generation of air superiority fighters is exemplified by the USAF's F-15 Eagle and the Soviet Union's Su-27 Flanker. The latter aircraft has been assigned to the Aviation Armies of the Soviet Union (AASU) specifically to provide escort cover for that command's Su-24 Fencers.

An air superiority fighter's need for long range and heavy air-to-air armament inevitably produces a large aircraft, which will need good ECM protection if it is to survive in enemy airspace. The F-15 Eagle's successor – the Advanced Tactical Fighter, which is currently being developed – will most probably make use of active electronic warfare (EW) measures (built-in threat-warning receivers and automatically controlled jammers) as well as the passive protection of its 'stealthiness'.

Above: A McDonnell Douglas/British Aerospace AV-8B Harrier II of the US Marine Corps. The V/STOL (Vertical/Short Take-Off and Landing) capability of the Harrier allows the Marines to operate it almost anywhere

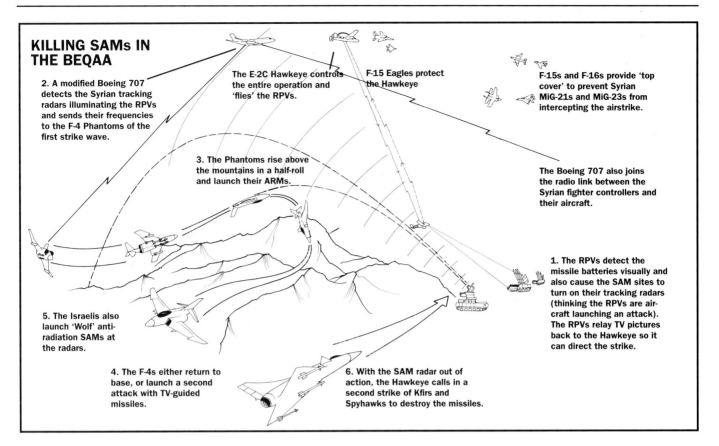

KILLING SAMs IN THE BEQAA

2. A modified Boeing 707 detects the Syrian tracking radars illuminating the RPVs and sends their frequencies to the F-4 Phantoms of the first strike wave.

The E-2C Hawkeye controls the entire operation and 'flies' the RPVs.

F-15 Eagles protect the Hawkeye

F-15s and F-16s provide 'top cover' to prevent Syrian MiG-21s and MiG-23s from intercepting the airstrike.

3. The Phantoms rise above the mountains in a half-roll and launch their ARMs.

The Boeing 707 also joins the radio link between the Syrian fighter controllers and their aircraft.

1. The RPVs detect the missile batteries visually and also cause the SAM sites to turn on their tracking radars (thinking the RPVs are aircraft launching an attack). The RPVs relay TV pictures back to the Hawkeye so it can direct the strike.

5. The Israelis also launch 'Wolf' anti-radiation SAMs at the radars.

4. The F-4s either return to base, or launch a second attack with TV-guided missiles.

6. With the SAM radar out of action, the Hawkeye calls in a second strike of Kfirs and Spyhawks to destroy the missiles.

Although both attack aircraft and escort fighters must carry EW equipment that can jam SAM and AAA radars, this individually-fitted equipment will not protect an attacking formation from these threats. So dedicated defence-suppression aircraft will join the escort force. The USAF designates such aircraft 'Wild Weasels'. Currently the USAF assigns F-4G Phantoms and F-16C Fighting Falcons to its Wild Weasel units, the two types operating together as 'hunter-killer' pairs. The Services Follow-on Wild Weasel project, set up to field a successor to the F-4G, has fallen foul of recent budget cuts, and so the present force is likely to continue in service until the early years of the next century.

The Wild Weasels operate at low level and on the flanks

The F-4G carries a complex threat detection system (the AN/APR-38), which is capable of locating and identifying a wide range of radars associated with ground-based SAM and AAA systems. Not only will the system give the range and bearing of these threats, but it will also indicate which of them is the most dangerous. The F-4G's backseater or 'Bear' can then deal with the trouble, either using his own stand-off or freefall armament, or by directing the accompanying F-16C against the enemy.

The F-16Cs are virtually standard aircraft, with only some changes in computer software required to suit them to the new role. They carry both freefall ordnance and anti-radiation missiles, with which to attack SAM and AAA sites and their associated radars, and (unlike the F-4G) also have a built-in gun armament. The Wild Weasels operate at low level ahead and on the flanks of the strike

force. They play a very dangerous game of cat and mouse with the ground defences, their primary objective being to create a safe corridor through enemy airspace for the strike force.

Specialised EW aircraft can also have a vital role in neutralising the enemy air defence forces, either through jamming their radars or by means of 'spoofing' tactics. For example, barrage jamming can be used to create a barrier behind which a strike force can assemble for its attack. Jamming escort aircraft, however, need to be able to perform better than most standard EW aircraft. The answer has been to use converted strike aircraft like the USAF's EF-111A Raven and the US Navy's EA-6B Prowler. The Raven's operations depend to a high degree on automation, since it carries only a pilot and one electronic warfare specialist. The Prowler is a more effective aircraft in this respect, since it can carry three specialist crew members, but it lacks the overall performance of its USAF counterpart.

Specialised diversions give the strike force valuable supprt

Other specialist aircraft can give the strike force valuable support. In-flight refuelling tanker aircraft, for instance, are often needed to provide the necessary range for a strike mission. During USAF operations over Southeast Asia during the Vietnam War they were particularly useful during the withdrawal phase of a strike, providing fuel to aircraft that otherwise would not have regained their bases. Then there are AEW aircraft, which monitor the progress of a strike at long range and if necessary provide advance warning of a developing threat from enemy interceptors.

Left: Soviet SAM-4 'Ganef' surface-to-air missiles on their tracked launchers. The SAM-4 has a maximum range of 70km, a minimum range of 9.3km and can reach up to an altitude of 25km. Many Soviet SAMs have been sold to countries throughout the Third World

In certain circumstances, the bludgeon of escorted strike may be preferable to the rapier of low-level evasion, as an attack force that has to evade enemy defences and to fight its way into the target area will find navigation and target acquisition all the more difficult. The ideal navigation system for an interdiction aircraft would be completely autonomous; that is, requiring no external data for position correction during the course of the flight. This would mean that the aircraft would make no EM emissions – which, as outlined earlier, are a potential means of detection and can provide an opportunity for jamming – and it would of course be thoroughly reliable. Modern electronic engineering has yet to produce such a system.

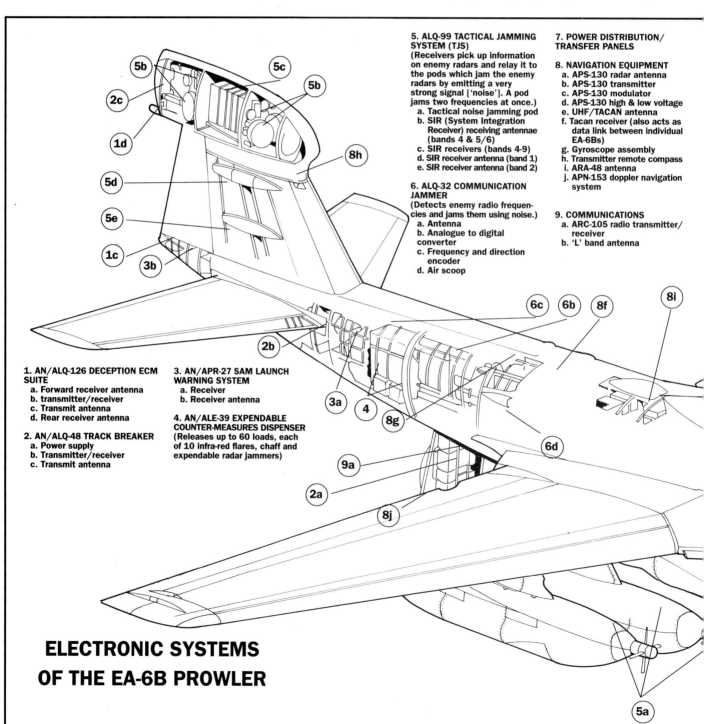

5. ALQ-99 TACTICAL JAMMING SYSTEM (TJS)
(Receivers pick up information on enemy radars and relay it to the pods which jam the enemy radars by emitting a very strong signal ['noise']. A pod jams two frequencies at once.)
a. Tactical noise jamming pod
b. SIR (System Integration Receiver) receiving antennae (bands 4 & 5/6)
c. SIR receivers (bands 4-9)
d. SIR receiver antenna (band 1)
e. SIR receiver antenna (band 2)

6. ALQ-32 COMMUNICATION JAMMER
(Detects enemy radio frequencies and jams them using noise.)
a. Antenna
b. Analogue to digital converter
c. Frequency and direction encoder
d. Air scoop

7. POWER DISTRIBUTION/ TRANSFER PANELS

8. NAVIGATION EQUIPMENT
a. APS-130 radar antenna
b. APS-130 transmitter
c. APS-130 modulator
d. APS-130 high & low voltage
e. UHF/TACAN antenna
f. Tacan receiver (also acts as data link between individual EA-6Bs)
g. Gyroscope assembly
h. Transmitter remote compass
i. ARA-48 antenna
j. APN-153 doppler navigation system

9. COMMUNICATIONS
a. ARC-105 radio transmitter/ receiver
b. 'L' band antenna

1. AN/ALQ-126 DECEPTION ECM SUITE
a. Forward receiver antenna
b. transmitter/receiver
c. Transmit antenna
d. Rear receiver antenna

2. AN/ALQ-48 TRACK BREAKER
a. Power supply
b. Transmitter/receiver
c. Transmit antenna

3. AN/APR-27 SAM LAUNCH WARNING SYSTEM
a. Receiver
b. Receiver antenna

4. AN/ALE-39 EXPENDABLE COUNTER-MEASURES DISPENSER
(Releases up to 60 loads, each of 10 infra-red flares, chaff and expendable radar jammers)

ELECTRONIC SYSTEMS
OF THE EA-6B PROWLER

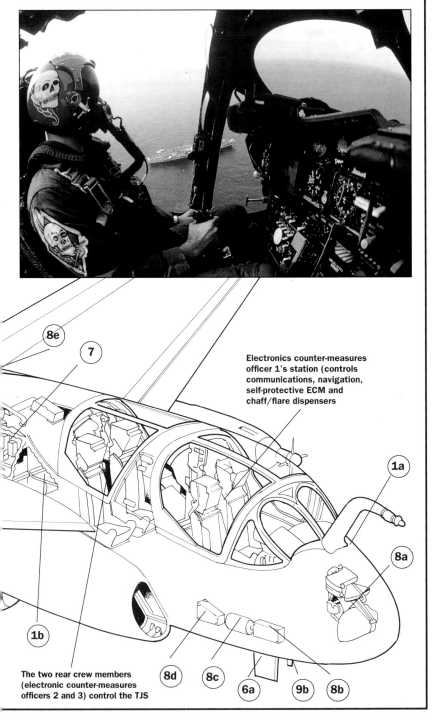

The Tornado interdiction/strike aircraft in service with the Royal Air Force, the German Luftwaffe and Italy's Aeronautica Militare relies on an inertial navigation system (INS) and a doppler velocity-sensing radar for its basic navigation information. The INS is autonomous in operation in the sense that it requires no external inputs, apart from feeding in the aircraft's precise position at the start of its flight.

The system, however, does suffer from 'slippage', and the accumulation of minor positional errors during the course of a two-hour sortie will create a significant circular error. For this reason, the Tornado crew must update the INS with position fixes during the flight. Typically, a series of prominent features (geographical or man-made) are selected as 'waypoints' along the pre-planned aircraft track. The navigator will pick them up on his radar and mark them by positioning a cursor over the waypoint's image on his radar screen, so correcting the flightpath. An experienced crew can do this very quickly indeed, but it does involve a telltale radar emission.

The Tornado crew must update the INS with fixes during the flight

The two separate sources of navigational data, the INS and the doppler, provide a cross-check on accuracy: a serious error in either system will immediately become apparent. However, the combined accuracy of the two is still insufficient for terrain-following flight. This calls for a specialised radar, which is of course another emitter, albeit one operating on a fairly narrow beam. Nevertheless, terrain-following by means of super-accurate navigation is certainly now within prospect. The system proposed for the Tornado's 'mid-life upgrade' will be verified by an apparatus similar to the cruise missile's terrain contour matching. This compares a radar image of the terrain below the aircraft with data stored in a navigation computer. Certainly the need for an emitter has not yet been entirely eliminated, but the new system won't be as easy to detect as terrain-following radar.

There can be no doubt that radar – used sparingly to avoid detection – will remain a valuable attack aircraft sensor for the foreseeable future. The USAF's new F-15E Strike Eagle, now coming into service to supplement the F-111 in the strike/interdiction role, has an especially valuable radar feature for target acquisition. Its AN/APG-70 radar can operate in a synthetic aperture mode for ground-mapping. This gives a high-resolution image of the target area after a few seconds' transmission. The image can then be 'frozen', allowing the radar to go onto standby if need be, while the aircraft's weapons system officer (WSO) sets up the attack using the stored radar data.

The need for an emitter has not yet been entirely eliminated

Synthetic aperture techniques, hitherto used for reconnaissance rather than attack radars, obtain an extremely detailed radar picture by electronically 'enlarging' the aerial, the physical dimensions of which are severely restricted by the limited space available on the aircraft. The F-15E also uses the pod-mounted LANTIRN system, which provides FLIR imagery for both navigation and attack. The main radar retains an air-to-air capability and so, unlike most interdiction aircraft, the F-15E can transform itself from an attack aircraft into an air superiority fighter.

FLIRs and laser rangefinders are extremely useful in target acquisition and weapons delivery. The USAF's F-111F's WSO can use the aircraft's Pave Tack system to acquire his target using FLIR and

Electronics counter-measures officer 1's station (controls communications, navigation, self-protective ECM and chaff/flare dispensers)

The two rear crew members (electronic counter-measures officers 2 and 3) control the TJS

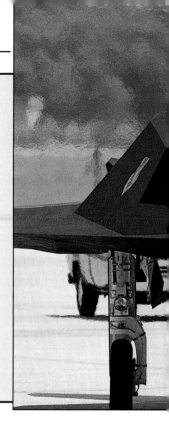

INVISIBLE AIRCRAFT
STEALTH TECHNOLOGY EXPLAINED

The next generation of tactical aircraft will all have some level of 'stealth' technology to improve their chances of survival in combat and against air defences. Various techniques will reduce the radar cross-section, infra-red, visual – and perhaps aural – signatures of aircraft to the point where they will no longer give the enemy an early enough warning of their approach or a sufficiently reliable means of target tracking and weapons guidance.

A 'stealthy' aircraft will also need to reduce or entirely eliminate its own electromagnetic emissions. These are essentially the aims of Stealth programmes. The idea that stealth technology makes an aircraft literally invisible is really journalistic hyperbole; the objective in the design of a high-performance fighter is rather to ensure that its pilot can pick up an enemy and

launch a missile against it before the target is aware of the danger.

The first Stealth aircraft, the US Air Force's Lockheed F-117A and Northrop B-2, largely rely on their much reduced radar signatures to allow them to penetrate defended airspace. The coming generation is likely to combine 'stealthiness' with other aids to penetration, such as a high service ceiling, agility and speed. Thus an interdiction aircraft such as the American A-12/ Advanced Tactical Aircraft will be able to operate again in the high- and medium-altitude bands that SAMs and interceptors have for long denied to unescorted strike aircraft. However, the US believes that Soviet aircraft designers will produce successors to the Su-27 Flanker and MiG-29 Fulcrum for service in the next century, so perhaps the ATF will not be entirely in a class of its own.

then laser-designate it for attack by his own or an accompanying aircraft; alternatively, he can use Pave Tack to determine the range by laser range finder. The accuracy with which weapons can be delivered has also been improved by increased computer capacity. For example, one RAF Tornado GR Mk 1 can deliver 'dumb' bombs with greater accuracy in a loft-bombing attack than its predecessor the Jaguar can achieve using laydown bombing.

In view of the tremendous improvements in attack aircraft since World War II, it is astounding that the weapons these aircraft will deliver on the majority of their sorties are freefall bombs no different in concept from the bombs dropped in that conflict. This phenomenon can be explained in part by the philosophy that it is better, and cheaper, to build sophisticated guidance into the aircraft – which (it is hoped) will return – rather than into the weapon, which will be expended. The other major inhibiting factor in air-weapon development has been a simple lack of adequate funding; aircraft development tends to absorb the lion's share of an air force's research-and-development budget.

Specialised bombs are available for many different purposes

There can be little doubt that this situation will change over the coming decade. Not only will increasingly effective air defence threats put a premium on long-range stand-off weapons, but budgets for new aircraft procurement are likely to drop. The latter will mean extending the life of aircraft currently in service, and developing and fitting more effective weaponry will be a good way of achieving this. The French Armee de l'Air has extended the useful life of its Mirage IVs long beyond their 'natural' span largely through fitting them with the ASMP stand-off missile.

The type of target to be attacked decides the sort of bomb that will be used against it. If the

bomb is to penetrate concrete – in an attack on a runway or hardened aircraft shelter, for example – the variables to consider include the depth and the quality of the concrete, the strength and shape of the bomb casing and the bomb's angle of impact. The need to operate at low level can complicate the problems of bomb design, as the weapon then needs to be retarded – that is, slowed down in flight – typically by extending braking vanes, as in the American Snakeye. This lets the aircraft escape the blast and fragmentation of its own bombs during laydown at low altitude.

New bombing techniques have been developed for new bombs

However, retarding the bomb reduces its velocity at impact and the steepness of its angle of impact, and thus its penetrative ability. Ideally, the bomb should be released at a comparatively high altitude and at an angle near to the vertical in order to obtain the optimum result against a hardened structure. This is how laydown bombing works, but the bomber must fly at altitude in order to make the weapons effective. To achieve this and yet allow the aircraft to fly at low level for protection, the loft-bombing method has been developed. This involves the aircraft approaching at low level and then climbing sharply and at speed some way short of the target, when the bomb is released and tossed on to the target following a parabolic trajectory. The technique is less accurate than laydown, however, and is therefore more effective against larger, fixed targets. But if the requirement is for surface blast (to wreck buildings, aircraft or vehicles) or fragmentation (to kill people), retarded bombs are perfectly adequate, and have the great advantage of being directly aimed from an aircraft which has not exposed itself to ground fire.

Cluster bombs extend the weapon's area of effective coverage and compensate in some degree

Above: Lockheed's F-117A Stealth fighter is probably the most radical development in aviation since the jet engine. The first generation flew in 1977, but it wasn't until 12 years later that one was used operationally, during Operation Just Cause, the invasion of Panama. The aircraft's relatively low maximum speed – just over 1000km/h – is a by-product of airframe design. The next generation can be expected to be considerably faster

for inaccuracies in delivery. These can be composed of anti-personnel or anti-tank bomblets, which are dispersed in a pattern, typically doughnut shaped, to cover a wide area. As with conventional bombs, they can be delivered either in laydown or loft manoeuvres. Unguided rockets fired in salvoes will also destroy anything in their way over a fairly wide area, but have largely gone out of fashion, due to their inherent inaccuracy.

The natural extension of the cluster bomb principle is the weapons dispenser, which releases bomblets directly from the aircraft rather than from a cluster bomb as it falls earthwards. Dispensers can carry a large load of bomblets and so are well suited to airfield attack or for dealing with large armoured concentrations. However, it does require the aircraft to overfly the target and for this reason alone the bomblet dispenser will probably not have much of a future beyond the present generation MW-1, used by the Luftwaffe, and the RAF's JP 233. Laser-guided bombs offer a new dimension in accuracy, but demand that the target be illuminated

STEALTH TECHNOLOGY OF THE F-117A

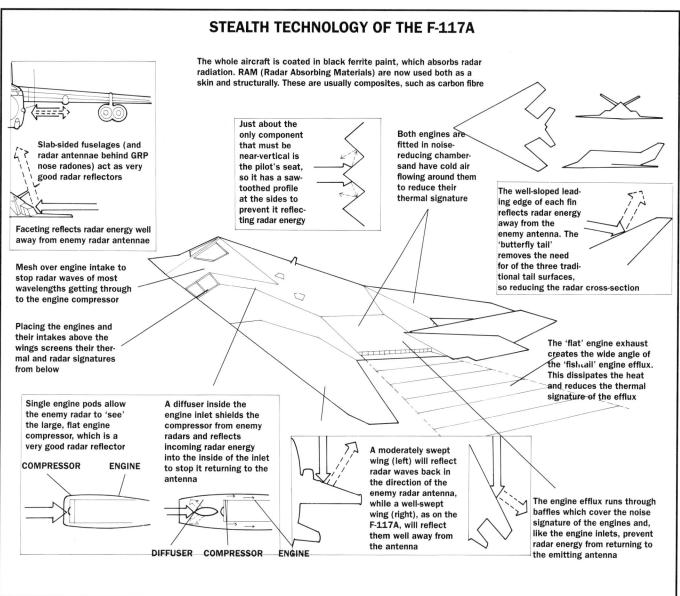

The whole aircraft is coated in black ferrite paint, which absorbs radar radiation. RAM (Radar Absorbing Materials) are now used both as a skin and structurally. These are usually composites, such as carbon fibre

Slab-sided fuselages (and radar antennae behind GRP nose radones) act as very good radar reflectors

Faceting reflects radar energy well away from enemy radar antennae

Just about the only component that must be near-vertical is the pilot's seat, so it has a saw-toothed profile at the sides to prevent it reflecting radar energy

Both engines are fitted in noise-reducing chamber-sand have cold air flowing around them to reduce their thermal signature

The well-sloped leading edge of each fin reflects radar energy away from the enemy antenna. The 'butterfly tail' removes the need for of the three traditional tail surfaces, so reducing the radar cross-section

Mesh over engine intake to stop radar waves of most wavelengths getting through to the engine compressor

Placing the engines and their intakes above the wings screens their thermal and radar signatures from below

Single engine pods allow the enemy radar to 'see' the large, flat engine compressor, which is a very good radar reflector

COMPRESSOR   ENGINE

A diffuser inside the engine inlet shields the compressor from enemy radars and reflects incoming radar energy into the inside of the inlet to stop it returning to the antenna

DIFFUSER COMPRESSOR ENGINE

A moderately swept wing (left) will reflect radar waves back in the direction of the enemy radar antenna, while a well-swept wing (right), as on the F-117A, will reflect them well away from the antenna

The 'flat' engine exhaust creates the wide angle of the 'fishtail' engine efflux. This dissipates the heat and reduces the thermal signature of the efflux

The engine efflux runs through baffles which cover the noise signature of the engines and, like the engine inlets, prevent radar energy from returning to the emitting antenna throughout the bomb's flight, by the releasing aircraft's laser designator, by an accompanying aircraft, or from a ground position within line-of-sight of the desired impact point.

Stand-off weapons (either missiles or unpowered glide bombs), minimise the launch aircraft's exposure to the target's point air defence, but at the price of making target acquisition much more difficult. Not all targets will be fixed in one position, and so the use of stand-off weapons presupposes the availability firstly of near-real time reconnaissance information and secondly of a weapons-guidance system that is able to recognise its target. A TV or imaging-infra-red guidance system, such as that on the American AGM-65 Maverick series, is one option; another is laser guidance. Millimetric radar seekers may prove useful for future air-to-surface missiles.

Unguided rockets fired in salvoes will destroy anything in their way

A formation attack helps solve the problem of how to hit the target and at the same time avoid exposure to air defences. A group of aircraft can provide a degree of mutual support against fighter attack, and a synchronised approach to the target from various headings will dissipate the concentration of defensive fire. Yet mass attacks have their problems. They call for accurate timing and co-ordination between individual aircraft, which must usually observe radio silence at the same time. For example, if following aircraft are not to run into the blast of the preceding aircraft's weapons and if collisions are to be avoided, each bomb run must be separated by a few seconds, yet too great a gap between attack runs will simply allow the defenders to deal with the attacking aircraft one by one.

Another disadvantage of attacking in formation is that the smoke and debris from the initial attack runs will also tend to obscure aiming points for the following aircraft. This could well render electro-

optically guided weapons ineffective, although free-fall bombs could be dropped blind if the pilot starts his bombing run from a predetermined point at a known distance from the target and precisely times the moment when he releases the weapon. Wind direction could therefore be significant in determining the direction from which he approaches the target, but the pilot would also balance other tactical considerations against the need to avoid the worst effects of smoke.

Smoke and debris from initial attacks will obscure later aiming

Many factors will lessen or increase the overall effectiveness and reliability of interdiction bombing. Weather conditions and hours of daylight, for example, could well affect accuracy, with the lower incidence of cloud and longer daylight hours of the summer months offering obvious advantages. The effectiveness and density of enemy air defences will dictate how far interdictors can penetrate his airspace. Also significant to the success of a mission will be the level of sophistication of the attacking aircraft, and of the weapons it carries.

Stand-off and precision-guided munitions will probably be in relatively short supply (if only because of their sheer expense) and are therefore likely to be set aside for use against the most difficult targets. Similarly, the most advanced aircraft will be carefully matched against the most demanding missions and some may well be held back from a conventional bombing campaign as a tactical nuclear delivery force. Even with an attrition rate of one per cent per sortie (and figures of around 10 per cent were nearer the norm during periods of heavy fighting in World War II), losses will soon mount.

Assuming that aircraft fly an average of 2.8 sorties per day, a one per cent attrition rate will reduce them by half over a 24-day period of continuous operations. Battle damage to aircraft, crew

CONVENTIONAL AN
DECOUPLED FLIGH
COMPARED

CONVENTIONAL FLIGHT
1. A modern aircraft has to roll in to bank in order to turn.

DECOUPLED FLIGHT
2. YAW-AXIS POINTING
The aircraft can move its nose witho
changing the direction of flight.

3. LATERAL TRANSLATION
The aircraft can move its nose witho
changing the direction of flight.

4. YAW-AXIS POINTING
The aircraft can move sideways (rela
to the air in which it is flying rather t
the ground) without changing the dir
tion in which it is pointing, and witho
banking, or yawing the nose.

CONVENTIONAL FLIGHT
5. When an aircraft increases its ang
of attack for a given airspeed, it clim
Increasing the angle of attack furthe
also increases the steepness of the
climb, until the aircraft reaches stall
point. The aircraft can also climb by
increasing its airspeed without incre
ing its angle of attack.

DECOUPLED FLIGHT
6. PITCH-AXIS POINTING
The aircraft can raise or lower its no
without affecting the flight path.

7 & 8. VERTICAL TRANSLATION
The aircraft can climb or descend wi
out changing its angle of attack or its
speed. It does this by using direct lif
Similarly, the aircraft can change its
angle of attack without affecting how
climbs or descends.

Right: A Stinger surface-to-air missile destroys a QF-106 target drone. The Stinger is a shoulder-launched weapon that homes in on the heat emissions from the aircraft – both from its engines and from the friction generated by its flight through the air. While the Stinger is relatively difficult to jam, earlier types of shoulder-launched, infra-red homing missiles are easily decoyed by dropping flares. In the 1973 Arab-Israeli War, for instance, of the 4356 Soviet-supplied SAM-7s that were launched, only 34 hit their targets

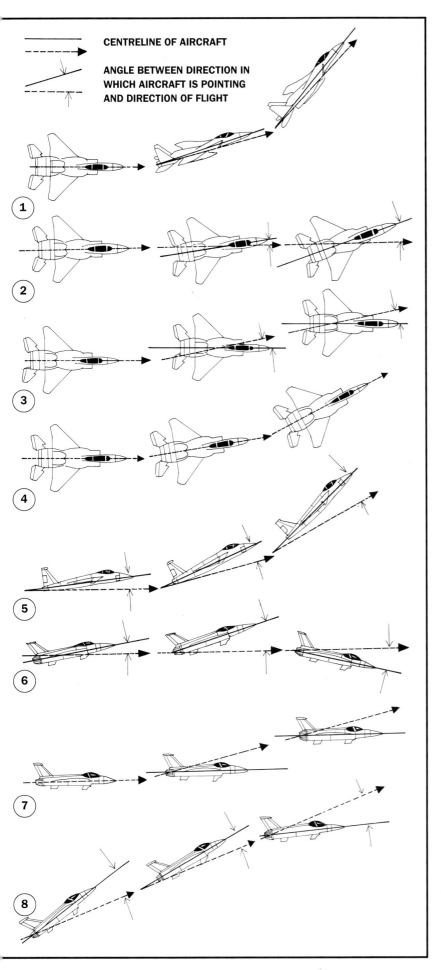

CENTRELINE OF AIRCRAFT

ANGLE BETWEEN DIRECTION IN
WHICH AIRCRAFT IS POINTING
AND DIRECTION OF FLIGHT

exhaustion and combat stress, together with the depletion of munitions stocks will all lead to diminishing returns from the surviving force as the campaign progresses. Target planning will therefore be at a premium, with the likely effect of any mission on the enemy to be carefully weighed against the price that his defences will exact.

There are some, however, who would argue that the day of the manned aircraft is fast drawing to a close, at least as a direct support weapon of the land armies.

Precision-guided munitions will be in relatively short supply

They point to the increasing vulnerability of manned aircraft over the battlefield, to the high cost of procuring and operating them and to the additional expense of providing highly trained air and ground crews. There is little, argue the proponents of unmanned aerial vehicles (UAVs – drones and remotely piloted vehicles, or RPVs), to be lost by taking the pilot 'out of the loop', and much to be gained. Airmen hotly contest this view, pointing out that a switch to UAVs would mean the loss of air power's much-prized ability to react to the unexpected when it occurs. Moreover, although RPVs are cheaper and can be fielded in greater numbers than manned aircraft, their loss rate from enemy action and accident is expected to be much higher. Complex and vulnerable communications links from air to ground will be needed to operate RPVs, while drones will need to be pre-programmed and thus will lose all flexibility.

Even with an attrition rate of one per cent, losses will soon mount

The Israeli experience in the Beqaa Valley in 1982 suggests that drones have a useful part to play alongside manned aircraft. This is a valuable lesson that is likely to be blurred in the present debate on manned versus unmanned aircraft as the various services fight for their interests. One of the attractions of drones and RPVs for the army commander is that he can operate them himself, while the air forces are, for obvious emotional reasons, aghast at the idea of replacing their fighter and attack aircraft with UAVs. The air forces' resistance to UAVs is likely to transcend that of the horse cavalry regiments to mechanisation in the 1920s and 1930s, though in its support, one should perhaps say that the case for the manned aircraft is intrinsically more sound than that for the 'well-bred horse'.

But there's more to air power than strike missions. Aerial reconnaissance is vitally important to the land commander, and its value is usually in direct proportion to its timeliness; hence the emphasis in modern reconnaissance systems on the 'real-time' transmission of data, which may be gathered either by optical sensors or in other parts of electromagnetic spectrum. The fighters' battle for air superiority is another area in which air power will decisively influence what happens on the ground. It is an area which has consistently been undervalued by

Left: It costs in excess of a million pounds to train a fast-mover pilot, who might have a life expectancy measured in days, in the event of war. This A-10 pilot, who has no air-to-air combat training (and lacks even rudimentary air-to-air combat weapons systems in his aircraft), has to absorb a different set of skills, which include feature and vehicle recognition and low flying.

Below: An F-14 Tomcat on the Grumman production line, giving an idea of the complexity of modern combat aircraft that makes them so expensive. Some of the systems are there purely because it is a manned aircraft. Having an unmanned aircraft makes it smaller and more capable, as machines can withstand stresses and manoeuvres beyond the physical limits of a human being

land commanders. This is well illustrated by the classic 1970s story in which two victorious Soviet tank army commanders meet on the banks of the Rhine and one is asked by the other, 'And who was it that won the air battle?' In real warfare, the answer to this question would be all too evident, since on the outcome of the fight for air superiority depends the freedom of one's own ground forces to operate without undue interference from enemy air power and also the ability of friendly tactical air forces to intervene directly in the ground fighting.

Fixed-wing transport aircraft can also deploy airborne forces

Finally, we come to air transport operations. Their role is significant in that it affects the speed at which ground forces can be deployed, reinforced and resupplied. Neither fixed-wing transport aircraft nor utility and heavy-lift helicopters will be able to move more than a small proportion of ground troops (and even less of their equipment), but nonetheless, airlift's ability to transport reinforcements into the theatre of operations at great speed is likely to play an important part in the opening moves of the battle. Similarly, the helicopter's ability to reinforce any part of the battlefield rapidly confers great tactical

DOES THE MANNED BOMBER HAVE A FUTURE?

Those who say that the manned bomber has a bright future, despite the threat from ET weapons, argue as follows:

• Stealth technology and other counter-measures give it unprecedented protection and make successfully completed missions far more likely

• Unmanned ET interdiction systems such as strike drones and 'smart' missiles are still untested in battle. The manned bomber, however, is a well-tried and tested tool for the same job

• Smart and brilliant weapon stores now allow a single bomber to fly missions that once would have required many aircraft

• Unlike a pre-programmed drone or missile, the manned bomber can attack targets of opportunity

• The manned bomber can be flown over and over again, whereas existing unmanned systems are regarded as disposable. The more missions a bomber can complete, the better value for money it gives. Unmanned weapons can be used only once – and consequently their final costs in terms of 'bang per buck' will be higher in a protracted war

The arguments against are:

• New and emerging missiles may be able to defeat the bomber's counter-measures

• Unmanned ET weapons may cost less in the long run than manned bombers if

bomber combat losses prove to be high – and ET weapons do not put pilots at risk

• New weapons will make airfields unusable, both by destroying runways and making repair impossible with chemical weapons

advantages on the army which is trained and prepared to use this asset with flair and imagination.

However, the Boeing CH-47 Chinook, the largest helicopter in use by NATO, can carry only 12 tons of cargo at the very most, and is a sitting duck to the new generation of SAM and anti-aircraft fire and even the most rudimentary form of air-to-air attack. Tactical heavy-lift helicopters, therefore, have to rely on their lighter, more agile and more heavily armed colleagues to keep them alive.

Fixed-wing transport aircraft can also deploy airborne forces, and 'special forces' will require both fixed-wing and rotary-wing airlift. The USAF and US Army have assigned dedicated air units to the support of their Special Forces troops – which is not only indicative of the importance that the United States accords to such forces, but also recognises one of the principal failings of air transport. Namely, that it will always be in short supply and that many difficult decisions will have to be made between conflicting claims on its services – all of which are likely to have strong arguments in their favour. US Special Forces at least do not have to get involved in those arguments – although the debate about the 'correct' tactical and strategic uses of air power will doubtless continue for as long as aircraft, manned or not, go to war.

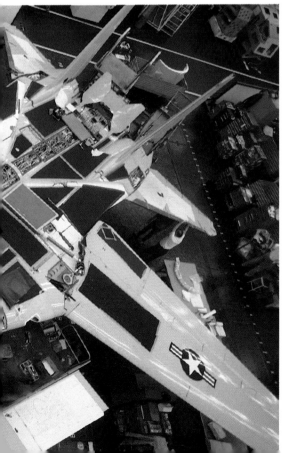

Above: Computer-aided design of the YF-23, one of the contenders for the USAF ATF (Advanced Tactical Fighter) competition. It remains to be seen if the ATF's successor will be unmanned, or whether the ATF will be amongst the last generation of manned aircraft

IS THE TANK DEAD?

In 1939, the German army astonished the world with the speed and efficiency with which its armoured columns over-ran vast tracts of Europe. In fact the success of those early advances probably owed more to other factors than to the tanks themselves. One was the brilliance of the German concept of *blitzkrieg* itself. The other stemmed from the opposing armies' disregard for the tank and for mobile armoured warfare. They failed to develop an anti-tank doctrine or to equip themselves properly. The lesson, however, has been well learned. Since the 1940s an 'extended family' of anti-tank weapons has appeared, and ever more complex and far-fetched systems are constantly being added to it.

A t first sight, modern developments could suggest that contemporary tanks would be destroyed almost as soon as they appear, and that battles will in future have to be based upon completely different types of weapons systems. However, the tank itself is now enormously more sophisticated than it was in 1939 – with the introduction of much-improved passive armour, reactive armour and active counter-measures; not to mention increased horsepower, electronic power and firepower. The tank can now move faster and hit harder than ever; it can see in the dark; and – perhaps most important – it can fight off most incoming warheads with a wide variety of self-defence mechanisms. Stealth technology for tanks, comparable to that used in the B2 bomber aircraft, is already being developed.

The tank can now move faster and hit harder than ever

All this means that we do not really know which currently has the edge: the tank or the anti-tank measures. Thus it may be true that the tank is finally dead, as lobbyists for the new AT weaponry continue to insist. Equally, it may be true that the armour lobby is right to claim that the tank is only just beginning a new lease of life. Both sides seem to have a case: in the 1973 October War between Israel and Egypt and Syria, and the 1980-89 Gulf War, most tank attacks were quickly stopped in their tracks, while in the 1982 invasion of Lebanon the tank was

LEFT: The detonation of the 155 mm HEAT (High Explosive Anti-Tank) warhead of a Copperhead CLGP (Cannon-Launched Guided Projectile). It has hit the side of an obsolete M47 medium tank being used as a range target. This photograph shows how the HEAT warhead explodes in every direction, though only that part of the explosion directed towards the tank is used to penetrate the target's armour. Today's main battle tanks are often fitted with reactive or composite armour which greatly reduce the penetrating power of even such large-calibre HEAT warheads

ARMOUR PROTECTION OF A MODERN MAIN BATTLE TANK

WHAT EACH ARMOUR REGION IS CAPABLE OF STOPPING:

GREEN: All but 120mm or larger APFSDS rounds and the largest HEAT warheads

RED: Automatic cannon fire (40mm or smaller) and most LAW (Light Anti-tank Weapons)

WHITE: HMG (Heavy Machine Gun) rounds and shell splinters

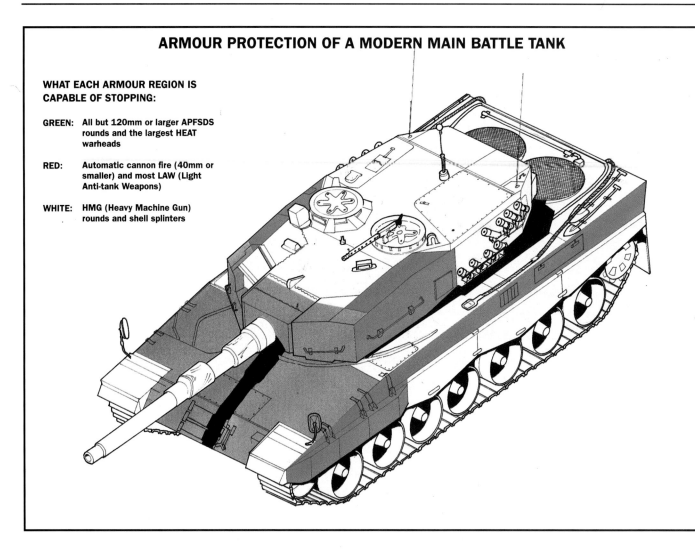

still able to fight its way forward despite taking heavy losses from infantry anti-tank weapons.

There is no doubt that the tank is vulnerable to an enormous range of weapons; not solely to those dedicated to AT duties. Straightforward primitive weapons have always posed a certain threat – for example the Madrid dynamiters of 1936 or the 1945 Japanese officers who occasionally got inside British tanks in Burma with their slashing swords. Equally, simple obstacles placed on the battlefield by engineers can exert an important channelling effect, as did the anti-tank ditches on the Golan in 1973. Even snipers armed with rifles are still lethal since, despite modern optics and communications, tank commanders still tend to operate best with

their hatches open and heads up. Then there are tank-killing infantry teams, which may infiltrate into leaguer areas to cause havoc among crews performing maintenance or replenishment work. Conventional artillery can also make its mark, with HE shelling seemingly much more damaging to tanks today than it was in the past, as a result of greatly improved accuracy, fragmentation and sheer blast power. The last-mentioned is useful in disrupting the array of sensitive sensors and antennae on a tank's exterior.

Modern armies field a wide range of relatively light (that is, between 75mm and 90mm) anti-armour guns that are designated for use against APCs but which, if they can achieve a lucky hit on

Above: Vickers Medium and Light tanks of the British Army in training between WWI and WWII. Many pundits in the inter-war years said that the tank had had its day, because of the anti-tank gun

Right: Soviet T-55 tanks ford a river during an exercise. More of this type of tank have been produced than any other in history

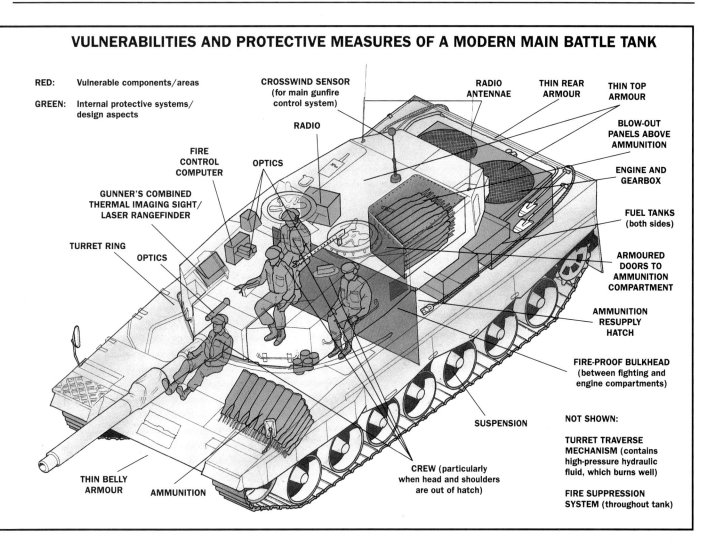

VULNERABILITIES AND PROTECTIVE MEASURES OF A MODERN MAIN BATTLE TANK

RED: Vulnerable components/areas

GREEN: Internal protective systems/
        design aspects

CROSSWIND SENSOR
(for main gunfire
control system)

RADIO

FIRE
CONTROL
COMPUTER

OPTICS

GUNNER'S COMBINED
THERMAL IMAGING SIGHT/
LASER RANGEFINDER

TURRET RING

OPTICS

THIN BELLY
ARMOUR

AMMUNITION

RADIO
ANTENNAE

THIN REAR
ARMOUR

THIN TOP
ARMOUR

BLOW-OUT
PANELS ABOVE
AMMUNITION

ENGINE AND
GEARBOX

FUEL TANKS
(both sides)

ARMOURED
DOORS TO
AMMUNITION
COMPARTMENT

AMMUNITION
RESUPPLY
HATCH

FIRE-PROOF BULKHEAD
(between fighting and
engine compartments)

SUSPENSION

CREW (particularly
when head and shoulders
are out of hatch)

NOT SHOWN:

TURRET TRAVERSE
MECHANISM (contains
high-pressure hydraulic
fluid, which burns well)

FIRE SUPPRESSION
SYSTEM (throughout tank)

ANTI-TANK PROJECTILES

Right: A Chieftain MBT simulates receiving a hit during a firepower demonstration. At the front of the hull is a dozer blade with which the tank can dig its own protective 'slot' – a cutaway into the ground so that only the top of the turret shows from the front

HOW A HESH WARHEAD WORKS

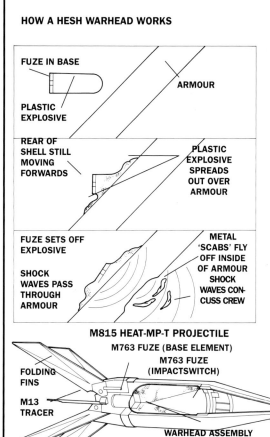

FUZE IN BASE

ARMOUR

PLASTIC EXPLOSIVE

REAR OF SHELL STILL MOVING FORWARDS

PLASTIC EXPLOSIVE SPREADS OUT OVER ARMOUR

FUZE SETS OFF EXPLOSIVE

METAL 'SCABS' FLY OFF INSIDE OF ARMOUR SHOCK WAVES CONCUSS CREW

SHOCK WAVES PASS THROUGH ARMOUR

M815 HEAT-MP-T PROJECTILE

M763 FUZE (BASE ELEMENT)

M763 FUZE (IMPACTSWITCH)

FOLDING FINS

M13 TRACER

WARHEAD ASSEMBLY

HOW A HEAT WARHEAD WORKS

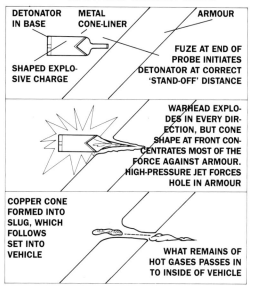

DETONATOR IN BASE

METAL CONE-LINER

ARMOUR

SHAPED EXPLOSIVE CHARGE

FUZE AT END OF PROBE INITIATES DETONATOR AT CORRECT 'STAND-OFF' DISTANCE

WARHEAD EXPLODES IN EVERY DIRECTION, BUT CONE SHAPE AT FRONT CONCENTRATES MOST OF THE FORCE AGAINST ARMOUR. HIGH-PRESSURE JET FORCES HOLE IN ARMOUR

COPPER CONE FORMED INTO SLUG, WHICH FOLLOWS SET INTO VEHICLE

WHAT REMAINS OF HOT GASES PASSES IN TO INSIDE OF VEHICLE

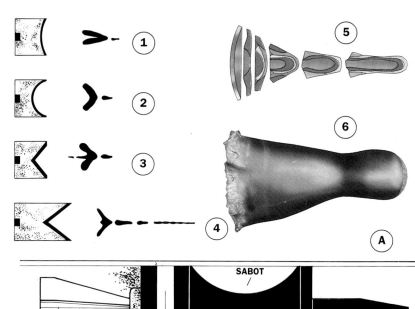

(1) (2) (3) (4) (5) (6)

(A)

SABOT

GASES

PENETRATOR

PENETRATOR FINS

SLIPPING DRIVING BAND

RIFLED GUN BARREL

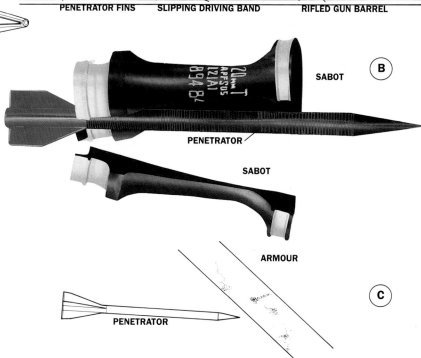

(B)

SABOT

PENETRATOR

SABOT

ARMOUR

(C)

PENETRATOR

THE SCI-FI BATTLEFIELD

Death rays, beam guns and other exotic devices that shoot down targets at the speed of light have traditionally been the exclusive property of science-fiction authors and comic-book heroes. But today serious money and effort is going in to developing hardware that bears an uncanny resemblance to these fantasy weapons. Known as directed-energy weapons (DEW), they fall into two main categories Lasers (below), and Particle Beam Weapons (on page 95).

Laser Death Rays

The laser (Light Amplification by Stimulated Emission of Radiation) works by electromagnetically 'pumping up' the energy levels of the atoms of a given material and then exposing them to light. This creates a reaction that generates a stream of exactly similar photons – the constituent particles of light – which all travel in the same direction and at exactly the same frequency. (The precise frequency, and so the colour of the light, depend on the material whose atoms are stimulated.) This 'coherent' light is remarkably intense, and can be made more so by bouncing the photons back and forth off opposed mirrors before releasing them. The combination of intensity and coherence creates a beam of light that does not diffuse easily and so retains the concentration of its energy over very long distances. Lasers can also throw out light in pulses – brief packets of energy.

A laser will destroy ordinary materials in its path when the energy of its narrow beam strikes an object and converts into heat, so making the object burn. Low-level, very fine laser beams are becoming common in eye surgery, where conventional tools are too crude. A powerful laser can generate enough heat to cut through sheets of metal.

Lasers are destructive over very short distances, however. Water vapour, carbon dioxide, the distorting effects of atmospheric gases and even the presence of ions (free-floating atoms) all diffuse the intensity of laser light over distances greater than a few centimetres. Lasers can still travel very long distances, however, but at energy levels better suited to carrying information (such as radio messages) than to causing physical destruction. To create a laser powerful enough to overcome these limitations would require phenomenally powerful energy sources that would be too big and cumbersome for fast-moving modern warfare. So, 'death rays' lasers would be far more useful in space than on the ground; although higher-frequency 'eximer' and X-ray lasers may be be able to overcome these natural obstacles.

Even if a laser cannot burn through armour at great distances, it can still blind a human being; and a tank with a blind commander or driver is as useless as one with a dead crew or with its tracks blown off. Some Royal Navy ships have already fitted experimental lasers that send out single pulses to disorientate enemy pilots. These may have the power, not yet exploited, to blind. So, in a land battle, just as fire from a single machine gun in World War I could rove systematically across a battlefield and pin down infantry, so a single retina-stripping laser could immobilise all enemy within its line of sight. If it randomly hopped frequencies, it would also defeat anti-laser goggles and other counter-measures.

Lasers in space

Outside the deleterious effects of the Earth's atmosphere, the rules change. With no water vapour or atmosphere gases to diffuse the coherent beam, even relatively low-powered lasers can disable sophisticated weapons systems. Smart mirrors, which not only re-direct the beam, but also re-concentrate it, allow a static source, in geo-stable orbit, to reach in any direction. Naturally, corrections have to be made in real time by the control systems, so the amount of raw computing power required to adjust the mirrors is colossal.

SMOOTHBORE VERSUS RIFLED TANK GUNS

FACTOR:	SMOOTHBORE GUN:	RIFLED GUN:
SECONDARY ARMOUR-DEFEATING NATURES	HEAT MP: Probably defeated by compound armour and skirting plates. Adequate against secondary targets. Advanced fuzing techniques may improve performance HESH: Impracticable, as its addition would reduce explosive payload below efficient minimum	HEAT: At present, HESH is preferred to HEAT by the UK, but rifled guns have fin-stabilised HEAT rounds, with slipping driving bands HESH: Effective against external tank components, and excellent against secondary targets
OTHER NATURES	Smoke, HE, Canister } Require bulky fins, therefore less payload. HEAT-MP may suffice in lieu of canister	Smoke, Canister } Ballistically similar to HESH. No HE required as HESH is very effective against 'soft' targets. Spin aids in dispensing canister payload. May be used in anti-helicopter role
ARMING	Only two stimuli (setback, creep) available	Additional stimulus of spin available as safety interlock
SENSING	—	Controlled spin rate may allow sensing for possible top-attack of armour by CE projectile
SABOT DISCARD	—	Additional spin assists in clean discard of Sabot pellets at muzzle
MUZZLE VELOCITY	No theoretical limit	Slipping driving band may impose practical upper limit on firing of KE projectiles
GUN MANUFACTURE	Possibly simpler to build, but precise control of surface finish is essential	Established manufacturing techniques for rifled guns do not present problems
BARREL LENGTH	A smoothbore barrel is short and lightweight	A rifled barrel must be longer than a smoothbore barrel to achieve the same muzzle velocity, which also makes it heavier

a soft spot, may incapacitate or even kill a tank. Still lighter anti-armour automatic cannons, furthermore, have been given enhanced importance by the emergence of new types of ammunition such as depleted uranium KE rounds, which can rip through a tank's side armour at ranges up to 300m. For all this, large kinetic-energy (KE) projectiles fired from heavy (that is, 90-125mm) guns are today the best way to destroy modern tanks. These weapons are themselves best mounted on tanks or heavy armoured cars, instead of being towed along without protection, which seems to revive the late-World War II maxim that 'the best anti-tank weapon is another tank.'

The KE round is still the most effective way to destroy a tank

This maxim, which has been called into question in recent times, stands to be reinforced if a hyper-velocity electro-magnetic KE gun can be produced in a mobile and armoured form, which it soon may be. Yet even now tank guns can fire a variety of ammunition out to two, three or four kilometres, with a total engagement time of little more than 10

seconds, a flight time of more than a kilometre per second and a first-shot-hit expectation of greater than 90 per cent. The shots may destroy the target by external shock waves, as with high-explosive squash head (HESH) rounds against light armour; by a penetrating jet of high- temperature, high pressure gas from high-explosive anti-tank (HEAT) shells; or simple high-velocity bolts of KE – especially armour-piercing fin-stabilised discarding sabot (APFSDS) rounds, or the improved Soviet high- velocity armour-piercing fin-stabilised discarding sabot round (HVAPFSDS).

All this ammunition can easily devastate lightly armoured vehicles, but against modern laminated or reactive armours the KE round is by far the most effective – and often the only – way to destroy a tank. The British inclination has been traditionally towards rifled guns, the bores of which impart spin to the KE bolt to give it stability in flight and accuracy; most other armies prefer smoothbore guns, which achieve the same effect by firing 'self-spinning' rounds with a rotating outer portion.

In addition to the guns, there are the anti-armour rocket and missile systems. The infantry has the rocket launcher – the descendant of the

World War II Bazooka – which provides a simple but portable 'fire and forget' anti-tank capability, even though it leaves a massive signature in the form of a back-blast when fired. The Soviet RPG-7, in particular, achieved a formidable number of tank kills in all the Middle East conficts of the 1970s and 1980s. Current types are accurate out to 300m and they are being upgraded all the time, but as HEAT weapons with relatively small warheads, they are of questionable penetrative power against the latest armour.

Programmes are in train to improve the portable rocket's performance by using two warheads in tandem – the first to disrupt 'reactive' armour (see box feature) and the second to penetrate the tank's main armour. Nevertheless, these weapons will not break through the latest Chobham armour on Western tanks; and all increases in weight inevitably limit the weapon's portability. Thus the one-man rocket launcher may in future be reserved for use only against light armour or bunkers, since the punch required to knock out a tank will become too heavy for a man to carry. The future of the rocket launcher as a tank killer would seem to lie with heavier, vehicle-mounted

weapons such as new versions of the recoilless rifles that filled this role in the 1950s. These are effective at ranges up to 700m, and modern tactics call for them to attack the weaker *sides* of the tank rather than its very hard and angled *front* (which induces ricochets).

Modern tanks will use surges of power for short sprints

More likely, perhaps, is a move away from unguided rockets altogether, towards anti-tank guided weapons (ATGW). These are far from light, having tandem charges and other improvements in the warhead to enhance penetration, but they do enjoy a number of advantages over the simple rocket launcher. Their 'firing signature' is far smaller, making their source harder to spot with infra-red detectors; they can be remotely fired at a distance from the operator; and they can often range out to 5km or further.

These missiles have traditionally been guided through a wire extruded from the rear of the missile, a system that forced the operator to keep the cross-hairs of the sight centred on the target

Below: A platoon of M1 Abrams on a night shoot in training. Because these tanks are fitted with TI (Thermal Imaging) night sights, they can shoot just as well at night as during the day. If the enemy is not equipped with TI sights, tanks that have such a sensor can also set up a 'thermal ambush' during the day or night. This involves laying a conventional smoke-screen between them-selves and the enemy. The Abrams can see clearly through the smoke with its TI sight, while all the enemy can see is the smokescreen

RESISTING TANK ATTACK

1. Ground attack aircraft hit the enemy armoured column when it is moving up using every weapon they have. The air attack goes in away from the defensive positions so that there is less likelihood of the aircraft hitting friendly forces, and aims to strike the enemy before he has dispersed into battle formation.

3. Just out of tank gun direct fire range (3-4 km), the defending artillery lays down fire as part of a pre-planned DF (Defensive Fire) task. This disrupts the attack, and forces the vehicles to close all their hatches, limiting both the driver's and the commander's vision.

2. Attack helicopters assist in steadily reducing the number of tanks that the defenders have to face. In particular, they try to destroy enemy air-defence vehicles, for both their own survival, and that of the fixed-wing aircraft, and enemy command vehicles, to disrupt the coordination of the attack.

4. Given time, defending engineers will have created or improved obstacles in front of the position. Combining different types (such as placing an anti-tank ditch in the middle of a minefield) makes crossing both more difficult. Even if there is little time available, engineers may use scatterable mines.

5a. Infantry ATGM (Anti-Tank Guided Missiles) cover the engineers' obstacles with direct fire. Their priority targets are the enemy engineer vehicles. Because the missiles and command wires are easily damaged by shrapnel and blast, friendly artillery fire into ATGM killing areas has to be carefully coordinated.

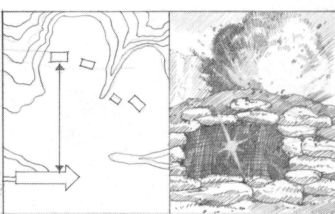

5b. The ATGMs will often be sited in "defilade" - firing at the flank of the advance and with cover on the side towards the enemy so that only those tanks in the ATGMs' "killing area" can spot the bunkers. The infantry may build dummy bunkers to deceive the enemy.

7. For close range defence (up to 500m) the infantry have their own shoulder-fired anti-armour weapons. Because the frontal armour of modern MBTs is usually impervious to the small HEAT warheads of these weapons, the infantry try to fire at the sides of the tanks.

6. If the enemy infantry "debus" to try and clear a position, then the infantry will use mortar fire to pin them down. If the friendly infantry are dug-in with overhead cover they can bring airburst mortar fire down right on top of their own positions.

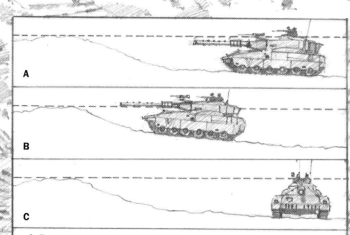

8. Each tank is initially "turret down" (A), so that only the commander is above cover. When he spots a target, the tank moves forward, so the gunner can see the enemy - a "hull down" position (B). As soon as the gunner has fired, the tank moves to a new position (C).

throughout what must always have seemed an agonisingly long flight time, during which he was vulnerable. The latest generations of missile, however, use handier systems, such as laser designators or on-board homing devices. With shorter flight times, and the imminent introduction of a fire-and-forget capability, these missiles greatly increase the operator's chances of surviving to score a hit. Indeed such weapons can be very effective, particularly when launched from 'pop-up/pop-down' tank-busting helicopters. The relatively unsophisticated American TOW demonstrated this early on during the Easter 1972 North Vietnamese invasion of South Vietnam. 'Smart' bombs launched from fixed-wing aircraft (for example, the Paveway from the A10 Thunderbolt) are essentially a heavier version of the same thing.

Some of these new munitions consist of a single heavy round

Many counter-measures have been developed to meet the threat from ATGW, ranging from 'prophylactic firepower' aimed at suppressing any reaction from all possible enemy firing positions, through laser-defeating smokes to thermally intense flares to decoy infra-red heat-seeking missiles. In future there may also be decoy radar corner reflectors towed on trailers behind the tank, or rapid-reacting anti-missile guns mounted on its turret. A tank that is aware of danger should

therefore be perfectly able to defend itself and may well escape entirely unscathed.

On the battlefield of the future it will be tanks that have been distracted and are looking at the wrong threat or in the wrong direction that are in serious danger. Yet, in the 'continuous battle', alertness will be continuously required. Although a tank cannot remain in battle for 24 hours a day – the crew must find moments to eat and doze, to maintain the vehicle and replenish it – it remains constantly vulnerable. Protection is no longer guaranteed to tanks that pull out of the front line to leaguer, since long-range weapons can seek them out as never before. For example, the multiple launch rocket system (MLRS) armed with 'smart' sub-munitions is an especially vital new element in a corps commander's battle, letting him attack specific armoured or radar and radio-emitting targets as far away as the enemy's second tactical echelon, at a range of 30km or more. These weapons may be guided on to the target by a single ground observer, or by data provided by surveillance aircraft or RPVs.

The development of 'smart' munitions promises, too, to revolutionise the anti-tank capability of the traditional indirect-fire weapons – that is, those lobbing shells, often out of direct line of sight from their targets, such as mortars and guns. Some of these new munitions consist of a single heavy round, while others dispense many homing sub-munitions around the target, producing a lethal shower of 'smartlets' that will strip off layers of

Right: French Airborne troops take their MILAN (Missile Infanterie Legere Anti-Char) ATGM (Anti-Tank Guided Missile) from their LOHR Fardier FL500 $^{1}/_{2}$-tonne light vehicle to take up a firing position. MILAN is has considerable range (up to 1950m) is highly accurate, man-portable, and can penetrate over 1000mm of rolled homogenous steel armour with its new 'MILAN II' warhead. The firing post (which the soldier on the right is carrying) weighs 18kg, while each ammuniton tube (which the soldier leaping from the vehicle is carrying) weighs 12kg with the missile pre-packed inside

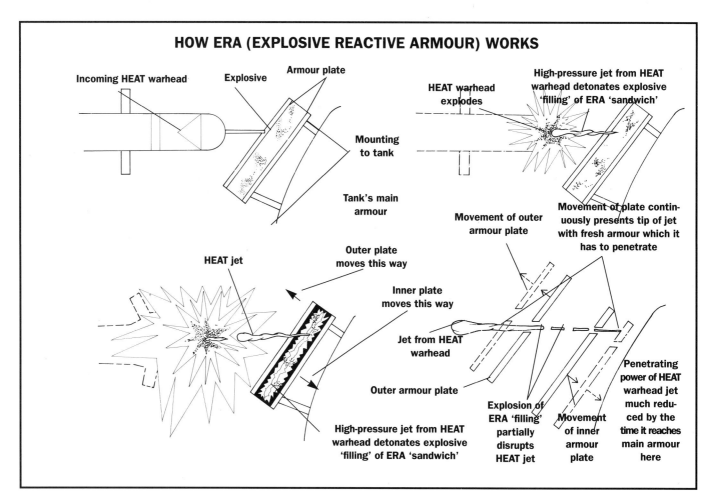

HOW ERA (EXPLOSIVE REACTIVE ARMOUR) WORKS

Incoming HEAT warhead — Explosive — Armour plate

Mounting to tank

Tank's main armour

HEAT warhead explodes

High-pressure jet from HEAT warhead detonates explosive 'filling' of ERA 'sandwich'

Movement of plate continuously presents tip of jet with fresh armour which it has to penetrate

HEAT jet

Outer plate moves this way

Inner plate moves this way

Jet from HEAT warhead

Movement of outer armour plate

Outer armour plate

High-pressure jet from HEAT warhead detonates explosive 'filling' of ERA 'sandwich'

Explosion of ERA 'filling' partially disrupts HEAT jet

Movement of inner armour plate

Penetrating power of HEAT warhead jet much reduced by the time it reaches main armour here

PARTICLE BEAM WEAPONS

The 'ammunition' for these is a stream of sub-atomic particles (protons or electrons, which are constituent parts of atoms), which may or may not be electrically charged. They are generated in the first place as the atoms of radioactive materials decay naturally, and are then accelerated by being given successive electromagnetic 'shoves'. To get them up to speed requires fairly massive distances, so the particles are whirled in a space-saving spiral or 'cyclotron' in which magnets keep them stable before they rocket out at near-light speeds in a straight line, or beam, to the target.

Wrecking the electronics

When they strike, the effects can be devastating if enough particles are fired at once at high energy. Enough heat is generated to burn metal; while the particles themselves are in any case so tiny that they will disrupt the molecules of armour and of human flesh, much as atomic or X-ray radiation will, as well as wreck electronic equipment and set off explosives (such as a tank ammo store). The West has suspected the USSR of experimenting with these weapons since 1975.

As with lasers, they are more effective in space than on the ground. Within the atmosphere, they travel in zig-zag fashion, like lightning bolts, so they are, to say the least, difficult to aim usefully. Even a very large ground-based accelerator would have an effective range of little more than 7 or 8km, so the main use of mobile Particle Beam Weapons (PBW) on the future battlefield will probably be as active armour or point defence systems.

The neutron bomb

Military planners have seen the 'enhanced radiation weapon' or 'neutron bomb' as something of an ideal ever since the earliest days of the atomic era. This is because it can kill people over a wide area while leaving buildings, equipment and the ground itself undamaged by blast or radiation outside a very limited central zone. Such bombs have been tested, and may well be stored, by the USA and by France; the Americans offered them to Western European forces as early as 1976.

Unfortunately for the military mind, neutron bombs are regarded as nuclear weapons, since they need a small nuclear explosion to initiate them. As such they

are unlikely to be used on the battlefield, if only for fear of escalating the conflict into a full-scale exchange of strategic nuclear weapons.

More appealing to those on the lookout for loopholes in disarmament treaties, therefore, is some form of DEW that would have the same effect without the blast and residual radiation of a nuclear bomb. It may be possible to devise a Charged-Particle Beam (CPB) weapon that scours the landscape with a directed ray of lethal nuclear radiation. Their scope could be enhanced by using satellite surveillance to select targets. If that satellite could itself be made secure from enemy attack, such a system could be an overnight war-winner.

The effect of 'Star Wars'

These advanced weapons may all seem a little far-fetched and futuristic — more like something used by Luke Skywalker than weapons for GI Joe or Tommy Atkins. Yet the massive spending on SDI (Strategic Defence Initiative, or 'Star Wars') in the 1980s led to a great leap in the development of weapons in the United States that seemed merely science-fiction just a decade before.

reactive armour and seek out the relatively thin top plates on a tank. While an alert tank's counter-measures may in theory defeat an individual sub-warhead, the sheer weight of numbers discharged will probably make self-defence all but impossible.

The 'smartlets' in an anti-armour cluster bomb, shell or rocket warhead can be small HEAT grenades, each of which will have terminal-homing on IR, radiation, magnetic or other signals. They are long-range, indirect-fire, area weapons, which can funnel very heavy firepower accurately into a small space without exposing a friendly tank force at close range – as would have been necessary to achieve the same effect in the past. The same systems can also carry warheads optimised for use against personnel or concrete runways. Some commentators have even suggested that a salvo of cluster munitions could have an anti-armour effect equivalent to that of a small nuclear device, but without creating the same environmental damage. Such deep-strike ET weapons are certainly a counter to the old adage that 'the best anti-tank weapon is another tank', and they have already caused a re-think over just how deep-lying armour needs to be before it is safe.

Sceptics, nevertheless, remain convinced that such weapons are doomed to failure because of their enormous cost and technological complexity. It is easier to believe in a weapon that utilises only two or three technologies – for example, an unsubtle KE bolt – than in a system that depends on 16 different technologies for its target acquisition, fire control, missile flight, mid-term guidance, warhead release, terminal guidance and finally penetration.

An anti-armour effect equivalent to that of a small nuclear device

Similarly there is a profound belief that relatively simple ECMs possess the power to throw the whole ET system into chaos. A few intense-heat decoys near the target, for example, may be all that is needed to draw the teeth of even the most perfect weapon release. Nor are these weapons yet combat-proven: Omdurman provided a vivid pre-1914 test run for the Maxim gun, while the first day of Cambrai in 1917 showed what the concentrated use of armour could achieve; but so far there has been no 'dress rehearsal' for these supposed mass killers of the future.

Below: Maintenance work on the drive sprocket of a Scorpion-series light tank. Work on some mechanical aspect of their 'mounts' is an all-pervading feature of life in the tanks. After a road march, for example, there may be hours of 'trackbashing' – adjusting track tension and replacing worn track links – to do. A tank that has broken down is out of action just as much as one knocked out by enemy action

HOW THE RAIL GUN WORKS

Despite its futuristic name, the rail gun is a relatively conventional piece of Kinetic-Energy (KE) kit. But it promises to fire an artillery round at 100,000m per second – just over 70 times the velocity of a tank's KE sabot round, which chugs along at 1400m/sec, 125 times faster than the average rifle bullet (800m/sec) and 333 times the speed of an advanced ATM (300m/sec). Experimental versions of the rail gun have already fired rounds at 10,000m/sec.

The rail gun consists of twin metallic rails that are given a high electro-magnetic charge. Gas pressure injects a bullet made of plastic or some other non-conducting material between them. Conductors at the base of the bullet then complete a circuit between the two rails. The massive current flowing behind the bullet, acclerates it due to the Lorenz effect, caused by movement of a current across a magnetic field.

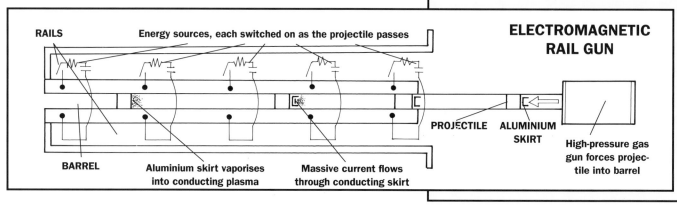

RAILS   Energy sources, each switched on as the projectile passes   **ELECTROMAGNETIC RAIL GUN**

PROJECTILE   ALUMINIUM SKIRT

High-pressure gas gun forces projectile into barrel

BARREL   Aluminium skirt vaporises into conducting plasma   Massive current flows through conducting skirt

Anti-armour cluster munitions may also contain anti-tank mines – with or without time delays and other 'smart' features. These can be scattered almost instantly by means of artillery, rockets, helicopters or aircraft, offering a commander an invaluable means of closing chokepoints behind the enemy's front, or plugging gaps that may suddenly appear in his own fighting line. This requires considerably less complex technology than that needed by fully active homing warheads, and is surely far more reliable and certain. Whereas the world's armies may not yet be truly capable of sniping moving tanks at 100km range, it is likely that they can lay effective anti-tank minefields at the same ranges. The mine itself has undergone radical changes since 1945, with many new sensing systems and an ability to discriminate between targets. One version 'stands off' by the roadside, automatically aiming and firing a self-forging fragment horizontally into its target.

It has always been much easier to knock out one or two of a tank's vital systems, to halt it temporarily or to kill some of its crew, than to destroy it definitively. Blast or shrapnel that does not actually penetrate the armour may strip off a tank's tracks or make aerials, optics or electronics inoperative. A projectile that does penetrate may simply draw a neat pencil-line of energy across the inside of the tank, hitting nothing important. On the other hand, it may kill men, smash vital equipment or – most devastating of all – ignite stored ammunition. Failing fire and explosion, however, it is quite normal in sustained combat for tanks to be 're-cycled' many times over by maintenance crews, often within a few hours of each hit. All this may change in the not too distant future when armies deploy particle and beam anti-tank weapons.

Particle and beam weapons, which are perhaps the most futuristic of the anti-armour systems currently under development, would be capable of destroying tanks along a line of sight virtually at the speed of light. Simultaneously, they would dispense with the current need for cumbersome fire-control and ranging apparatus and render useless all armour and counter-measures within their range. The drawback to these would be that their effectiveness would be restricted to line of sight only, thus limiting their range and scope of action. They would also need to be armoured and supported to exceptionally high standards, since they would be no better protected than any other weapon against an enemy their crews had not noticed. Until such devastating weapons arrive, however, armies will have to make do with the existing complex mixture of partially effective anti-tank weapons to hold in check ever more fearsome tanks.

Tanks would not be deployed as an independent battalion

In theory, modern tanks should be a great rarity, thanks to their high sophistication and cost. Oddly, this is not the case: the tank parks of the advanced nations are today fuller than ever. Whereas in July 1943 a total of fewer than 6000 tanks took part in 'the greatest tank battle in history' at Kursk, NATO and the Warsaw Pact could until very recently indeed deploy a staggering 40,000 tanks within a month, to fight a battle for Germany. That would mean on average some 50 tanks per kilometre of front; that is, 25 on each side. Allowing for inevitable mechanical breakdowns along the way, 25 tanks represents about the strength of one armoured battalion (a major sub-unit of a tank division), as it might realistically expect to go into action. In reality, however, the tanks would not be deployed as an independent battalion, but would form part of a battlegroup together with infantry, ATGW, anti-aircrat artillery (AAA) and the like.

Above: Chieftain MBTs on a training exercise without the 'bazooka' plates usually fitted on the lower hull sides. They are viewed from within a 'closed down' tank (one with all hatches shut). The restricted view shows why tank commanders like to have their heads out of their turrets. It also shows how difficult it would be to spot an anti-tank missile launcher 2000m away

THE TANK OF THE FUTURE

There are four broad directions in which tank designers have been moving in recent years. These are:

The heavy armoured car

This is a small, agile, lightly armoured wheeled vehicle that carries a heavy tank-killing gun. The French in particular have pioneered this technology. Panhard have already produced a number of wheeled vehicles mounting 90mm guns – as heavy as anything on any British or American tank in World War II – and it seems logical that they should further adapt the vehicle to carry a 105mm gun.

Some designs, notably those developed experimentally by Ford, feature multiple wheels and an articulated chassis to give cross-country performance far superior to the classic four-wheel-drive design with a rigid chassis. The major problem so far with these vehicles is that their complexity has resulted in a drop in mechanical durability and reliability.

The turretless tank destroyer

This is a direct descendant of the many low-profile turretless tanks and self-propelled assault guns developed during World War II. Many armies have experimented with this configuration since 1945: the Swedish 1966 S-Tank is often held up as a milestone example.

In this tank, the driver is also the gunner, for the gun is fixed in the hull and aimed by moving the whole tank. It is 105mm in calibre and loaded automatically from a magazine of 50 rounds. The two engines – one gas turbine, the other diesel – are placed in front of the crew compartment to protect it with their own mass. Additional protection comes from an exceptionally low angle of slope to the glacis plate. These two features have been followed in the equally unconventional, but turreted, Israeli Merkava of 1978.

The 1965 West German Jagdpanzer Kanone is another example of a turretless tank destroyer. This caries a 90mm gun and belongs to a family of relatively lightly-armoured vehicles that includes the Marder infantry fighting vehicle.

Tanks with automatic turrets

Various experimental tank configurations feature a low profile and a heavy gun mounted on a swivelling external pylon. The gun is entirely automatic, being fed from a hopper of shells tacked onto the back. The 1966 Swedish 155mm Bandkanon SPG already uses such a sys-

tem for its gun, although this is housed in a crewed turret. The Bandkanon, fed by an automatic magazine, can fire a full complement of 14 rounds within one minute.

A future tank based on this concept would need both a greater magazine capacity and a system for automatically selected and loading different kinds of shell for different kinds of shot. Given the current state of robotics and computerisation, this should prove no difficulty. Many tanks already have semi-automatic loading systems within manned turrets.

Tanks without crews

The problem with the external gun concept seems to be that, if all human operators are taken out of the turret, the crew will need a whole new array of advanced and expensive technological kit to let them do their jobs from within the body of the machine. This may ultimately strain the design of the vehicle to unacceptable levels, and it does not seem worth while to do this merely to achieve a lower frontal profile and a higher rate of fire.

The next logical development after a tank with no turret is a tank with no crew at all. Just as unmanned aircraft, or

remotely piloted vehicles (RPVs), are playing an increasingly important part over the battlefield, so we can expect to see more and more remotely-controlled AFVs on the ground. Even in World War II the Germans had an armoured, self-propelled, wire-guided AT mine, the 'Goliath'. More recently the British have used a tracked robot for bomb disposal in Northern Ireland – the 'Wheelbarrow'.

There is no logical reason why the tank squadron of the future should not include remotely-controlled vehicles designed for specialist tasks such as armoured reconnaissance or AT sniping. If every manned tank controlled one or two unmanned vehicles, the saving in manpower would be enormous – as would the human losses when things went wrong – without any loss of firepower. Unmanned vehicles would also be braver than manned ones, and their controllers would be able to send them into positions that no human crew could contemplate taking up. They could also be built with much lower profiles than conventional tanks, as they would not need internal compartments high enough to house human crews.

Left: The Swedish turret-less Strv-103 S-Tank. Hailed as revolutionary when it first appeared in 1966, the S-Tank has a 105mm gun which is fixed in the hull. The gun is traversed by turning the whole tank using the tracks, and it is elevated and depressed by raising or lowering the forward or rear part of the hydro-pneumatic suspension. This means that the S-tank cannot track targets, or fire, on the move – a tactical handicap. It is very effective in defence as a tank destroyer, in the manner of the German 'SP guns' of World War II. The S-Tank has a very low silhouette, good protection for the crew and ammunition, and a high rate of fire

One battalion per kilometre – a tank every 40 metres of front – at first sight looks like an awful lot of tanks, but on the ground each battalion commander would be very conscious of how limited his force actually was. Advancing into an enemy-held locality, he – and his crews – would want to go slowly and cautiously, only too well aware of how quickly his force could be reduced to a mere handful. A unit commander would know that a hidden and waiting enemy holds many advantages over a moving unit, so he would try to leapfrog forward in short bounds, consolidating each new position in turn. Every movement would be overwatched by tanks ready to fire as soon as the enemy revealed himself – and those tanks in turn would be overwatched by air-defence guns and missiles. Infantry or fire would have to check out every potentially threatening piece of cover along the way – which artillery would perhaps smoke off while the tanks manoeuvred past it. Every potential minefield or patch of boggy ground would have to be skirted. Reconnaissance units would probe forward, flanks would be watched for any attempt at penetration.

This type of all-arms battle can quickly become very complex, needing especially efficient communications if the commander is to retain control. All too easily he can find sub-units becoming detached or getting involved in small local combats of their own, spreading out laterally as well as in depth – so diluting the spearhead and using up the force. In this way, all too quickly, the 'battalion concentrated on a kilometre of front' can melt away to an isolated troop fighting on its own.

The tactics for individual tanks are based on the principle of maintaining maximum concealment up to – and even during – the moment of opening fire. Where possible tanks will take position behind a ridge or in scrapes which can be dug in less than an hour by modern earth-moving plant. Defilade positions are preferred so that the enemy can be engaged from a concealed position on his flank. If there is time, the tank crew will camouflage the vehicle and, where appropriate, lay out dummy positions and decoy heat sources to divert enemy surveillance and fire.

Where possible, tanks will take position behind a ridge or scrape

When waiting to make contact with the enemy, tanks may be turret down – that is, showing only the commander's cupola above ground level; then to fire they may come hull down – showing only the turret. During the engagement, they may put down suppressive fire – terrorising the enemy, in short – with their machine guns, as well as firing their main guns, and employ a variety of ECMs, such as flares to decoy heat-seeking warheads. Once they have fired, the tanks may revert to their concealed positions or – preferably, in view of the threat from both direct and indirect fire – move to an altogether new position. If they are caught in the open, they can lay down a screen of smoke and hastily retreat to the nearest cover. Despite the risk of throwing a track, modern tanks will use surges of power for short sprints at high speed from one piece of cover to another; the American M1 and Soviet T80 can both manage up to 70km/h on a good surface.

Life in a tank is not as easy as the infantry might like to imagine. It is cramped – especially in Soviet main battle tanks (MBTs), which are much smaller than their Western counterparts – and very bumpy when travelling at speed. There are many hard objects inside a tank: broken noses are an occupational hazard among tank crews. Needing to know what is going on outside only makes life harder. Even with modern all-round optics, the commander has difficulty seeing what he needs to see unless he opens his hatch (a move that can be fatal), while the remainder of the turret crew can see next to nothing of what is going on. The driver has a better view to the outside if the commander has 'buttoned up'. But it is a very restricted view, and he is isolated from his comrades in a lonely station in the front of the hull, from which, in many tanks, he cannot escape as long as the main gun is facing forward. In fact, evacuating the tank quickly in an emergency is difficult for everyone. Smoke, fire and especially explosion are the main enemies of tank crews, although the Israelis have pioneered innovative fire-suppression systems, which use halon gas to starve the flames of oxygen, with considerable success in their Merkava tank. The American Abrams M1 and German Leopard 2 tanks now use the same means to control internal fires.

Smoke, fire and explosion are the main enemies of tank crews

Manning a tank demands split-second decision-making from all crew members. The commander must communicate with other tanks, while selecting targets and designating them to his own crew; the gunner must see and lay on to these targets quickly; and the driver must keep the vehicle positioned to optimum effect. On the modern battlefield these life-and-death decisions will need to be made faster than ever, and more complex equipment – such as apparatus to control the tank's main armament, ECMs and camouflage – will be involved than ever. In the stress and fatigue of battle, a moment's inattention may break any link in this complex chain, possibly with disastrous results.

And there are many disasters that may befall an inattentive tank crew or tank unit. The fate of the 4th County of London Yeomanry at Villers Bocage, Normandy, 1944, is eloquent. A column of its Cromwells and Sherman Fireflies, along with a company from the Rifle Brigade in Universal Carriers and half-tracks, were caught without flank protection while lined up along a narrow road, so just three German Tiger tanks were able to destroy them, vehicle by vehicle. On the modern battlefield a much greater number of such incidents may be expected to take place – and tanks will not be at

PROTECTIVE MEASURES OF THE A-10A THUNDERBOLT II

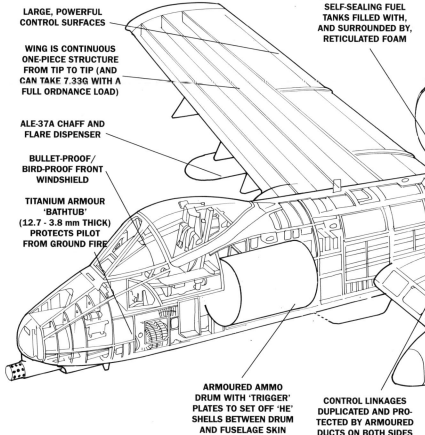

LARGE, POWERFUL CONTROL SURFACES

WING IS CONTINUOUS ONE-PIECE STRUCTURE FROM TIP TO TIP (AND CAN TAKE 7.33G WITH A FULL ORDNANCE LOAD)

ALE-37A CHAFF AND FLARE DISPENSER

BULLET-PROOF/ BIRD-PROOF FRONT WINDSHIELD

TITANIUM ARMOUR 'BATHTUB' (12.7 - 3.8 mm THICK) PROTECTS PILOT FROM GROUND FIRE

SELF-SEALING FUEL TANKS FILLED WITH, AND SURROUNDED BY, RETICULATED FOAM

ARMOURED AMMO DRUM WITH 'TRIGGER' PLATES TO SET OFF 'HE' SHELLS BETWEEN DRUM AND FUSELAGE SKIN

CONTROL LINKAGES DUPLICATED AND PROTECTED BY ARMOURED DUCTS ON BOTH SIDES OF AIRCRAFT (A-10 ALSO USES CABLES RATHER THAN RODS, AS THEY ARE LESS LIKELY TO JAM AFTER BATTLE DAMAGE

OTHER POINTS:
1. The interchangeability of many port and starboard components of the aircraft reduces the number of spares needed
2. Most of the skin area of the aircraft is unstressed, which simplifies the repair task

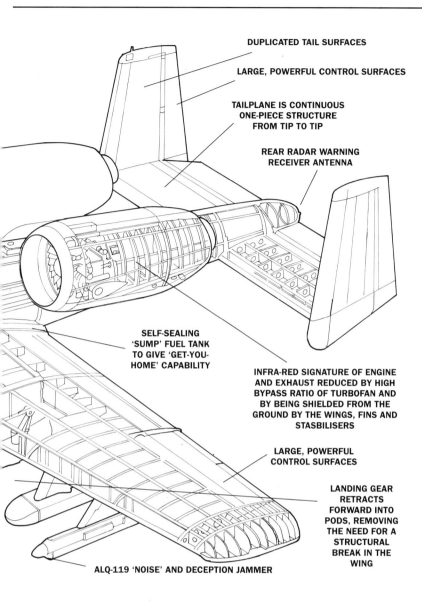

DUPLICATED TAIL SURFACES

LARGE, POWERFUL CONTROL SURFACES

TAILPLANE IS CONTINUOUS ONE-PIECE STRUCTURE FROM TIP TO TIP

REAR RADAR WARNING RECEIVER ANTENNA

SELF-SEALING 'SUMP' FUEL TANK TO GIVE 'GET-YOU-HOME' CAPABILITY

INFRA-RED SIGNATURE OF ENGINE AND EXHAUST REDUCED BY HIGH BYPASS RATIO OF TURBOFAN AND BY BEING SHIELDED FROM THE GROUND BY THE WINGS, FINS AND STASBILISERS

LARGE, POWERFUL CONTROL SURFACES

LANDING GEAR RETRACTS FORWARD INTO PODS, REMOVING THE NEED FOR A STRUCTURAL BREAK IN THE WING

ALQ-119 'NOISE' AND DECEPTION JAMMER

risk merely from enemy armour, but from the whole range of new indirect-fire weapons as well.

Nor has the sheer physical toil facing tank crews been abolished by such ostensibly labour-saving features as bagged charges and other 'separate' ammunition or automated ammunition handling. Crews still have to tension tracks on most tanks, and have to service engines; to bring ammunition aboard and manhandle camouflage nets. Merely mounting and dismounting these giant 60-ton monsters is something of an athletic feat in itself. Admittedly mechanical digging equipment can now help add protection to a static position, but in general a tank's crew gets precious little help from outside. It is a distinct unit that must fend for itself, 24 hours a day.

The very size of the tank makes for hard work

The main threat to combat efficiency, however, may well rest not with stress, physical fatigue, or new weapons, but with the very ancient problem of making a successful rendezvous (RV). It has always been notoriously difficult for commanders to manoeuvre their own forces, and for troops to navigate their way, to a particular spot to arrive at a particular moment, especially through terrain with restricted lines of sight, such as forest or mountain country. When two separate forces are both trying to reach the same RV at the same time, the problem becomes more than twice as difficult to overcome. New, satellite-based navigation aids may tell units exactly where they are and where they have to be, but they do not necessarily speed their progress. An infantry force travelling by truck may be tied to roads that have been interdicted by the enemy, whereas tanks can crash across country: whichever makes the deadline first will be exposed to attack while it waits for the other. Making these manoeuvres work requires a

Left: Rearming the 30mm GAU-8/A 'Avenger' cannon on an A-10A. Built specifically as a tank-busting aircraft – with the cannon as its main anti-armour weapon – the Thunderbolt II follows the WWI Junkers J1 and the WWII Il-2 Sturmvoik in being heavily armoured itself

Right: The awesome firepower of a GAU-8. This weapon can fire at 2100 or 4200 rpm, but to prevent overheating the 1174 rounds the A-10A carries are fired in 10 two-second bursts

Right: US Marines firing a SMAW (Shoulder-launched Multi-purpose Assault Weapon) at a T-72 tank. The SMAW is a modification of the Israeli B-300 82mm anti-armour weapon. Because of the small size of the warhead, it can only penetrate 400mm of rolled homogenous steel armour, which means that it has to be fired against the side of a modern main battle tank, rather than the front, to be effective. But against more lightly armoured targets – such as APCs and IFVs (Infantry Fighting Vehicles), such weapons are devastating

high level of 'staff work' – often from very junior commanders or even individual vehicle crews. As the speed of operations increases, so does the number of RVs that are needed. The schedules become tighter and the possibility of failure increases.

There is probably nothing in land warfare more difficult than orchestrating an impromptu, fast-moving armoured battle fought by small sub-units. In World War II only a few commanders – for example, O'Connor (whose motto was 'offensive action whenever possible', but whose potential was cut short when he was captured), Rommel, Von Balck and Patton – could ride this particular bronco for very long, and Patton often did so only by bypassing and so isolating heavy concentrations of enemy units. The general consensus was that it was always safer to plan for a deliberate, slow-moving, attritional battle in which massive force could be remorselessly lined up against identified enemy weak points and, in the end, the Allies' greater industrial resources justified this stand. Montgomery, for all his bluster about chasing the enemy 'like a frightened rabbit', stuck firmly to this strategy both in North Africa and in the European theatre. This sedate and resource-intensive style did ultimately win the war – but the whole thing might have been a shorter and less bloody business had the Allied high command had the talent available to follow, or had encouraged, a more swashbuckling approach.

Opportunistic attacks, brilliant improvisation and lightning responses may be the only way to win a future war. But such a fighting style presumes that supplies will always be available on demand to continue the battle, to exploit advantages or recoup losses. On the battlefield of the future, there is no problem that will be more acute than logistics.

Heavily armoured columns must fight an unpredictable battle of wide-ranging manoeuvre, then link up almost instantly – still somewhere not far away from the battlefield – with their soft-skinned supply echelons. The rate at which modern armour will consume ammunition makes this a crucial matter. Making it succeed will make heavy work for combat and staff troops alike: for the armoured troops there are all the difficulties of disengaging from the fighting and moving to find a particular – and reasonably safe – spot in the rear; for the logisticians there is the hardly less daunting task of predicting where the 'tankies' will want to be, and when.

Tanks can be as vulnerable as any soft-skinned vehicle

We may well be entering an era in which armoured vehicles will have to carry out all logistic replenishment, since the present soft-skinned ones will be unable to survive in the places where tanks must resupply. But even this provision may not be enough, for while tanks and heavily armoured vehicles may be becoming proof against hand-held infantry weapons, they can be as vulnerable as any soft-skinned vehicle to almost any other type of weapon if they are caught off guard. Furthermore, the appearance of effective indirect-fire anti-armour weapons, in particular, has now abolished the tank's traditional safety outside the enemy's line of sight. The tank's freedom of action is today being restricted from many directions at once, and it is unlikely to dominate the battlefield of the future in the same way that it dominated the battlefield in the past. The tank may not be dead, but from now on it will have to be more wary than ever.

IS THE TANK DEAD?

Some answer this question with an unequivocal 'yes'. Their reasons:

• The tank now faces a bewildering range of anti-tank weapons, and many, many more of them it ever faced before. As well as direct-fire weapons there are tube artillery-launched scattered field mines, smart 'search-and-destroy armour' mines and self-forging projectiles that hang beneath parachutes, waiting for a target to appear below them

• Thermal imagery and other new surveillance devices highlight tanks when they move, although they can be defeated by tanks lurking in ambush. This reverses the traditional offensive role of the tank

• Other classes of AFV – for example, SPGs, armoured cars and attack helicopters – may take over the tank's role

• The complex all-arms battle that the tank

demands will be very hard to fight if tactical communications are lost and logistics are uncertain

Others disagree. Their reasons:

• Many new AT weapons are expensive, complicated, and little tested in combat. Even if enough of them can be put into the field, it is uncertain that they will work properly

• New passive, reactive and perhaps even active armour, ECMs and fire suppression systems make the tank safer than ever, especially against portable HEAT weapons

• The heavy KE gun will be the best AT weapon, and only another tank can carry it. If the electro-magnetic rail gun can be fielded, this will be more true than ever

• Modern all-arms teams contain a mix of powerful AFVs and other kit that is better designed for the integrated battle than ever

HELICOPTERS IN DANGER

Ever since Vietnam, the helicopter has been a potent symbol of modern warfare, surpassing even the tank. It has been portrayed as capable of doing almost anything that a tank can do, five times faster, and without touching the ground. Many commentators have seriously suggested that it might soon supersede the tank as the main front-line combat vehicle; even if it does not, they continue, it may still be able to lift tanks or 'near-tanks' into combat and thus become vital to the mobility of armoured forces.

Below: Since the advent of the dedicated helicopter gunship, the rotary-winged attack aircraft has become the queen of the battlefield. But for all its awesome appearance and firepower, it is still a very vulnerable machine

I f the helicopter really can become the tank of the future, then all of the 68,000 (very expensive) MBTs currently deployed in Europe – that is, west of the Urals – are in imminent danger of becoming militarily obsolete, just as they are already diplomatically negotiable. If, on the other hand, the helicopter cannot supersede the tank, then certain current military and civilian expectations will remain sadly unfulfilled and the helicopter will continue in something like an auxiliary role. What, then, is the outlook for the helicopter?

Although the tank-hunting helicopter may indeed be better able to look after itself than the tank, nevertheless it faces a number of aerial dangers; far more in fact than does the fast jet. AAA weapons or light surface-to-air missiles (SAMs), which a jet would expect to avoid relatively easily, will pose a very serious threat to the slower-moving helicopter.

The helicopter in the air battle will be just as vulnerable as the APC in the tank battle: it will face destruction from many types of bullet and warhead that its faster and better protected 'senior partner' can almost ignore. This is especially true of laden transport helicopters that lack the agility or freedom to take cover enjoyed by attack and observation machines. Even the hybrid aircraft with variable-geometry rotors or twin counter-rotating rotors seem unlikely to increase helicopter speed to much more than double the present standard. The helicopter is, apparently, doomed by its own technology to remain a slow-mover.

Because of their slow flight, helicopters are vulnerable to relatively unsophisticated weapons. In the Vietnam War the most important killer of helicopters was the simple 12.7mm, or 0.5in, machine gun and the Viet Cong (VC) and North Vietnamese Army (NVA) had these weapons in plenty. There will be many more of them on any advanced armoured battlefield, as most modern AFVs carry a machine gun

Right: Alongside the gunship, the heavy-lift helicopter has come to play a vital role in bringing up equipment and supplies more rapidly than a soldier of even 50 years ago would have dreamed possible. The Sikorsky CH-54 'Tarhe', or Sky Crane, was designed to transport standard shipping containers, hence its odd shape. It is capable of lifting 10 tonnes at a time

HEAVY-LIFT HELICOPTERS

In Vietnam the heavy-lift helicopter was an essential element in the war against North Vietnam and the Viet Cong. In the ground battle, it ferried heavy guns, ammunition and fortification materials to and from advanced fire bases. It also significantly assisted in the helicopter war by bringing fuel and ammunition to forward helicopters, and transporting damaged light helicopters rearwards to the repair shops. It even occasionally helped the 'Brown Water Navy' in the Mekong Delta, by lifting armoured boats bodily from one waterway to another.

In any future war heavy-lift helicopters would still carry out duties similar to these, and would doubtless very quickly be called upon to perform many others.

For example: they could transport advanced armoured cars mounting up to a 105mm gun from one end of the theatre of operations to the other, adding enormous extra mobile punch to any *desant*; they could quickly lift heavy engineer plant and munitions such as mines from one point in a defender's line to another to obstruct a threatened enemy breakthrough; they could move entire pre-packaged command bunkers in a series of bounds, to where engineers would dig them in using the heavy plant already lifted in; fuel and ammunition could be vectored into threatened units at a moment's notice; they could move support echelons for helicopters, Harriers or even conventional fixed-wing aircraft, allowing air assets to be concentrated where they were most needed.

Two major problems affect heavy-lift helicopters, however. First, there may not be enough machines to go round on the day of battle and, second, those that are available will probably be highly vulnerable even on the fringes of the combat zone. In the Falklands war of 1982 the single British Chinook gave invaluable service – but it was the only one that survived anti-shipping missile attacks on the way to the battlefield.

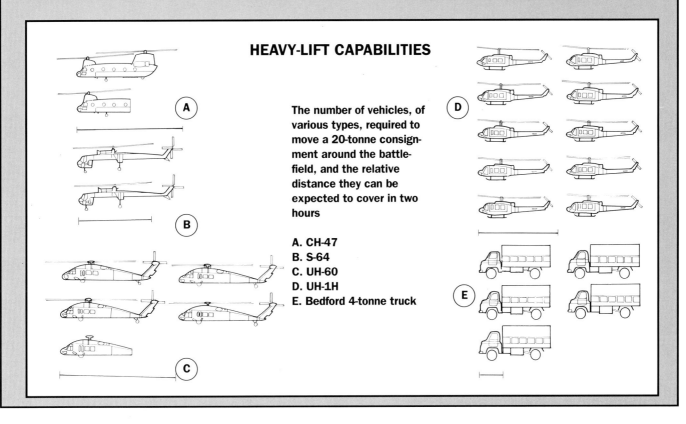

HEAVY-LIFT CAPABILITIES

The number of vehicles, of various types, required to move a 20-tonne consignment around the battle-field, and the relative distance they can be expected to cover in two hours

A. CH-47
B. S-64
C. UH-60
D. UH-1H
E. Bedford 4-tonne truck

of at least this calibre, and most of the latest Infantry Fighting Vehicles (IFVs) mount a heavier weapon still; for example, the German Marder carries a 20mm cannon, the US Bradley the 25mm Chain Gun and the British Warrior the 30mm Rarden.

Most light or medium machine guns (MGs), on the other hand, can be countered simply by flying nap-of-the-earth behind cover, or out of range at an altitude of 2000ft or higher. Nevertheless in combat neither of these solutions may be possible and in Vietnam even AK47 assault rifles proved deadly at close range, particularly when an aircraft was moving very slowly in transitional lift just before landing or after take off. An 'ace' pilot was the one who could take off in a smooth forward parabola, rather than by rising vertically, then pausing in the air as a

static target before moving off in normal flight; and a high priority was placed on setting a helicopter down at a 'cold LZ' – that is, a Landing Zone not covered by enemy fire. On the modern armoured battlefield such LZs may be considerably harder to find than they were in Vietnam, especially when the increasing threat from accurate, quick-response indirect fire is taken fully into account.

Helicopters on the modern armoured battlefield face far worse direct-fire threats than rifles and traditional machine guns, however. Today's infantry carry hand-held SAMs, such as the SAM7, Stinger and Javelin, which are highly effective against the helicopter, especially if it is cruising at higher altitudes. They in turn are backed up by heavy automatic cannon mounted on vehicles specifically

Above: Transport helicopters are expected to supersede the truck one day, but they still have a long way to go

PROTECTIVE MEASURES OF THE AH-64 APACHE

HIT AVOIDANCE

1. Flat canopy panels greatly reduce 'glint' from sun
2. Four rotor blades produce less 'flicker' than two
3. Receiving antenna for AN/ALQ-136(V) radar jammer
4. Space, weight and power available for AN/AVR-2 laser warning receiver
5. Well-separated engines
6. AN/ALQ-144 infra red jammer
7. Rear AN/APR-39(V)1 radar warning receiver
8. Asymmetrical layout of tail rotor blades attenuate noise they produce
9. M-130 chaff and flare dispenser
10. Ventral AN/APR-39(V)1 radar warning receiver
11. 'Black Hole' infra red-suppression exhaust ducts
12. AN/ALQ-136(V)1 radar jammer
13. Forward radar warning receiver for AN/APR-39(V)1

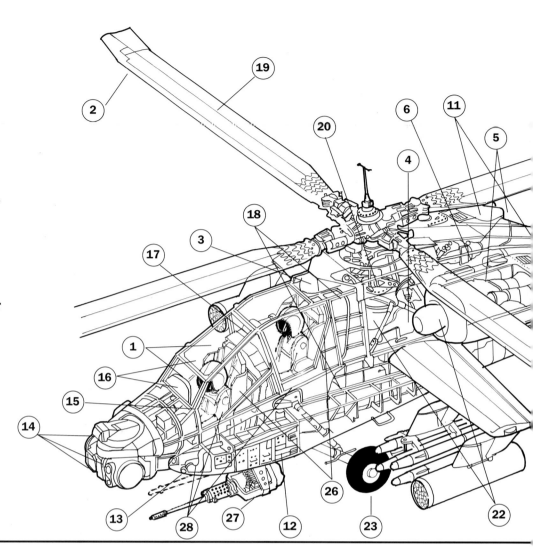

designed for the anti-aircraft role, and with fire control to match. Such systems include the US M163A1 20mm Vulcan, the Oerlikon 35mm GDF-DO3, and the Soviet ZSU 23/4 Shilka. The last-mentioned accounted for around 40 per cent of Israeli aircraft losses in the 1973 October War, and though it now looks somewhat aged and lightweight against fast jets, it still poses a very potent threat to helicopters. Today's more advanced AAA tends to fire 30mm or 40mm rounds with special features such as burst-fire capability and cluster-pellet warheads (as in the 40mm Bofors Trinity). These weapons can reach many thousands of feet higher than traditional MGs, thus depriving helicopters of the protection of altitude that they enjoyed in Vietnam.

Behind the hand-held missile launchers and AAA lie the heavier SAMs, many of which now enjoy the same battlefield mobility as tanks and APCs. The British Rapier system, for example, which was effective against fast jets in the Falklands War of 1982, is today mounted on an armoured vehicle, while the Soviet SAM6, a fearsome proposition in 1973, has now been superseded by the still more mobile SAM8. Other advanced systems include the American Chaparral

and Patriot, and the French Roland and Crotale.

Yet today's helicopter has more to deal with than the surface-to-air threat; it is also part of a full-blown air battle in which good 'airspace management' – in civilian terms, 'air traffic control' – is critical to survival and success. For example, a helicopter should not try to fly through the same three-dimensional space that another helicopter is already working, or in which an artillery bombardment or a fast jet strike is taking place.

Hand-held SAMs are efficient helicopter killers

Rather, deep-penetrating interdiction strikes must be passed through the close support air battle over the Forward Line of Own Troops (FLOT), with friendly surface-to-air gunners being warned in advance in case they make a fatal mistake in identification. All this involves considerable staffwork and effective communications, neither of which may be available under modern combat conditions. This being the case, perhaps the greatest threat to the helicopter in combat may come from friendly air defences and stray aircraft. This was certainly an unexpected major concern in the 1983

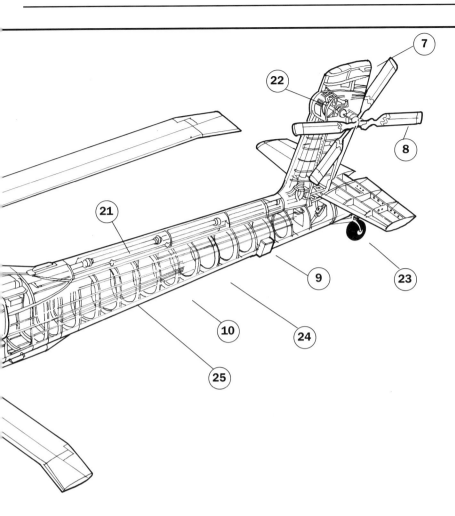

DAMAGE LIMITATION

14. Recessed, protected sensors

15. Dual-control column allows co-pilot/gunner to fly aircraft if pilot is incapacitated

17. Transparent inter-cockpit acrylic blast-shield (also acts with with canopy frame in 'roll-bar' protective effect)

18. Control-rod linkages and other operating systems duplicated and well-separated

19. Each main rotor blade includes five stainless-steel spars to withstand 25mm cannon fire

20. Transmission has collar of ESR (Electro-Slag Refined) steel (proof against 12.7mm rounds)

21. Transmission runs through duct of ESR steel (see 20)

22. Gearbox designed to withstand battle damage and can run for one hour after loss of oil supply

23. Impact-absorbing landing gear collapses in a crash

24. Critical structures made of ESR steel to withstand 12.7mm rounds

25. Back-up fly-by-wire tailplane hydraulic actuator

26. Kevlar armoured seats in energy-absorbing seat mountings

27. Collapsible turret for 30mm gun protects crew in crash

28. Boron carbide armoured cockpit floor and protective panels

Right: Putting the pilot and the gunner in tandem, as do all the modern purpose-built gunships, allows the aircraft's fuselage to be little wider than a man's shoulders. The crewmen's positions are the reverse of those found in fixed-wing aircraft, the pilot being positioned behind and above the gunner

HELICOPTERS IN COMBAT - DUEL IN THE SKIES

One particular aspect of air war yet to be seen is the airborne duel between helicopters. The diagram illustrates a scenario which would be very likely in a desert war between two well-equipped powers - one supplied from NATO sources and the other from the Soviet armoury. An armoured column, composed of the usual mix of MBTs, IFVs and support vehicles, is advancing towards an objective when it is ambushed by Mi-24 Hind D gunships. The armoured column has its own helicopter support, however: flying unseen by the Hinds but close by are AH-64A Apaches and Bell AH-1T Cobras. These are primarily designed to take out any tanks that might oppose the ground advance, but as soon as the Hinds move in, the friendly helicopters feel impelled to come to the aid of the vulnerable column.

The Hinds are big and rather clumsy - the heavy armour that protects them against ground fire makes them a liability when it comes to manoeuvring in the air. So the Hind unit has its organic support in the form of the speedier Kamov Hokum. In this scenario, a helicopter dogfight would be inevitable: neither side could give way, and the helicopters would engage each other for some minutes before fixed-wing aircraft could intervene.

Given these possibilities it is clear that helicopters will have to be able to look after themselves. They will need gunsights and air-to-air guided missiles such as Sparrows and Sidewinders just to fight others of their kind.

US operation in Grenada, where rotary-wing losses were relatively high.

Also very worrying to helicopters is the likelihood that enemy helicopters and jets will be specifically tasked with searching them out and engaging them in air-to-air combat. The weapon mixes currently carried by many combat helicopters and jets would be utterly devastating were they to be used against rotary-winged aircraft. In the future, helicopters will therefore have to learn to fight a thrust-and-parry air battle of their own, just as the tank has had to learn to fend for itself in tank-to-tank duels. This air battle will be an almost entirely novel feature of warfare, since in most helicopter campaigns of the past – especially those in South Vietnam and Afghanistan – the side that had the helicopters was not opposed by enemy air power at all.

Counter-measures, more than armour, will save the helicopter

The helicopter's air battle will be quite different in scale and scope from the main deep-strike air battle of advanced fast jets with their airfield-cratering munitions and air-to-air missiles (AAMs). Nevertheless it will have the same general structure and will be fought according to similar basic rules. The humble helicopter will have to exploit its own special tactical agility to out-fight enemy attack helicopters and jets in the air: it will have to jink and dodge behind trees and other ground clutter, making split-second decisions whether or not to take the risk of pursuit across the FLOT, and it will have to dash, climb and manoeuvre at super-high speed, as only the latest attack helicopters can.

In addition to this, the helicopter will have to use its own brands of ECM, stealth technology and firepower to suppress the opposition. Devices to counter IR-homing warheads are already being fitted, in the form of exhaust-gas coolers and decoy strobes. However, there is still some way to go in areas such as radar jamming and suppression of the distinctive rotor-wash signature; the complete 'stealth helicopter' remains some way in the future.

Despite their shortcomings, helicopters, no less than jets, will have to clear a path through enemy air defences before they will be able to operate effectively. They will need to adopt the 'Wild Weasel' concept, and an EW helicopter will accompany any helicopter force and smooth its way to the target both by jamming and by direct air-to-ground strikes.

In general, all this implies that there will be a relative increase in the number of EW, SAM-busting and dog-fighting helicopters, compared to other types. There will also have to be new munitions and specialised EW pods developed to make this battle possible. The helicopter, in short, will have to start learning to take the air battle as seriously as it already takes the ground battle.

Rational analysis of the future battlefield and the helicopter's role on it ought to pay greater attention to the remarkable Harrier Vertical/Short Take Off & Landing (VSTOL) 'jump jet'. Like the helicopter, the Harrier does not need a formal airfield and can hover, while it can pack a much greater payload and can move at almost Mach 1. Because it is completely decoupled, relying on thrust rather than aerodynamic lift when it chooses, it can change direction in mid-air to confound incoming combat

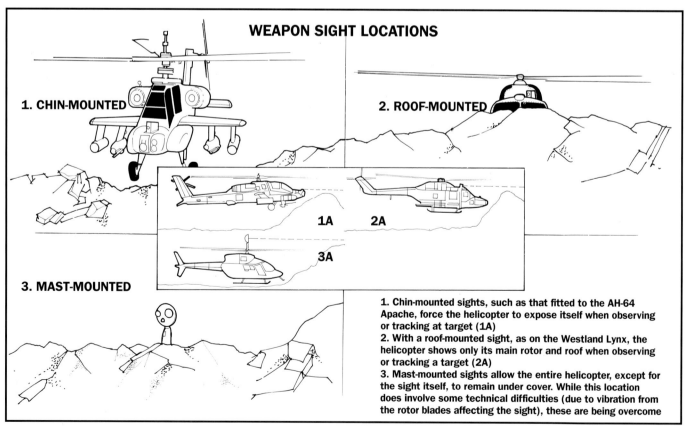

WEAPON SIGHT LOCATIONS

1. CHIN-MOUNTED

2. ROOF-MOUNTED

1A 2A 3A

3. MAST-MOUNTED

1. Chin-mounted sights, such as that fitted to the AH-64 Apache, force the helicopter to expose itself when observing or tracking at target (1A)
2. With a roof-mounted sight, as on the Westland Lynx, the helicopter shows only its main rotor and roof when observing or tracking a target (2A)
3. Mast-mounted sights allow the entire helicopter, except for the sight itself, to remain under cover. While this location does involve some technical difficulties (due to vibration from the rotor blades affecting the sight), these are being overcome

ANTI-TANK HELICOPTER TACTICS

Tank-killing helicopters hunt in packs of perhaps half a dozen machines assisted by target-locating LOHs. Once the LOHs have identified a potentially fruitful enemy target, the team will first try to manoeuvre out of sight to a covered fire-position, perhaps behind a ridge or a treeline. From here, the LOHs – sitting 'rotor down' but still managing to keep the enemy in constant view through their mast-mounted scanners – may send tactical information to the fire team. This may be relayed by radio – if it is still working – or alternatively it may come in the form of target designation by laser.

With the enemy pinpointed, the attack helicopters will start to 'work' the target, each one bobbing into sight momentarily, firing and then quickly retreating into cover. Identified enemy air-defence weapons will be targeted first, then command tanks, and lastly ordinary tanks. If the ambush can be completed before the enemy takes cover or vectors effective counter-fire on to the helicopters, a team of six firing units could very

well expect to annihilate an entire battalion of 31 tanks in less than half an hour.

Even if it is forced to break off the engagement prematurely, or if it is fighting under-strength, the tank-hunting team can still hope to inflict serious losses on the enemy. Armoured formations will have to keep alert, not only so they can activate their own air defences, ECMs and other counter-measures, but also to call up artillery and anti-helicopter helicopters.

Helicopters currently rely on missiles and unguided rockets to attack hardened targets such as armoured vehicles – the GAU-8A cannon, as fitted to the A-10A Thunderbolt would probably stop a rotary-winged aircraft in its tracks. Should the helicopter come upon soft-skinned vehicles mixed in with the armour, however, then its guns will be brought into play. Both Soviet and NATO helicopters are armed for this eventuality, and future generations of attack helicopters are unlikely to lose their capacity to destroy vehicles and material so cheaply.

Above: The AH-1 Huey Cobra first saw service in Vietnam, where its small size and comparatively huge weapons load made it a firm favourite with hard-pressed ground troops. More recently, it has been recast in the anti-armour role, which it shares with its larger successor, the AH-64 Apache. Rocket-powered projectiles, whether guided or unguided, have the great advantage of not upsetting the weapons platform by their recoil, so are particularly well adapted to helicopter use

Fast troop-carrying helicopters, such as the UH-60 Blackhawk (Right), and the Mi-24 Hind (Below) have given the modern generation of infantryman a way of getting into battle quickly, and at minimum risk to himself in the dangerous moving-up period. The Soviet solution to the problem of how to protect the aircraft was to equip the helicopter as a gunship, so allowing it to put down massive suppressive fire before inserting a small group of infantrymen. The Blackhawk – a much bigger aircraft – relies on dedicated gunships to neutralise enemy forces

Left: The helicopter's short ferry range means that it, itself, must be air-portable if it is to be of any use in the rapid-intervention role. One of the constraints placed on the designers of the UH-60 was that it should be transportable by the C-141 Starlifter, the front-line transport aircraft of the USAF's Military Airlift Command. They had to fold it a couple of times to achieve the desired result!

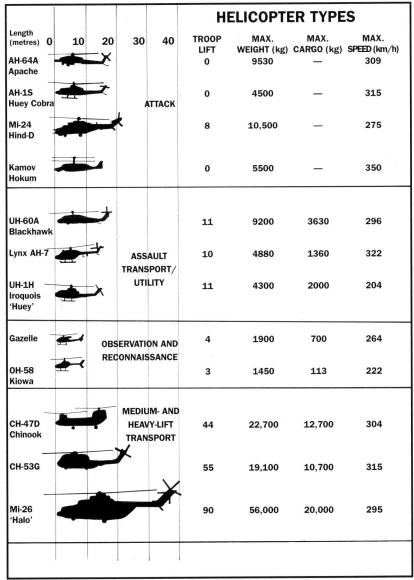

HELICOPTER TYPES

Length (metres)	0	10	20	30	40	TROOP LIFT	MAX. WEIGHT (kg)	MAX. CARGO (kg)	MAX. SPEED (km/h)
AH-64A Apache					ATTACK	0	9530	—	309
AH-1S Huey Cobra						0	4500	—	315
Mi-24 Hind-D						8	10,500	—	275
Kamov Hokum						0	5500	—	350
UH-60A Blackhawk					ASSAULT TRANSPORT/ UTILITY	11	9200	3630	296
Lynx AH-7						10	4880	1360	322
UH-1H Iroquois 'Huey'						11	4300	2000	204
Gazelle					OBSERVATION AND RECONNAISSANCE	4	1900	700	264
OH-58 Kiowa						3	1450	113	222
CH-47D Chinook					MEDIUM- AND HEAVY-LIFT TRANSPORT	44	22,700	12,700	304
CH-53G						55	19,100	10,700	315
Mi-26 'Halo'						90	56,000	20,000	295

aircraft and missiles alike; this gives it a crucial advantage in dog-fighting. In practice, 'viffing' (vectoring in flight) is not the sudden stop that some commentators would have one believe, but it is none the less effective for all that. Admittedly, when taking off and landing vertically, the Harrier has a very heavy IR signature, and it requires a larger support echelon than a helicopter and cannot transport troops. Nevertheless, in the microcosm of the overall air battle that is the helicopter battle, the Harrier is a lethal interloper.

Fixed- and rotary-wing aircraft compliment each other

More heavily 'hyped', although perhaps ultimately less promising than the Harrier, is the A-10A Thunderbolt II. This is a purpose-built tank-busting close-support fixed-wing jet, low, slow and heavily armoured. It mounts a heavy cannon as well as a wide variety of smart (and other) bombs. If it is allowed to manoeuvre close to the enemy, the A-10 is well able to take out AAA, SAMs, tanks and helicopters alike. However, its ability to survive is in some doubt, since it lacks the agility of an attack helicopter. And even if the A-10 does not fall victim to its intended target, it still needs to return to a large, fixed infrastructure, though not necessarily an airfield proper; A-10s on exercise have used straight stretches of autobahn as runways quite successfully, just the same as the Harrier.

It is certainly likely that a mixture of these fixed-wing aircraft will take part in the close-support air battle along with the helicopters. Relatively large numbers of unsophisticated light jets such as the Alpha Jet and the Hawk may be added to the brew as reinforcements for the Harriers and A-10s, making the sky over the FLOT more crowded than ever. This will surely intensify the nightmare of airspace management at the same time as it gives anti-aircraft

HELICOPTER WEAPONRY

Standard 7.62mm general-purpose machine guns (GPMGs) were originally fitted to transport helicopters, while on attack and LOH machines these were normally supplanted by electrically powered, hydraulically powered or blowback-powered multi-barrelled rotary aircraft guns. These weapons could fire between 1600 and 10,000 rounds per minute of ammunition ranging from standard 5.56mm and 7.62mm ball to 30mm HEAT and KE anti-tank rounds. The 40mm grenade- or bomblet-launcher has also traditionally been a mainstay of the helicopter's armoury; this can fire at a rate of up to 230 rounds per minute.

When the need for heavy firepower support for helicopter operations was originally recognised, the first thought was to transport underslung conventional artillery pieces to an advanced fire-position. This happened in the European powers' colonial wars, such as the Malayan Emergency (1948-60) and the Algerian Insurrection (1954-62), and 'displacing' artillery remains an important service that the helicopter can offer. However, in the 1960s, the Americans came up with another approach when they fitted massed 2.75in rocket pods on to the helicopters themselves.

This was the birth of aerial rocket artillery (ARA). At first up to 72 HE rockets, each weighing between 5 and 8kg, could be fired either individually or in salvoes to a range of up to 3km; today, the Soviets mount up to 128 2.24in rockets per helicopter. The great advantage of rockets is that they have no appreciable recoil to jar the helicopter, whereas the recoil from a number of guns can, at least initially, throw the aircraft violently out of alignment; the disadvantage is that rockets are not especially accurate.

From unguided rockets, the natural next step was to equip helicopters with guided weapons. Early on, the French pioneered heli-borne ATGW, and the move has captured the imagination of the world's armies. The classic US wire-guided TOW is today giving way to various 'fire and forget' systems that can follow the target once a laser beam has designated it or otherwise locked on to it. The AH-64 Apache can carry 16 Hellfire laser-guided AT missiles.

These anti-tank weapons have already been joined by guided weapons for other duties, such as dog-fighting or radiation-seeking; inevitably these will at some stage be joined by many more varieties. The attack helicopter of the future may well be capable, at least in theory, of firing a single salvo of four missiles that simultaneously downs an enemy helicopter, takes out an air-defence radar, kills a troop of tanks and makes a helicopter 'airfield' uninhabitable for 12 hours.

gunners yet more plentiful targets. Admittedly it also implies a bigger threat to the anti-aircraft gunners, but they will at least enjoy the defender's advantage of sitting in place waiting for targets, whereas the aircraft will have to seek them out actively and co-ordinate their efforts to destroy them.

The balance of advantage between attack and defence will vary widely according to local circumstances, but overall the defence is surely likely to have the upper hand. The aerial element of a future war may well resemble the standoff over the FLOT that marked the middle period of the 1973 October War. On that occasion both sides came to believe it was impossible to operate aircraft safely beyond the enemy's front line. It was only later in the war that the Israelis successfully carved out SAM-free corridors for air operations.

The attack helicopter's first task is to suppress local anti-aircraft fire

Quite apart from fighting its complex battle in the air, the helicopter will in future have to protect its own home base, just as the jets already do. The difference is that in the case of the helicopter, the 'airfield' may consist of little more than a forest clearing containing some POL trucks, a small ammunition train and a skeleton maintenance crew. Although helicopters can land in any field or small clearing – or even on a flat roof or at an urban crossroads – their overall mobility and oper-ability is still quite severely limited by the mobility and vulnerability of their supporting rear echelon.

This soft-skinned echelon was previously highly secure, since it could be protected both by dispersal beyond the range of enemy artillery, and by making its signature so small and insignificant that it would be easily overlooked. In a future high-tech war, however, it is likely that neither of these arrangements will work. Even the smallest installation deep behind enemy lines may in future be perfectly visible at a considerable distance, while the greatly increased range of surface-to-surface gun and rocket weapons will make it entirely vulnerable once it has been located.

Insofar as helicopters depend on fuel, ammuni-tion and maintenance, therefore, they are more at risk today than they ever were in the past. In Vietnam between 1965 and 1972 each machine needed at first three, then eventually 10 hours of maintenance for every hour in the air; in the future this ratio is unlikely to be significantly improved. Mechanical reliability is certainly on an upward curve, but so too is mechanical and electronic com-plexity, bringing with it increased potential for a systems failure somewhere down the line. As far as logistics are concerned, helicopter operation is by no means an easy option. In 1967 each brigade in the US 1st Cavalry Division (Airmobile) in Vietnam consumed some 250 tonnes of supplies per day. This is roughly equivalent to the 650 tonnes that an armoured division in Patton's Third Army needed to fight in Europe in 1944.

In Vietnam, helicopters needed 10 hours maintenance for one in the air

The general conclusion must be that, while the helicopter's 'home airfield' and logistic infrastruc-ture are no less important to its survival today than they were in the 1960s, these essential lifelines have become very much more accessible targets for enemy attack. And the more dangerous the heli-copter is thought to be to tanks and other ground units, the more ardently the enemy will seek new

While they are almost a generation apart, the AH-64 Apache (Far Left), and the Mi-24 Hind (Left) are inevitably compared one with the other. The Hind D, (not the most recent evolution, but the most common), mounts a four-barrel 12.7mm cannon in an electrically operated chin turret. Wing pylons accommodate four ATGWs – either AT-2 Swatters or AT-6 Spirals – and four UV-32-57 rocket pods. The Apache mounts a 30mm M230A1 chain gun and up to 16 Hellfire anti-tank missiles, but an air-to-air version, fitted with Sparrows and Sidewinders, is on the stocks

ways to wipe it out – not least by turning his gaze towards its vulnerable rear echelon.

The vulnerability of its 'airfield' aside, the helicopter is itself essentially a very fragile machine. In time of peace it is involved in approximately twice as many accidents for every hour flown as are fixed-wing aircraft, while in wartime its radar, thermal and other signatures are often prodigious and it has a multiplicity of 'soft spots'. The AH-64 Apache, for example, is designed to be landable even after suffering hull hits from a ZSU 23mm cannon, but it cannot function without its rotor blades – a weak feature, despite advances in materials science, and

unprotectable. Yet even if a serious hit destroys nothing vital and does not kill anyone, it may disorient the pilot sufficiently to provoke a catastrophe. And as a final entry in this catalogue of woes, it should be remembered that if troops are to be carried on board, they will be notoriously difficult to protect even from casual small-arms fire. Rounds from an assault rifle may not stop the helicopter, but they can certainly puncture its skin and kill its passengers.

The answer seems to be to operate helicopters only at low altitude, safely behind cover and behind the FLOT; here they would be relatively well protected from both surface-to-air and air-to-air threats.

THE JOINT AIR-ATTACK TEAM IN ACTION

The light observation helicopters (such as the OH-58D Kiowa) patrol likely enemy approach routes, watching for the enemy advance. They use their agility to fly 'NOE' (Nap Of the Earth) – flying very low, and using the shape of the terrain for protection. The mast-mounted sight on the Kiowa allows it to observe from behind cover.

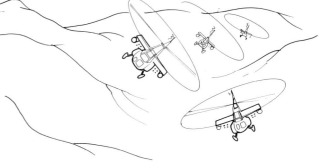

On sighting an armoured column, the observation helicopter calls forward the anti-attack helicopters (such as AH-64 Apache). These fly NOE to the ambush point, carrying ATGMs (Anti-Tank Guided Missiles) to destroy the tanks, and rockets and 30mm cannon to destroy light armour and soft-skin vehicles.

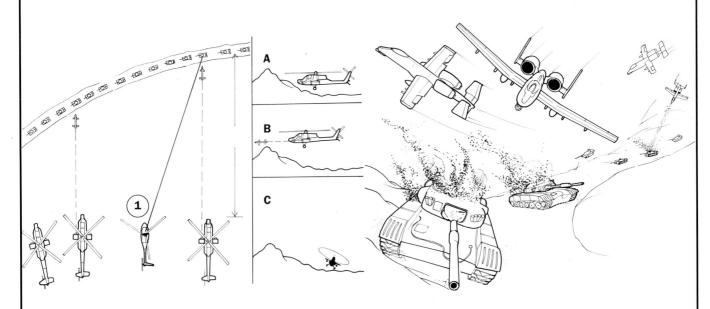

At the ambush site the Kiowa 'illuminates' targets with its mast-mounted laser (1) for the Apache's Hellfire missiles. The Apache pops up from behind cover (A), launches a Hellfire (B), then moves off behind cover (C). Meanwhile, the Hellfire homes in on the laser light reflected by the target. Apaches can also illuminate their own targets, and protect the flanks against enemy helicopters.

One of the priority targets for the attack helicopters is air-defence vehicles. With these destroyed, fixed-wing aircraft are called in. These can destroy the armoured column much more quickly than helicopters. The A-10, for instance, has a powerful 30mm GAU-8 rotary cannon that can fire 4200 rounds per minute; it can also drop 'Rockeye' anti-armour cluster bombs.

But even this cannot guarantee their survival, though it does severely restrict their freedom of action. The increased effectiveness of both long-range indirect-fire weapons and long-range 'look down' surveillance is today starting to bring this 'safe option' into question. For instance, there is no physical law that prevents a long-range artillery rocket or shell from making a soft impact on the ground and then firing a terminally guided anti-helicopter cluster bomb vertically into the air. In Vietnam there were already several types of anti-helicopter 'windmill' mines designed for deployment on LZs; tomorrow there may well be a far more advanced, computer-controlled form of the same thing.

The helicopter's mobility and agility are the key to its success

Helicopters are by no means all the same, of course. They range from slow, super-heavy-lift Sikorsky CH54B Sky Crane-type machines, capable of lifting loads of some 50,000 lbs, all the way down to light and manoeuverable two-man scouts, such as the 'Loach' (the Hughes OH-6 Cayuse). Since the 1960s, at least, there has been a deliberate effort to design machines for specific tasks, with the highest power-to-weight ratios being found among the heavy-lift and attack types. The former are designed for sedate, level flight behind the front line; the latter must be optimised for aerobatic evasive manoeuvres in close contact with the enemy. In Vietnam there was an attempt to combine the two in the shape of the formidable 'Go Go Bird' Chinook gunship. What it lacked in manoeuverability it more than made up for in firepower – its twin 20mm Gatling guns, 40mm grenade launchers and a row of 0.5in machine guns laying a truly murderous carpet of fire over a given area. Troops that it supported

HELICOPTER LOSSES IN VIETNAM

During its first 18 months of operations in Vietnam – from 1965 to 1967 – the experimental US 1st Cavalry Division (Air Mobile) recorded a loss rate of only one helicopter destroyed out of every 21,194 flights. The figure seems somewhat less spectacular set against the fact that for every one destroyed, 20 more were hit; nevertheless it is still a fine record.

By 1968, however, the picture had changed as the enemy improved his anti-helicopter awareness and tactics. One helicopter was then being destroyed out of every 6600 flights and, more ominously, the kill rate was up to one helicopter destroyed out of every five hit. Ground fire was thus becoming much more lethal, although this improvement owed very little to improving technology. The fire was still coming almost entirely from calibres of 12.7mm or lighter, and losses almost never occurred of aircraft flying at altitudes higher than 2000ft.

One enemy hit per 1320 flights nevertheless seems an amazingly safe record. However, these figures do not differentiate between rear area or administrative flights, which were relatively peaceful, and combat assault flights, which could be hair-raisingly dangerous. During the 1971 Operation Lam Son 719 in Laos, no less than 107 machines were lost and 618 were damaged during the eight-week operation (8 February to 6 April) because every LZ was covered by enemy fire. It should also be noted that these losses were overwhelmingly to troop carriers rather than attack helicopters or LOHs, indicating that agility and freedom to avoid predictable flight paths are keys to survivability.

In the Vietnam War the USA lost more than 4000 helicopters in all; the current NATO holding in Germany is little more than half that figure. It therefore seems reasonable to suppose that in any future high-tech war, the helicopter would rapidly become an attractive item in very short supply.

Above: American infantry tactics in Vietnam called for the rapid deployment of two groups of fighting men – one to act as a stop group, the other to drive the enemy into their arms. Without the troop-carrying helicopter, this would have been unthinkable, let alone unworkable. Nonetheless, the aircraft were vulnerable to the Viet Cong's 12.7mm machine guns over ranges of at least a mile, making the job of inserting and extracting troops very dangerous indeed

described the experience as 'unforgettable', but overall the experiment was no more successful than the many abortive attempts to create a super-heavy tank. The conclusion to be drawn from the 'Go Go Bird' is that an attack, or gunship, helicopter must be lean, mean, small and fast.

Of all rotary-wing aircraft, the attack helicopter has the greatest potential to affect the general battle most directly. As a dog-fighter it may prove to be absolutely essential protection for the less glamorous troop-lift helicopters, and the brunt of the air-to-air battle will almost certainly fall on its shoulders. As anti-tank snipers, attack helicopters have also been widely advertised as incomparable, while as flexible and fast-moving general firepower assets, they undoubtedly have a very great deal to offer. A hand of caution should perhaps be raised here. In Vietnam it was found that helicopter gunships suffered from many limitations that the artillery did not: they were hard to concentrate or co-ordinate in large numbers, and their rockets or grenades – while undoubtedly lethal to troops caught in the open – were markedly less effective against infantry that was properly dug in. With modern 'smart' ammunition and fuel-air bombs, however, the advantage may well now be shifting back to the helicopter.

Alongside the attack helicopter lies the scarcely less manoeuvrable light observation helicopter (LOH), or scout. This type of machine has long been used in very close co-operation with attack helicopters, and in future the same practice will doubtless continue. The dashing 'air cavalry' scouts will roam far and wide in search of targets, perhaps using centrally mounted electronic periscopes above their rotors to allow inconspicuous observation from behind treelines. When the enemy has been found, the LOHs may engage him directly or, more likely, report him for general tactical reaction,

designating him by laser as a specific target for artillery or the missiles fired from attack helicopters.

Alternatively, the LOH may be used in a less aggressive and less vulnerable mode as an airborne surveillance vehicle, as a command post, as a liaison vehicle or as a re-broadcasting station. Even if they never overfly the enemy, this class of helicopter will be indispensable to the process of command on the modern battlefield – not least if radio communications are difficult.

Pairing LOHs with gunships introduced a new flexibility

As a contrast to the 'air cavalry' vision of the LOH/attack helicopter combination as an aggressive source of firepower, many soldiers believe that the main battlefield role of the helicopter should be as a troop transport. Infantry can be given enormously greater mobility and flexibility if it can travel by air, as is ably demonstrated by the story of the US platoon in Vietnam that made three combat assaults in three different provinces during a single day. Even anti-tank operations may be conducted efficiently in this way, with helicopters being used to offload infantry tank-killing teams at suitable ambush sites along the enemy's expected path. The West German *Fallschirmjaeger*, especially, have trained for this role, in which they use MILAN, supported by heavy ATGWs mounted in light, air-portable four-wheeled 'Kraka' vehicles.

The *fallschirmjaeger* concept is nevertheless still defensive, exploiting the helicopter's mobility behind the FLOT only. Many other potential employments of troop transport helicopters would also take place in this zone, with the helicopter's mobility being exploited to shift reserves from one part of the friendly rear area to another. Such

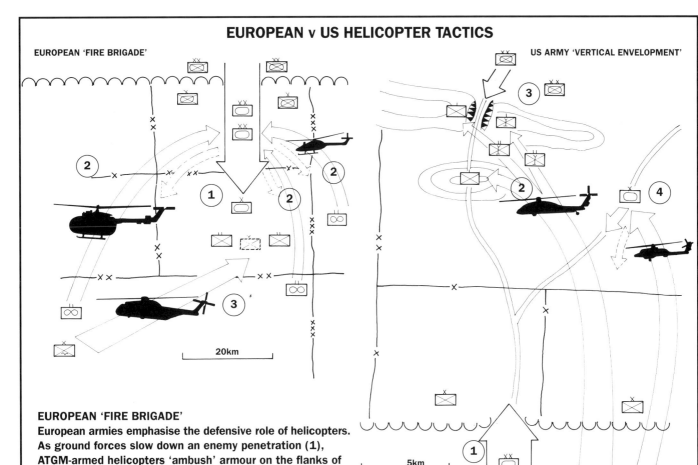

EUROPEAN v US HELICOPTER TACTICS

EUROPEAN 'FIRE BRIGADE'

US ARMY 'VERTICAL ENVELOPMENT'

20km

5km

EUROPEAN 'FIRE BRIGADE'
European armies emphasise the defensive role of helicopters. As ground forces slow down an enemy penetration (1), ATGM-armed helicopters 'ambush' armour on the flanks of the thrust (2), while transport helicopters carry ATGM-armed infantry to a blocking position in front of it (3).

US ARMY 'VERTICAL ENVELOPMENT'
US Army doctrine places greater emphasis on the offensive role of helicopters. While the main ground force pushes through the enemy FEBA (Forward Edge of the Battle Area) (1), Blackhawk helicopters lift 'Air Assault' infantry to seize objectives in the enemy rear (2). This force seizes choke points – such as defiles or bridges – to prevent the enemy blocking the ground advance. It also acts as a blocking force itself, stopping enemy reserves from counter-attacking the main force (3). Attack helicopters will also ambush enemy attackers from the flank (4).

Left: Even the first generation of surface-to-air missiles were lethal to helicopters, with their huge, slow-moving heat signatures. Designers tried to combat this by insulating the engines and deflecting the hot exhaust gases up into the air, but the SAMs have technology on their side: modern sensors are so finely tuned that they easily penetrate the deception

Right: To be able to survive in the modern battle, helicopters have to rely on technological solutions – the pilot simply cannot cope with a greater workload. But technological solutions demand complex technology, and that in its turn builds in a higher degree of risk of failure. Add to this the difficulty of maintenance operations in the front-line area, and the result is a nightmare. American helicopter losses in Vietnam were in excess of 4000; more than half of those were through systems failure

Below: Red team on the warpath. A hunting party of AH-64 Apache helicopters setting out on a search-and-destroy armour mission at dusk

HELICOPTER PERFORMANCE

Type	Max. Speed (km/h)	Typical range (km)
Aerospatiale/Westland Gazell	264	360
Aerospatiale/Westland Puma	257	580
Aerospatiale/Westland Lynx	322	540
Bell 'Huey' Iroquois	204	400
Boeing CH-47 Chinook	304	185
Hughes OH-6 Cayuse	241	611
Hughes AH-64 Apache	309	611
Mil Mi-2 'Hoplite'	200	170
Mil Mi-8 'Hip'	260	480
Mil Mi-24 'Hind'	275	550
Sikorsky UH-60 Blackhawk	296	600

Compare these with:

Sikorsky experimental XH59A	487(+)	?
Typical modern MBT	70	450
Typical modern fighter-bomber	Mach 1-2	1200-3000

operations would include flying in troops for counter-attacks against enemy heli-borne or airborne *desants* (Soviet parlance for commando raids that are launched deep into the enemy rear and then left to fend for themselves). In future a major role of the troop transport helicopter may be to counter enemy air mobile assault troops, just as a major role of the attack helicopter may be to intercept enemy attack helicopters.

Insertion and extraction are the worst times for heliborne troops

Troop transports will also certainly be invaluable in a counter-penetration role: to bring up fast-reacting reserves to fill unexpected gaps in the line in what amounts to a human equivalent of the rapidly deployed air-scattered minefield. In any fast-moving battle such interventions may well be decisive for a defender; indeed, on a future battlefield this might be the most important role of all for the helicopter. It certainly seems to have been so for the Iraqis in the 1980-88 Gulf War.

However, the troop transport helicopter has traditionally been thought of as an offensive weapon as much as – or even more than – a defensive one. Many tacticians have seen its greatest potential in its

ability to launch surprise attacks on the enemy's side of the front line. The persuasive and alluring argument for this is that helicopters can accelerate the infantry's speed of advance from some 5 km/h on foot or 50 km/h if riding in trucks or APCs to more than 200 km/h. Since the infantry has always sought some means of crossing the zone beaten by the enemy's weapons at a double-quick pace, the helicopter seems to be a godsend. In Vietnam a jungle attack from a distance of just three kilometres might have taken all night to organise and carry out on the ground; by helicopter it could be mounted in 30 minutes from a distance of 30km.

This sounds simple, but there are plenty of dangers facing helicopters that try to operate on the enemy's side of the front line. At the start of the 1973 October War, for example, Egyptian heliborne *desants* across the Suez Canal were rapidly wiped out, without exception. With the yet more fearsome array of defensive anti-aircraft weapons available to today's armed forces, the chances that a heli-borne attack on the modern battlefield would get far enough even to begin to surprise its target seem slim indeed. This has driven many of the world's armies to confess tacitly that they lack the wherewithal to mount significant airmobile assaults beyond the FLOT – apart, that is, from special

For all its agility, the helicopter is the bumblebee of powered flight – it's sometimes hard to understand how it works as well as it does! It has long been the designer's dream to find an effective way of combining the helicopter's vertical take-off and landing capabilities with the aerodynamic properties of fixed-wing aircraft. The Osprey (Above) is one of the more successful attempts, and the US Government is under considerable pressure from strategists to procure it in large numbers

forces operations, or operations against an unsophisticated opponent. The two superpowers, who possess helicopters in far greater numbers than do the other powers, nevertheless both retain faith in (for the Americans) 'vertical envelopment' or (for the Soviets) 'the heli-borne *desant*'.

How can it be done? The American solution is to use a co-ordinated assault team consisting of a large number of aircraft. While Wild Weasel helicopters mask the enemy's electronics, reconnaissance aircraft and RPVs map out his defences. Artillery, rockets and air strikes can then be called in to suppress the enemy, while specialised aircraft (for example, the A-10 or the Apache) attack specific AAA and SAM sites. This phase over, the initial combat assault wave of Blackhawks can go in, supported by prep-fire Apaches, air-to-air combat air patrol (CAP) helicopters, and diversionary, command and heavy-lift helicopters. This all adds up to a mass attack – a major operation of at least battalion, perhaps even brigade, size. Such an assault cannot be especially quickly or easily laid on, but it may still be able to win vital prizes.

A serious shortcoming of massed heli-borne infantry assaults is that they place relatively lightly armed troops of low mobility in an exposed position behind enemy lines. If the troops can complete their job quickly and fly straight back to friendly territory, then all is well. If, however, they become pinned down and have to hold ground for more than a few hours, they will in effect become 'hostages' surrounded by converging enemy reaction forces. They will then have to be supported by helicopters using a now-hazardous corridor that the

enemy can be confidently expected to have identified; and they may have to be relieved or rescued by friendly ground forces in considerable strength. The airborne assault on Arnhem in September 1944 took on this character, as did many of the helicopter assaults in Vietnam during the 1960s. Thus unless really major ground forces can be landed with a full complement of heavy weapons and transport, there remains a strong risk that any future air mobile operation may also follow this pattern.

The helicopter gets ground forces in and out of action fast

The Soviet approach differs from that of the USA in two respects. Firstly, although the air mobile *desant* is not dissimilar to the American concept of vertical envelopment, insofar as a relatively large number of infantry transports, supported by gunship helicopters, are 'shot in' to the target by a variety of other weapons, the assault troops are regarded as a 'fire and forget' weapon deposited in the enemy rear to create the maximum distraction, disruption and damage. They have no particular right to expect relief or rescue by other friendly forces. If the war ends quickly – as it is supposed to under Soviet norms for speedy exploitation and pursuit – then all should be well; if not, these forces are completely on their own.

The second major way in which the Soviet approach differs from Western practice is that Soviet *desants* may include para-dropped or helo-lifted light armoured vehicles, which enable the infantry to motor away from their LZ at high

Speed and flexibility of movement are so essential to modern tactics that despite its vulnerabilities, there is no substitute for the helicopter as the vehicle for rapid intervention, both on the local, tactical level, and within broader strategic areas.
Below: A fire team, its job done, returns to its aircraft for extraction

Since it first appeared in the battlefield role in the 1950s, the helicopter has undergone considerable evolution. The next phase, as portrayed in this artist's impression (Above) of a new American attack helicopter, will rely on speed, lightweight titanium armour and ECMs to safeguard it, and a huge weapons load to accomplish its task of defeating both enemy ground forces and incoming gunships, such as the most recent Soviet Havocs and Hokums. Each new generation of fighting helicopters incorporates every piece of new technology available. Thus, the succeeding generation will appear only at the end of a long, drawn-out development programme

speed, and provide them with heavier firepower. Apart from the terror they inspire, these vehicles give the incursion a far greater range and pace, allowing it to continue long after all the helicopters have returned to base. Modern commentators, suspicious of the value of 'static' *desants* that may later come under siege, can still get excited at the possibilities of this type of dynamic thrust outwards from the LZ. It is likely to be a technique that becomes more widespread in future as further technical advances are made in both helicopters and light armour.

The helicopter must watch out for the dangers that lurk all around it

In summary, the helicopter today still promises exciting new horizons to tacticians, just as it did in the early 1960s. However, Vietnam and other helicopter wars have exposed limitations that can only be intensified by the very dense air-defence firepower likely to be encountered on the modern battlefield. Like the tank, the helicopter is not yet dead, but it must watch out for the escalating dangers that lurk all around it.

The survivability of troops inserted behind the enemy lines by helicopter depends on two factors: their firepower, and their training. Special Forces teams have long proved their ability to work effectively in very difficult conditions, but they are elite forces, who spend years acquiring the necessary skills. The 'ordinary' infantryman cannot be expected to perform in the same way, especially when inserted in small numbers, unsupported.

The increased range and improved accuracy of both tube and missile artillery adds another positive factor, however. MLRS, especially, in its third incarnation, can support troops out to ranges of perhaps 70km, with the necessary accuracy, and this may well swing the balance back in favour of the heli-borne raiding party.

HOW REVOLUTIONARY IS THE HELICOPTER?

The arguments for the helicopter are:

• They are far more manoeuvrable than tanks and can carry powerful AT weapons – so making the tank obsolete

• They can shift light AFVs around the battlefield, adding vast extra mobility to ground vehicles as well as infantry

• They can use ECMs and flak suppression systems to create safe corridors for troops and aircraft, even on the enemy's side of the FLOT

• The helicopter's ground support may itself be airmobile and hence very flexible: it has operational as well as tactical mobility

The opposing arguments run:

• They are no substitute for tanks: they cannot carry heavy KE guns and rely on HEAT warheads, which are decreasingly effective on the modern battlefield

• They face an awesome array of surface-to-air and air-to-air weapons, making them far more vulnerable than fixed-wing aircraft – and far more vulnerable than they ever were in Vietnam

• They are expensive in logistics and maintenance. Their ground-based support units are also more vulnerable today than ever before

THE ARTILLERY BATTLE

Artillery's ability to dominate the battlefield has been constrained in the past by the limits of technology. Gun ranges have been too short, rates of fire too slow and communications difficult. In a dramatic hardware revolution, however, technology has now solved most of these problems, allowing artillery to unleash its full potential, though what the eventual effect will be is still open to question.

Below: The 155mm gun is the most widely used artillery piece in the world. This version, the M185, is mounted on the M109A2 chassis. Rocket-assisted projectiles push its range out to 24km

FIRING A COPPERHEAD CLPG MISSILE

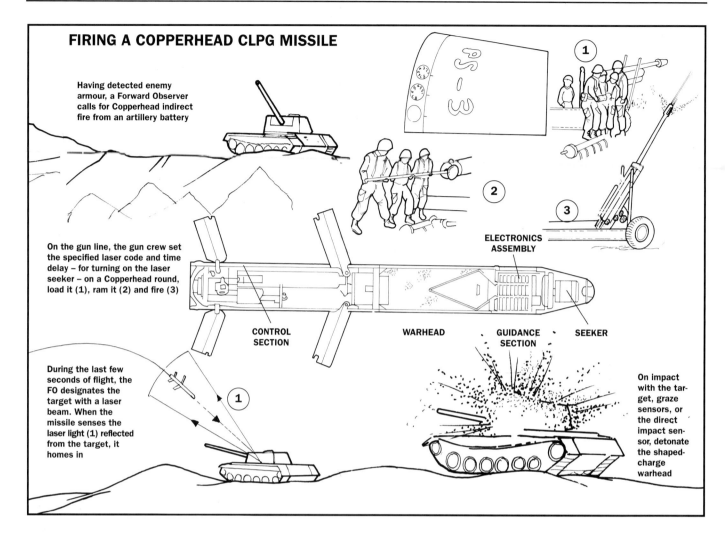

Having detected enemy armour, a Forward Observer calls for Copperhead indirect fire from an artillery battery

On the gun line, the gun crew set the specified laser code and time delay – for turning on the laser seeker – on a Copperhead round, load it (1), ram it (2) and fire (3)

During the last few seconds of flight, the FO designates the target with a laser beam. When the missile senses the laser light (1) reflected from the target, it homes in

CONTROL SECTION

ELECTRONICS ASSEMBLY

WARHEAD

GUIDANCE SECTION

SEEKER

On impact with the target, graze sensors, or the direct impact sensor, detonate the shaped-charge warhead

D uring the 1980-88 Iran-Iraq War, a brutal stalemate of entrenched defenders and massed attacks, artillery was a major factor in maintaining rigid battle lines and preventing either side's tanks from breaking into open ground and fighting a fluid, mobile, armoured battle.

The Iran-Iraq deadlock may well represent the battlefield of the future, the manoeuvre units completely pinned down by fast, concentrated, accurate artillery response, but in a less pessimistic scenario, the artillery, by winning the depth-fire battle, prevents reinforcements reaching the front, thus reducing the numbers involved in the contact battle. Either way, the quantum increase in artillery power and accuracy will certainly affect battlefield mobility. Anything moving within the extended range of the guns risks death.

The basic unit of artillery is the battery and a battery's worth of fire is the minimum normally employed, although in certain specialised situations, less firepower may be used. For instance, a single gun might fire from a forward position in the jungle; a quick infantry attack might be covered by just one or two guns firing smoke rounds.

The number of guns in a battery reflects the desired weight of munitions landing at the other end. The heavier calibre guns are arranged four to a battery, while the lighter calibres are grouped in sixes or eights. The basic organisation of the guns

The British and American armies both use 155mm towed howitzers, as well as the self-propelled version. Both the British FH-70 (Left) and the US M198 (Above) are capable of firing the Copperhead cannon-launched guided projectile (Above left), as are the M109A2 and Abbot SPGs. Copperhead is said to be so accurate that it can be dropped down the open hatch of a moving tank from up to 16km away

PRINCIPLES OF ARTILLERY FIRE PLANNING

Surprise and shock action are the artillery's stock-in-trade. Most casualties occur in the target area in the first seconds of a firing mission, as incoming shells catch troops diving for the cover of trenches and pulling down the hatches of armoured vehicles. After the initial shock action, artillery can only really keep the enemy's heads down, unless heavier calibres are being used or lucky shells hit armoured vehicles or enter trenches.

Initially, therefore, as much artillery ammunition as possible must be put on to the target in as short a time as possible, preferably with the first salvo striking home. The process of adjustment, although guaranteeing that fire on a target will soon be accurate, gives a warning, and surprise and shock action are often lost. It is also preferable to co-ordinate several batteries to fire in a burst on to one target as this is dramatically more effective as a shock weapon (and the chances of direct hits are higher) than just using one battery – even though the same number of rounds might be fired overall.

Ammunition must be carefully tailored to the target. Proximity ammunition that explodes overhead is particularly useful if fired without warning at troops in the open or at armoured vehicles travelling with hatches up. Judicious mixtures of ammunition are often used. For example, HE mixed with Delay is useful once troops have gone to ground in trenches (and some Smoke and Proximity may increase the confusion), while mixing HE with Smoke deters anyone from trying to extinguish the burning smoke canisters, though HE must always be ready to be fired as an alternative if a smoke screen proves not to be effective. It is important that rounds land at exactly the times ordered (to the second); for this reason everyone involved in an operation must synchronise his watch with that of the artillery commander.

Time must be allowed for the batteries to switch targets – one minute for light calibres, and more for heavier calibres. To maintain fire on a target when several batteries are operating, target switches can be staggered. Batteries must be kept 'superimposed', so that guns may switch to opportunity targets without affecting the fire plan.

When the artillery is covering a friendly infantry or armoured advance, fire on the objective should always be adjusted. This can be done either before the advance begins or even while it is taking place. As attacking troops enter the near edge of the fall of shot, the FO creeps it forward on to the enemy's rear positions.

is much the same in all modern armies. The battery is controlled by the battery command post, which consists of signallers, computer operators and command post officers. They employ three radio nets: the battery net connects the battery with the battery commander and his forward observers; the regimental net connects the batteries, forward observers and battery commanders with the commanding officer; and the regimental logistic net controls the delivery of ammunition to the batteries, according to battle requirements.

A battery may operate as a single entity, or it may split into two troops, each with its own command post, capable of operating independently of each other. Because artillery is constantly in action, there is always an alternative command post in existence. Even when the battery is operating as one unit, the two command posts will take turns to control it. For example, the alternative post would take over while the main command is

in transit to a new location and when it is necessary to rest key personnel.

The guns themselves also need rest. At any one time, one gun is likely to be out of action for routine servicing – barrel bores must be kept clean, recoil systems topped up with hydraulic fluid and barrels changed from time to time. There will also be mechanical breakdowns and battle damage to contend with. The gun batteries themselves remain back on the gun line, out of reach of enemy direct-fire weapons, and rely for guidance on information passed back by forward observers. The FO's job is to control scheduled fire and find targets of opportunity. Organised in teams of three, and assigned to infantry companies and armoured squadrons, FOs work alongside the company (or armoured squadron) commander, maintaining radios on the company and battalion nets; they follow the battle closely, bringing down fire on targets that they detect for themselves, or on request.

Artillery has changed in its own basic technology

In the attack, the FO moves with the 'point' platoon. As the leading platoons approach enemy positions, he directs the artillery fire forward, keeping the worst of it just in front of the leading troops. Although the attackers may suffer some casualties from their own artillery, the enemy will not be able to engage them from their trenches until the very last moment.

During the attack, one FO will usually set up an 'anchor' OP, from which he can observe the operation in relative safety. With good radio communications between himself, the attacking force, other

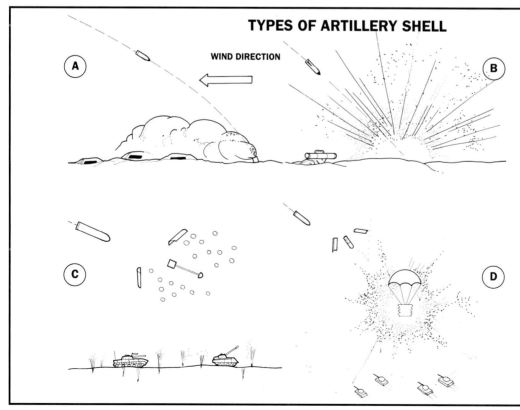

TYPES OF ARTILLERY SHELL

WIND DIRECTION

Apart from guided projectiles such as Copperhead, the artillery has a variety of ammunition types to draw on for different tasks:

A. SMOKE
Used to conceal movement

B. HIGH EXPLOSIVE (HE)
Used against point or area targets. Also available in this category are White Phosphorous (WP) shells.

C. 'CARGO' (Scatterable sub-munitions).
Include both anti-armour and anti-personnel mines. Also used to deliver objects such as disposable jammers

D. ILLUMINATION
Flares suspended below small parachutes (duration: about 30 seconds)

**Left: An instructor uses the MILES 'scope to check where his trainees simulated fire is going. The MILES system employs a laser on the M-16 rifle, in place of live ammunition, for training purposes
Below: An artillery barrage at night**

FOs and the guns, the observer in the anchor OP can co-ordinate fire: particularly important when assaulting observers lose radio communications or are killed or wounded.

The introduction of a new generation of armoured command and control vehicles, such as the USA's Emerson FIre Support Team Vehicle (FISTV) and the British Army's Warrior Observation Party Vehicle (OPV) will enlarge the FO's responsibilities considerably. Thus mounted, FOs will be

able to keep up with the advancing armour, and stay at the forefront of the battle. However, there is one drawback. These vehicles are manifestly not tanks, so when working with armoured units, FOs, who are already among the highest priority targets on the modern battlefield, are likely to attract even more attention than they do at present.

As well as providing this new mobility for its eyes and ears, the artillery has changed in its own basic technology, too. The destructive power of

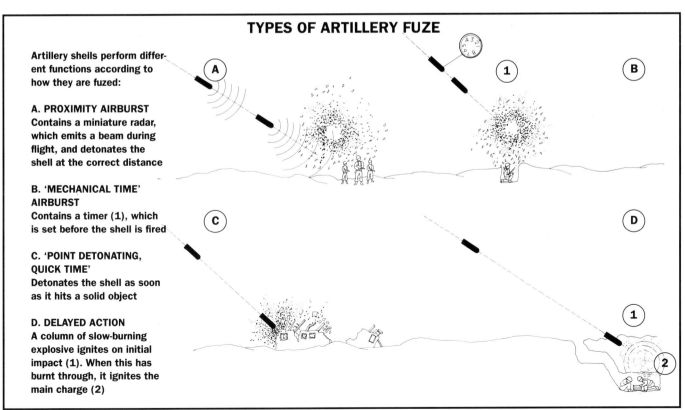

TYPES OF ARTILLERY FUZE

Artillery shells perform different functions according to how they are fuzed:

A. PROXIMITY AIRBURST
Contains a miniature radar, which emits a beam during flight, and detonates the shell at the correct distance

B. 'MECHANICAL TIME' AIRBURST
Contains a timer (1), which is set before the shell is fired

C. 'POINT DETONATING, QUICK TIME'
Detonates the shell as soon as it hits a solid object

D. DELAYED ACTION
A column of slow-burning explosive ignites on initial impact (1). When this has burnt through, it ignites the main charge (2)

even the simple HE shell has increased dramatically in the last decade, though limits on the size and weight of shell that can be fired probably preclude further development. Instead, artillery ammunition is becoming more 'mission-oriented', using sophisticated warheads to hit point targets. Thus the explosive punch is directed much more accurately to where it will do the most damage.

Among these new weapons are Precision Guided Munitions (PGMs), such as the USA's Copperhead round. Fired from a 155mm gun, the Copperhead projectile homes on to a target illuminated by a laser designator aimed by the FO. An individual tank is thus vulnerable to individual artillery shells.

Artillery ammunition is becoming more 'mission orientated'

Terminally-Guided Sub-Munitions (TGSMs) are also intended to kill individual tanks, but without human intervention. TGSM shells burst over the general target area, releasing sub-munitions that float to earth under small parachutes. Relying on their own sensors to locate moving targets, they attack the vulnerable top armour of tanks, using shaped charges to achieve penetration. The MLRS's TGSM, with six sub-missiles that seek, track and home in on tanks, should be in service by the end of the century. With the right sort of fuzing for top-cover attack it will be a serious 'assault breaker' and force multiplier.

Both PGMs and TGSMs can destroy specific targets in the same manner as direct-fire weapons, but without the restrictions imposed by line-of-sight target acquisition. Furthermore, the accuracy of these sub-munitions will not depend on the operator's vision (which is often impaired by dust, mist

or smoke on the battlefield), nor by the weather or the condition of the gun, all of which greatly restrict the effectiveness of direct-fire weapons.

These new projectiles can be controlled from inside a vehicle by just one man, who has no need to expose himself to the enemy in order to acquire his target and destroy it. Tied into a comprehensive system of battlefield surveillance and communications, he can orchestrate a colossal instantaneous barrage in total isolation from the actual weapon delivery systems themselves, so that his position will not be compromised by the guns' own IR and sound signature and still guarantee a significant number of one-hit kills.

Today, greater range allows guns to engage the enemy earlier

Supporting the contact battle is only part of the modern artillery's role. In the fluid fighting of World War II's European theatre, artillery was mainly used in the close support role. Today, greater range allows guns to engage the enemy earlier, in the depth-fire battle, breaking up enemy columns long before they fire a shot, hammering resupply routes and shattering enemy morale before the fight has even been joined.

Its extra range and increased accuracy means that the priorities for the use of artillery will have to be rethought. The cosy concept of every infantry or armour commander having his own artillery unit on call will disappear. On the battlefield of the future, competition for artillery assets will be fierce, the demands of the depth-fire battle often overriding the needs of the contact battle. The manoeuvre arms will at last become occupiers of ground won by artillery, but armour and infantry will hold this ground only if the artillery

Above: The mapboard is still essential to the Forward Observation (FO) Officer when he is planning fire missions

Left: The control and monitoring panel for a Heron-26 RPV battery. The drone aircraft is controlled from here, and the pictures it sends back inspected and recorded

TYPES OF ARTILLERY AMMUNITION

High Explosive shells can have either 'point detonating' fuzes, which explode on impact, or 'delay' fuzes, which allow the round to penetrate before exploding, collapsing trenches or exploding inside buildings. HE can also be fitted with 'Variable Time' (VT) fuzes – either the old-fashioned 'mechanical time' or the more accurate, faster 'proximity' fuzes – which explode the shell at a set height above the ground, showering the splinters forwards and downwards in a shotgun effect. Against troops in the open, particularly if fired without any warning, VT fuzes are lethal.

Against unprotected people, particularly in the jungle, 'flechette' rounds are used. These shells contain thousands of darts – flechettes – which are often made of plastic so as not to show up on hospital X Rays. In Vietnam, Viet Cong victims of flechettes were often discovered completely impaled against trees.

Another nasty anti-personnel weapon is the exploding shell packed with White Phosphorus (WP). On contact with the air, phosphorus ignites, producing intense heat and thick, white smoke. Phosphorus will burn through clothes and flesh, the water of the human body further encouraging the chemical reaction. The burning, which is excruciatingly painful, can only be stopped by cutting away all flesh containing phosphorus.

Smoke is delivered using a shell with a base that ejects the contents when over the target. The smoke takes a minute to build up, each canister burning for several minutes, producing thick, white smoke. Smoke rounds are used to conceal forces from the enemy, during an advance or a withdrawal, for example. They are quite the opposite to 'marker' rounds, which produce a coloured smoke to indicate targets to attacking aircraft or to signal one's own position – for example, in dense jungle.

depth-fire battle is successful in preventing enemy reinforcements from counter-attacking.

Although all guns within range can be used for depth-fire targets, it is usually the heavy guns at corps level and above that are entrusted with the task. Those guns are often deployed as close to the Front Line of Own Troops (FLOT) as the close support artillery, so their extra range can be used to reach as far as possible into the enemy's rear areas.

The greatest threat to artillery is fire from enemy artillery batteries

Because the depth-fire battle is fought beyond the limits of the FOs' vision, it depends on a wide variety of other means of target acquisition. At the higher formation headquarters, the artillery cell will co-ordinate the various means of target acquisition at its disposal, such as sound ranging and mortar and gun locating radars, special forces teams acting as observation parties, and monitoring the enemy's radio transmissions to locate his headquarters and artillery positions.

One further advance in depth-fire target acquisition is the drone or Remotely-Piloted Vehicle (RPV). Until now, the forward observer was the artillery's only means of 'real-time' target observation and aquisition, but today RPVs such as Phoenix and Cobra send back pictures as they fly, enabling

missions to be fired immediately. Drone flights over enemy rear areas identify his artillery batteries, headquarters and logistic areas, as well as resupply routes. The depth-fire battle will extend as far as RPVs will allow the guns and rockets to reach, making all rear areas liable to accurate artillery attack.

Although the depth-fire battle must start as early as possible in order to prevent the enemy reaching the contact battle, the timing and weight of this fire must be incorporated into the overall battle plan. The heavy guns are particularly vulnerable to counter-battery fire so must be used judiciously. While guns sit mute, they are safe, but completely useless; once they have been fired they must be moved. Decisions to 'unmask' the heavies are taken at a high level.

The Counter-Battery (CB) battle – that is, knocking out enemy artillery – is fought at divisional level and higher, using 175mm and larger calibre guns and rockets. The greatest threat to artillery is fire from enemy artillery batteries, and modern technology is reducing the time it takes to detect the gun positions and then fire back. The only certain way of avoiding counter-battery fire is for guns to fire in bursts, then move at least 500m, so that the incoming fire lands on an empty position. However, it is unacceptable to have artillery break off in the middle of a fire plan, or not available while ensuring its own safety by moving.

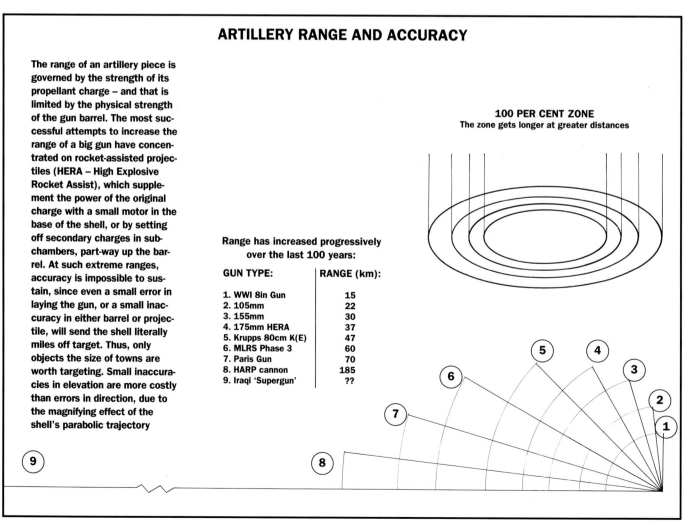

ARTILLERY RANGE AND ACCURACY

The range of an artillery piece is governed by the strength of its propellant charge – and that is limited by the physical strength of the gun barrel. The most successful attempts to increase the range of a big gun have concentrated on rocket-assisted projectiles (HERA – High Explosive Rocket Assist), which supplement the power of the original charge with a small motor in the base of the shell, or by setting off secondary charges in sub-chambers, part-way up the barrel. At such extreme ranges, accuracy is impossible to sustain, since even a small error in laying the gun, or a small inaccuracy in either barrel or projectile, will send the shell literally miles off target. Thus, only objects the size of towns are worth targeting. Small inaccuracies in elevation are more costly than errors in direction, due to the magnifying effect of the shell's parabolic trajectory

100 PER CENT ZONE
The zone gets longer at greater distances

Range has increased progressively over the last 100 years:

GUN TYPE:	RANGE (km):
1. WWI 8in Gun	15
2. 105mm	22
3. 155mm	30
4. 175mm HERA	37
5. Krupps 80cm K(E)	47
6. MLRS Phase 3	60
7. Paris Gun	70
8. HARP cannon	185
9. Iraqi 'Supergun'	??

FIELD ARTILLERY ACCURACY

The artillery concept of accuracy is often misunderstood by soldiers used to direct-fire weapons. Whereas direct-fire weapons either hit or miss specific targets, artillery is an area weapon. Even if set into a concrete mounting, an individual gun would not place 100 shells into the same shell-hole. This is because the inherent characteristics of a gun barrel cause every round to behave very slightly differently during firing. The shells actually land in a large cigar-shaped pattern called the '100 per cent zone'. In the same way a machine gun on a rock-solid mounting will spray bullets into a 'beaten zone', and even the most accurate precision small arms will 'group' its shots.

When a battery fires, the rounds land in the same pattern as the layout of the gun position, with each gun covering its own 100 per cent zone. This reproduction of the gun position layout occurs because the guns are carefully aligned when a battery moves into its location. First 'battery centre' (that is, the centre of the battery position) is accurately established and then an operation known as 'passing of line' takes place, whereby each gun is lined up to fire in exactly the same direction. The accuracy of artillery fire then depends upon the FOs sending the guns precise target information.

However, when several batteries are firing on the same target, optimum accuracy happens only when each battery is surveyed into a common grid, or survey grid – each to the same level of accuracy. This process is similar in principle to the 'passing of line' from director to guns on battery positions, but is carried out by the 'locators', using the latest surveying instruments to bring the common 'line', or bearing, to each battery. When several batteries fire at the same target, they use the FO's grid reference as the centre of the target, and the rounds fall within around 200m of this reference.

From the diagram of the 100 per cent zone, it is obvious that shells coming from behind and flying overhead are more liable to fall short and explode among friendly troops. Similarly, shells fired from a flank appear to spread over a large area lateral to the front line – even though they will in fact be on target. It is the job of the FOs to advise unit commanders when close-in fire is likely to be dangerous, so commanders can decide whether to risk injuries to their own men.

The different characteristics of special types of ammunition must also be borne in mind. Illuminating shells, for instance, can be blown in the wrong direction by wind changes, making them a real double-edged weapon. Wind changes and temperature similarly affect smoke, delivered in base-ejection shells. Hot, rising air can make smoke pillar, diminishing or even eliminating its screening effect. Smoke shells must also land well in front of enemy positions, as water will easily extinguish the canisters.

Above: A Forward Observation Officer. Artillery almost always fires at greater ranges than the gunners themselves can see, so an experienced officer has to be positioned far enough forward to be able to gauge where the artillery shells are falling, and order changes of direction and elevation accordingly

Left: The gunner's view of an M198 155mm howitzer

Below: Computer technology allows a number of fire missions to be pre-planned down to the finest detail, and then called up with just a few key strokes. Battlefield computers need to be hardened against EMP – the pulse of radiation created by a nuclear explosion, probably high in the atmosphere

Current doctrine has it that if batteries move every couple of hours they remain one step ahead of incoming counter-battery fire. With artillery expected to begin firing early in the war – and remain in action throughout – the constant 'shooting and scooting' will be exhausting and severely debilitating. A likely scenario has batteries moving not to completely new locations, but around a circuit or within an overall gun area. Battery positions may also be split into two smaller troop areas, and the whole spread over more ground than usual, so that at least part of a battery might be unaffected by accurate CB fire. A fully prepared alternative position nearby is sensible, too, allowing individual guns to be moved quickly out of danger, with the minimum of disruption to their own activities.

All these solutions to the CB problem require large areas of land to be allocated to the artillery. Apart from the premium on actual grid squares for alternate gun positions, no-one is going to be too happy at having a gun battery next door that draws enemy artillery fire, then pushes off before it arrives!

Winning the counter-battery battle depends completely on accurate target designation. While general artillery targets at this level are identified for the depth battle by RPVs, special forces teams, and SIGINT, the CB battle is fought using data mainly from locating units. Locating artillery

encompasses a wide range of different skills and tasks. Sound ranging uses strings of microphones to triangulate bearings to enemy gun positions in relation to the sound of their firing. Radar location equipment calculates enemy battery locations by detecting shells in their irregular parabolic trajectories, and RPVs fly over enemy territory and photograph depth targets.

The regular collection of meteorological data is also vital to the accuracy of field gunnery. Helium-filled balloons acting as remote radar stations double as weather stations, sending back air temperatures and densities, wind speed and direction, at vertical intervals of 15m. Every few hours, battery command post computers are up-dated with new 'met', greatly increasing the accuracy of the firing data they calculate for the guns.

Every few hours, battery command post computers are updated

Despite all this, the gunners are not constrained by sophistications. If they have to, forward observers can still make their own maps simply by firing the guns on given bearings and elevations, then plotting the fall of shot on to blank graph paper. Then they can adjust the fire taking these bearings as their reference points, whether the round has landed anywhere near the target or not.

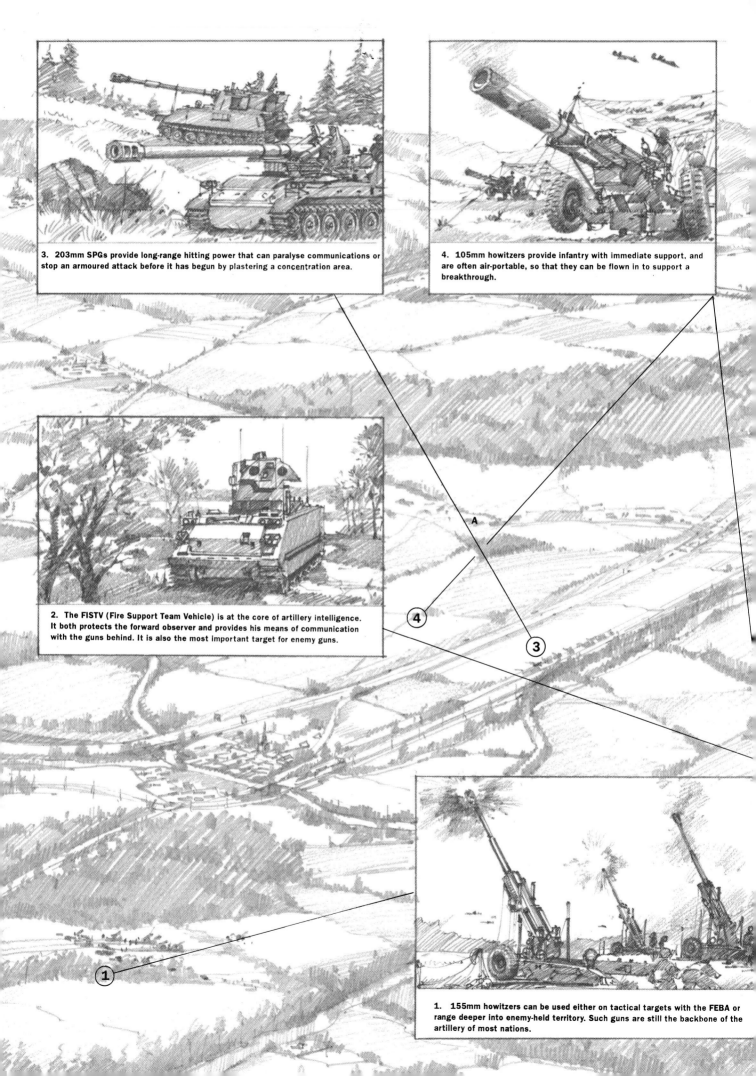

3. 203mm SPGs provide long-range hitting power that can paralyse communications or stop an armoured attack before it has begun by plastering a concentration area.

4. 105mm howitzers provide infantry with immediate support, and are often air-portable, so that they can be flown in to support a breakthrough.

2. The FISTV (Fire Support Team Vehicle) is at the core of artillery intelligence. It both protects the forward observer and provides his means of communication with the guns behind. It is also the most important target for enemy guns.

1. 155mm howitzers can be used either on tactical targets with the FEBA or range deeper into enemy-held territory. Such guns are still the backbone of the artillery of most nations.

5. As their electronics have improved, so RPVs have become more and more important in getting information from behind enemy lines - even when fired on successfully by AAA, they reveal the position of such guns which then become vulnerable.

6. Despite new and improved armour, tanks and AFV's are still vulreable to modern artillery-launched sub-munitions. They're obvious, too - so they would be a priority target.

7. MLRS are one of the most feared modern weapons systems, because of the weight of fire and the range of munitions they can put down within a short space of time.

A

THE ARTILLERY
KING OF THE BATTLEFIELD?

A typical arrangement of modern artillery, with the front line (A) running at 90 degrees across a major communications route. At the FEBA (Forward Edge of Battle Area) itself, the most noticeable artillery presence would be small pieces, such as the air-portable 105mm howitzer, giving immediate direct support to an infantry battalion. The most important artillery presence at FEBA, however, are the observers, in armoured vehicles or well dug in. They can call down an immense weight of fire from the batteries behind them, and on any battlefield are the most marked men. Behind the front line, the artillery is deployed in two main parks, and consists of 203mm SPGs and 105mm conventional artillery pieces. The 105s guns can be directed either onto targets within the FEBA or at deeper targets, while the 203s will normally be used exclusively on these deeper targets - supply lines, enemy batteries, armoured concentrations or headquarters. Information on where the enemy can be hit hard may come from piloted reconnaissance aircraft or even from satellites; it is, however, very likely to come from RPVs (Remotely Piloted Vehicles) - drones that can be catapulted up at any time and are expendable.
The final element in the equation are the MLRS (Multiple Launch Rocket Systems) that can put down the biggest weight of fire. They can be used for any task that requires a swift response - crushing down on a tank attack, scattering an air-launched minefield, or putting in fuel-air explosions over enemy infantry dug-in in a town. They are on the road and have to be ready to move very quickly, as they are prime targets for counter-battery fire.

Below: The Germans built their biggest guns in fortifications. This one, on the Somme, had to be abandoned when the British offensive got under way

Artillery is limited in its maximum range and in the payload it can deliver. The USSR adopted the Self-Propelled (SP) system in the 1970s, and underlined its overall artillery superiority with the range advantage these weapons had, over equivalent NATO systems. The West tried to counter this superiority by extending the range of its existing guns, and the development of Extended Range Full Bore (ERFB) base-bleed ammunition was one attempt to redress the balance. The principle of ERFB is to fit a light projectile that is smaller than the bore of the gun barrel into a jacket that does fit the bore. The rifling in the barrel acts on this to give the round spin, and it is discarded when it leaves the barrel.

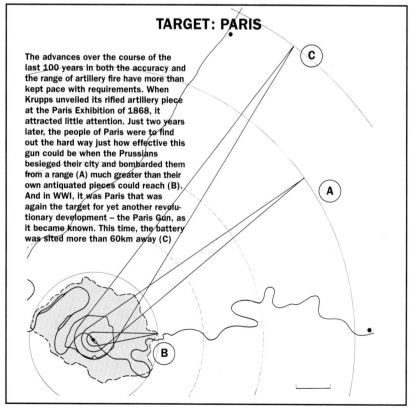

TARGET: PARIS

The advances over the course of the last 100 years in both the accuracy and the range of artillery fire have more than kept pace with requirements. When Krupps unveiled its rifled artillery piece at the Paris Exhibition of 1868, it attracted little attention. Just two years later, the people of Paris were to find out the hard way just how effective this gun could be when the Prussians besieged their city and bombarded them from a range (A) much greater than their own antiquated pieces could reach (B). And in WWI, it was Paris that was again the target for yet another revolutionary development – the Paris Gun, as it became known. This time, the battery was sited more than 60km away (C)

'Base bleed' means that the round carries its own additional propellant, fired once it has left the muzzle, to gain extra velocity.

The two techniques combined to give the gun considerably more range than it had with conventional rounds, but, as is often the case in any attempt to super-charge an existing design, ERFB ammunition had serious drawbacks: at maximum range the lightweight projectiles became too dispersed and the barrels wore out too quickly. Rocket Assisted Projectiles (RAPs), which include a small rocket motor within the artillery round, are in the latter stages of development, and seem likely to be used widely. There will, however, be the inevitable penalty for the extra range achieved – less explosive in the warhead.

If its guns are limited in range, the artillery arm can still use rockets

Muzzle Velocity (MV) is the critical factor determining a gun's range. When using solid propellants, the maximum MV possible is around Mach 6. Looking well ahead into the 21st Century, liquid propellants may replace the current 'solid' (actually powder or grain) propellants, giving increased muzzle velocity. Although easy to replenish and store – in shaped tanks around the gun – they are complex and volatile, and crew morale might suffer, surrounded by gallons of such dangerous material.

Another possibility to be explored is the so-called 'rail gun', an indirect-fire weapon which ups the velocity of the round by generating an electromagnetic charge in a rail running parallel to the gun barrel or in a coil wrapped around it. So far, the rail gun's power supply problem has not been overcome. Current models need a 15hp jet turbine engine with instantaneous switching to charge their induction coils.

Although increased range can be coaxed out of existing design – as has been effectively demonstrated by the late Dr. Gerald Bull's so-called 'superguns' – higher charges require heavier recoil systems and longer barrels, not to mention more frequent barrel changes. But there are ranges beyond which guns of a given calibre just cannot go. The new generation of guns, such as the Royal Artillery's new 155mm SP gun AS90, probably approach the optimum combination of range, manoeuvrability, rate of fire and size, though better breeches will

Above: The British, on the other hand, preferred the greater flexibility of moveable guns. The 15in howitzer – seen here being prepared for action – fired a 635kg projectile over just 10km

Below: Camouflage won't be much use as soon as the guns start firing; their heat signatures will give them away

Below: The American MLRS is the true successor to the big guns: one launcher alone is equivalent in fire power to four batteries of 155 or 205mm howitzers (Bottom). The MLRS warhead can carry a great number of submunitions – 644 shaped-charge anti-tank 'grenades', for example

allow higher pressures, and modular charges will simplify loading procedures.

But if its guns are limited in range, the artillery arm has another possibility in store: rockets. Rockets can deliver massive warheads over very long distances, and since the Soviets used multi-barrelled rocket launchers in World War II to reinforce their tubed artillery, free-flight systems have been seen as the most cost-effective option for achieving range and payload. The one proviso was that accuracy could be improved; rockets have hitherto been too inaccurate for front-line use near friendly troops.

Although rockets can be expected to increase their range, and are more likely to be used against depth targets and for massive strikes against armoured columns and the like, guns will remain the weapon of choice in general support of ground combat operations. Nevertheless speed into and out of action will be vital to surviving hostile, efficient CB fire.

One way to speed things up is to increase the rate at which guns fire. The brass cartridge case has survived over a century without much modification, but it is cumbersome, takes up too much room and has to be removed and disposed of after

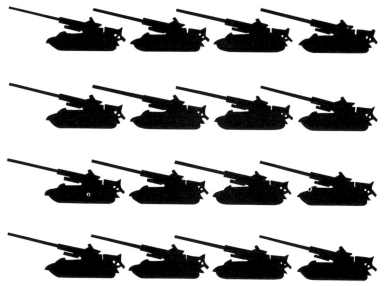

use. Combustible case charges, whose cases burn away at the same time as the propellant should speed things up. Rates of fire are also affected by the type of breech (screw-in or block), and by the presence of any special feed trays to offer shells to the open breech. Split-block breeches combine the range-enhancing effect of the screw-in breech with the far speedier operation of the block breech, and are also coming into service. Liquid propellants would speed things up further.

Rates of fire are quoted in two ways: as burst rates and sustained rates. On the battlefield of the future, it is envisaged that guns will fire in bursts, moving continually to avoid CB fire. Systems such as the British 155mm FH70 towed howitzer can line up three rounds at a time, and newer systems have burst fire 'clips' – the equivalents of small-arms magazines. With limber vehicles operating as magazines for an automated gun, feeding ammunition automatically through fireproof doors, rates of fire could be raised dramatically. Vickers' 4.5in naval gun system already uses a basic version of such a loading system. In addition, as already mentioned, a modular system of bag charges – of equal-sized bags to replace variously sized and colour-coded bags – would also help, and lessen the likelihood of mistakes.

More and more, the solution to artillery problems is systemised

On the battlefield of the future, all artillery delivery systems will operate independently with small crews, probably of three men. The emphasis will be on simplicity and speed – of ammunition-handling as well as gunnery. The arrival of the burst-fire capability has already revolutionised the effect of artillery, but just as important has been the development of equipment and techniques for co-ordinating the fire of many batteries on to one target. The likelihood is that the really big changes to artillery now and in the near future will probably not be in the field of ET weapons, but will be driven by improvements to Communications, Command, Control and Information.

More and more, the solution to artillery problems is systemised, rather than relying on ad hoc improvements to components. The British Army's BATES (Battlefield Artillery Target Evaluation System) and DROPS (Demountable Rack Offloading and Pickup System) are fine examples of this philosophy, but it remains to be seen whether their complexity will work in practice.

The task of defending the battlefield against attack from the air has fallen to the artillery almost by default. The basic problem of air defence is that aircraft can swamp ground defences simply by weight of numbers. It is certainly impossible to deny the entire battlefield to enemy aircraft, so defence strategy has to concentrate on key areas. Hand-launched systems, like the British Javelin, US Stinger, French Mistrale or Soviet SA-7 Grail, can protect likely point targets such as bridges and cross-roads, and medium systems like the British Rapier or Franco-German Roland can cover small areas or linear features like a main supply route. But the number of tasks

Below: The American MLRS can fire its 12 rockets in a three-second ripple-salvo. Each projectile incorporates its own guidance system, and each one can saturate an area 200m by 100m. Reloading takes just minutes

THE ROCKET'S RED GLARE

The first serious Soviet battlefield rockets were the crude but terrifying M-8 Katyushas (also known as 'Stalin organs') of World War II, which fired 36 82mm rockets each carrying 2kg of HE to a maximum range of 6km. The 40-barrelled BM-21, introduced in 1964, has a maximum range of 20.38km, and was upstaged in the late 1970s by the formidable BM-27. The latter, which was designed to augment rather than replace the BM-21, is mounted on a ZIL-135 chassis and has 16 220mm rockets, each carrying 100kg and reaching out to between 35 and 40km. Although MLRS – the Western equivalent – is considered more sophisticated, the BM-27 is very accurate, has the longer range and has been in service since the late 1970s. Today, each Soviet division has 18 BM-21s at their disposal and BM-27s form part of artillery brigade formations at Army level – 54 systems to each brigade. Both systems are used in conjunction with guns to create the devastating mass concentration of fire known

as 'Fire Blow' required by Soviet artillery doctrine.

As mentioned above, the Western answer to the BM-27 is MLRS, a highly mobile, all-weather, self-propelled rocket artillery system which can launch 12 surface-to-surface, free-flight rockets to ranges over 30km. It is carried by a 25-tonne tracked vehicle with a top speed of 64km/h and is designed for a three-man crew, but can be operated by one man on his own. The rockets can be launched singly with great accuracy, or in rapid-fire ripples delivering all 12 in under a minute, the computer re-laying for each rocket. The vehicle can be driven into position and all 12 rockets fired in under four minutes – thus avoiding CB fire.

The actual MLRS rocket is four metres long, of 227mm calibre, and propelled by solid fuel. The basic warhead contains 644 M77 dual-purpose bomblets that are released in mid-air, armed in free fall and oriented for impact by a drag ribbon that acts against air resistance rather like a rudder. The

M77 contains a shaped charge that can penetrate armour steel plate, with high fragmentation to kill people. Each launcher is thus able to deliver 7728 M77s in less than one minute. At mid-range (around 15km), one rocket will saturate a target 200m by 200m – an area equivalent to that covered by three gun batteries. One launcher can cover a larger area, the size depending upon the ripple pattern being fired, the range, and the different aim points that might be selected within the target area. At maximum range, the target area is about the size of four football pitches.

Other mission-orientated warheads are being developed – the West German AT2 with 28 anti-tank mines, and the TGW, mentioned earlier. Resupply for MLRS comes in two sealed rocket pods, each with six rockets, requiring no alignment on re-loading, and disposable once the rockets have been expended. These pods require no maintenance, withstand robust handling and can be reloaded by one man in minutes.

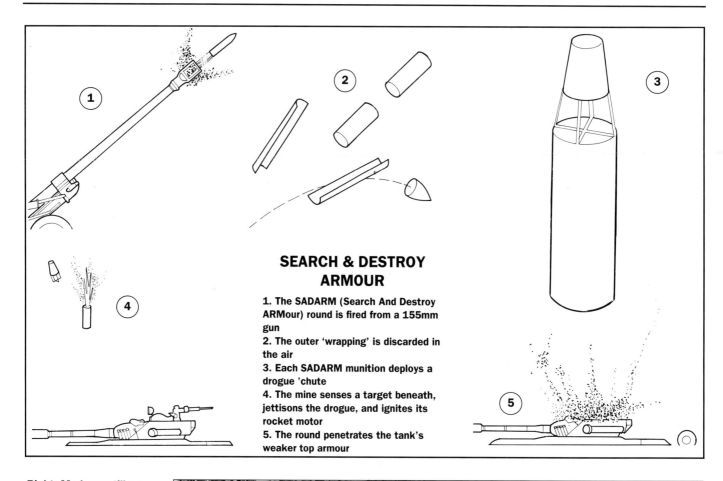

SEARCH & DESTROY ARMOUR

1. The SADARM (Search And Destroy ARMour) round is fired from a 155mm gun
2. The outer 'wrapping' is discarded in the air
3. Each SADARM munition deploys a drogue 'chute
4. The mine senses a target beneath, jettisons the drogue, and ignites its rocket motor
5. The round penetrates the tank's weaker top armour

Right: Modern artillery pieces are lighter in weight than their predecessors, due to advances in materials technology, but they are still extremely cumbersome. Moving them is a time-consuming business

always exceeds the available resource, so the aim must be simply to induce a sense of uncertainty in the minds of enemy pilots, while hoping that friendly air forces can achieve superiority.

Unmanned AD sites are a distinct possibility (they are in service on certain warships already), and it may be true that modern weapons are able to shoot down all enemy aircraft entering forward airspace, but friendly aircraft, too, have to fly through that airspace and survive. One initially attractive way to protect these aircraft from misplaced friendly fire is to equip the AD batteries with 'Identification Friend or Foe' (IFF) systems, which use an exchange of radio codes as 'passwords' to confirm that an aircraft is friendly. There are, unfortunately, monstrous difficulties in adapting them for AD use. Not only are they susceptible to jamming, but they are also not entirely reliable. And it would only take a small enemy special forces team to capture a single gun position and interpret the codes for the system to be invalidated across an entire front.

So far, only human operators possess the split-second aircraft recognition skills that form the basis

SUPERGUNS

There have been superguns as long as artillery has existed, ranging from the subject of C S Forester's novel *The Gun* to the railway guns used in WWI and WWII. But today's incarnation, largely the brainchild of one dedicated man, is such a large step forward that it deserves further examination.

Canadian Gerald Bull was a precocious young man, the youngest (at just 21) PhD to ever emerge from the University of Toronto. An aero engineer by training, Bull was a cross-disciplinarian, and his abiding interest was in the development of guns as launchers for ballistic missiles and earth-orbiters. By 1967 he had developed a 16in gun that had 'fired' a Martlet three-stage rocket to a height of 180km.

Bull next turned his attention to munitions and cargo carriers, working chiefly for the US Government. They so liked his work that they granted him US citizenship by means of a special act of Congress, and even back-dated it

10 years. Bull's life now becomes complicated; a muddy picture involving the CIA, the Pentagon, the South African government and Armscor, its arms procurement agency and manufacturer, the Israeli government and IDI, its armaments arm, not to mention the Iraqi government, the Chinese, the Russians, the Yugoslavs, Swiss, Swedes... The list goes on and on. To some observers, it appeared that Bull was unique – the one man in the entire world who could take a gun design and stretch its operating characteristics out of all proportion or, if you had the money, design and commission a true supergun, like the 16in smooth-bore HARP cannon he tested in Barbados and Canada in the 1960s.

The unanswered – and probably unanswerable – question is: did Dr Bull design and commission an even larger 1000mm cannon for the Iraqis, as the British government has insisted? Bull himself can't tell us; he's dead, gunned

down in a Brussels apartment building with a silenced 7.65mm pistol.

There is no clear picture of Bull's work to be drawn. In order to get even an outline sketch, half-a-dozen mutually suspicious agencies, ranging from Mossad, Israel's secret service, to its Iraqi equivalent, would have to suddenly start co-operating. One thing begins to emerge – Bull was working on plans for an artillery piece with a range in excess of 1200 kilometres, for a consortium that comprised Iraq, Egypt and Argentina, with Iraq by far the senior partner. At the time the project was conceived, Iraq was at war with Iran; Tehran was very definitely within range of the proposed weapon. Iraq has never been anything but hostile to Israel; Tel Aviv was, likewise, definitely within striking distance. Whether or not Bull's theories will ever be realisable we will not know, until another such unlikely genius comes along and takes up where he left off.

---

of all air defence, and so a human decision has to govern every weapon launch. In the end, we are likely to see a hybrid system, with men supervising a network of unmanned forward observation points, authorising their computers to attack specific unrecognised aircraft, as the best solution to a growing problem.

The battlefield of the future will be a new sort of nightmare

One alternative might be for all ground troops in forward battle areas to carry lightweight hand-launched 'fire and forget' weapons, with which they could engage attacking aircraft, thus discouraging enemy incursions into the FLOT. Such weapons, in the shape of Starstreak High Velocity Missiles (HVMs), could even deter attacks by massed helicopters, which will become a growing menace in the future. Radio-arming of weapons in a given area might maintain fire control and prevent friendly aircraft being blown out of the sky. Larger, more effective weapons would then be carried by AD artillerymen only.

The battlefield of the future will be a new sort of nightmare for everyone concerned. For artillery crews, scampering from one firing position to another, the stress, isolation and inhumanity of a prolonged war would be very great indeed. In sleep deprivation trials, artillerymen have been able to continue working – albeit not at peak levels of performance – for days at a time without rest. But the skills tested were routine – humping ammunition and carrying out drills on the gun. But

the reality is grossly different. Crews will be operating the on-board computer and making important decisions. Routine work will be automated, and that in itself could lead to further difficulties. If the automated systems break down, for instance, the three-man crew – the norm for future guns – would not be able to load and fire manually for more than a short period.

On the front line, the FOs would dominate a mobile war and would be the most prized and sought-after targets. Their life expectancy in war has always been low; in the future, they can expect

Above: Just a small portion of the mountain of brass shell cases left behind after the preparatory barrage that heralded the Battle of the Somme

enemy recce to hunt them ruthlessly and to survive only if they have superior fieldcraft and constant vigilance. Although each FO will be able to command larger areas than ever before, round-the-clock working inside the OPV, staring through periscopes and into computer screens, will be disorienting and very exhausting. It is unlikely that anyone would last more than a week – if that.

The artillery must be seen as the dominant battlefield force

The much-vaunted future battle of swirling high-tech hardware is splendid from the point of view of the weapons industry. High-tech threats must be countered, and obsolescence is inevitable. Only war can prove if the hardware works as claimed, and complex artillery will no doubt be just as prone to problems as any other advanced equipment. There is an argument that those who have high-tech kit come to rely on it and cannot do without their expensive toys. Yet some attention has been given to alternatives in the event of artillery C3I systems failing. BATES for example is designed to operate with whole levels of command removed, the individual batteries operating on their own, using traditional methods if necessary. In such circumstances, command post crews would have to be re-formed, and the guns grouped together into normal gun positions.

It is unlikely, then, that artillery would be paralysed and it would therefore be unwise to underestimate its value on the modern battlefield, something which non-artillery soldiers are sometimes wont to do. The problem is that artillery is too dangerous to include in combined arms training during peacetime. Armour can manoeuvre and fire its main armament in exciting live exercises with infantry, who can in turn use their small-arms and missiles in very realistic battle simulation. In peacetime, the power of artillery can never be demonstrated effectively – the nearest to reality is the British Bombard OP, where unrealistically small amounts of light calibre (105mm) shells are fired at targets 100m away and viewed from a deep bunker, behind inches-thick armoured glass.

It is hardly surprising therefore that, in peacetime, tank soldiers, for example, have misconceptions about the true power of modern artillery. The experience from World War II leads modern armoured soldiers to believe that only medium (155mm) or larger calibre shells pose a threat to them inside their vehicles, and that only a (rare) direct hit could put them out of action. Armoured infantry are similarly confident inside the thin plate of their APCs.

With today's ammunition, the reality is that tank and infantry operations are seriously affected, even when exposed only to light-calibre artillery fire. Shrapnel shatters the drivers' and commanders'

Right: A Blackhawk helicopter lifts in an American 105mm gun, together with a load of ammunition. Helicopters give the big guns a flexibility they have never enjoyed before

Below: Enough for a day's sport? Each ammunition box holds just two 155mm rounds. A battery in action would get through this pile in a matter of hours

optics, blinding any armoured vehicle; destroys the radio antennae, cutting communications; and seriously incapacitates the crews by creating electrical short-circuits that generate noxious fumes. Misses can deafen and concuss infantry in APCs, and direct hits kill them. Main battle tank crews are concussed and seriously disorientated by hits from even 105mm artillery. Anything larger penetrates and kills.

More than any other fighting arm, the artillery has successfully exploited the last two decades' stunning advances in military science and technology. As a result, it must be seen as the dominant battlefield force. As automation techniques become more reliable, so the prospect of the remote-control battle, using artillery alone, or in the company of remotely-piloted fighting vehicles, comes ever closer to reality – and the people most thankful for that will doubtless be the gunners themselves.

Whether or not the artillery can actually survive the attention it will bring upon itself is another matter. If it does succeed in fighting a 'battle by remote control', there must be grave doubts about how long that state of affairs can last.

HAS MODERN ARTILLERY CHANGED THE NATURE OF WAR?

Some argue that new developments have altered the way battles will be fought in future. The arguments to support them are:

• Improved surveillance, longer range and smart warheads promise to give artillery far greater effectiveness

• Increasingly discriminating warheads mean that fewer will be needed for each task, so reducing logistic pressures on the guns

• Modern artillery is both armoured and mobile: it can 'shoot and scoot' to avoid counter-battery (CB) fire

Against this case are these arguments:

• Armour or ECMs and EOCMs may turn out to be effective against indirect-fire AT weapons and their surveillance and guidance systems. In any case, AT artillery relies on HEAT warheads, which are not necessarily the best for killing tanks

• Adding to the artillery's tasks means increasing its consumption of ammunition, perhaps to the point where it can no longer be supplied.

• The improved efficiency of long-range artillery will bring more effective CB fire.

THE EMPTY BATTLEFIELD

The infantryman has always been the pawn on the chessboard of combat. In World War II, casualties in the infantry were three times greater than those suffered by armoured forces, nine times greater than in the artillery. It's 'all in the day's work' for the infantryman, to be crushed by tanks, battered by artillery and air strikes, raked by machine-gun fire and blown up by mines.

Left: In the final analysis, no matter how much technology advances, only the individual fighting man can hold ground. His confidence in his own abilities is paramount, and that can only be achieved by a combination of skill and good equipment. These infantrymen from the United States Marine Corps, waiting to debus from their M2 Bradley IFV, epitomise the no-nonsense style of the dedicated professional soldier, calm and sure despite the fears that always precede battle

Would one of Wellington's infantry even recognise his modern counterpart for what he is? On the face of it, probably not. Weapons, tactics and methods of waging war have changed so much over 200 years as to guarantee that. Yet, perversely perhaps, the task is virtually unchanged – the infantryman is still the only being who can hold territory, no matter what the methods used to sieze it might be. So does today's infantryman still qualify as the sacrificial pawn, or has he been exchanged for a piece of greater value? And where exactly does he stand?

On the modern battlefield, even the infantryman's traditional method of seeking safety – by wide dispersal – is often denied him; instead, infantrymen are forced to sit packed together in lightly armoured vehicles or in helicopters, vulnerable to weapons as light as high-velocity machine guns.

THE ULTIMATE WEAPONRY

Right: Increasingly, the modern infantryman is reverting to a style of personal armour that was out of fashion by the end of the17th Century. Newly-developed lightweight materials have finally made it possible to offer the soldier a real measure of personal protection from projectile weapons and from NBC threats. This design exercise, mounted by Scicon, attempts to show how the infantry soldier of the 21st Century will be equipped

The infantryman has many enemies and few friends on the modern battlefield – yet he is as essential now as in the days before armour and artillery were even thought of. As Tom Wintringham said in his 1939 book, *English Captain*, the infantry has a rare ability to 'hide... go to ground, become dangerous vermin hard to brush out of the seams of the soil'. The infantryman has a far smaller surveillance signature than any AFV, and often greater 'tactical agility'; and good infantry is not limited to roads or mountain passes. It can cross any sort of terrain, given time, including that which is impassable to armour. It has a unique ability to carry out *coup de main* attacks, special reconnaissance or sabotage raids, set-piece assaults and improvised defences; it can hold ground and clear

towns in a way that no other arm can, and in favourable circumstances its battalions, companies and platoons can produce an unapproachable intensity of team spirit and gutsy fighting morale.

There have been recurrent attempts to fight battles without large infantry formations. The British tried thinning out their front-line infantry in the Western desert in 1941-42, as did the Israelis in the first few days of the 1973 October War. In neither case was the experiment successful. The modern Soviet Army in central Europe is moving sharply away from a similar doctrine. Overall, the qualities of the infantry far outweigh its disadvantages, and it remains indispensable to victory.

On the battlefield of the future this general situation is unlikely to change, although the specific

THE 20TH-CENTURY INFANTRYMAN

Until about 1916, an infantry battalion consisted almost entirely of riflemen. In defence they would simply line up and fire their rifles – with or without the cover of trench works – and in attack they would advance in a loose line, go to ground close to the enemy to 'win the firefight', then charge home with the bayonet. As recently as 1914 only two machine guns were attached to each battalion of some 600 men. During the course of the big battles of 1916 – Verdun and the Somme – changes took place in both the armament and tactical philosophy of the infantry. The infantry, already protected by clothing of sub-dued colour, now had steel helmets and respirators. It was given increased fire-power in the shape of light machine guns, mortars, hand grenades, and even flame throwers and sniper rifles; these weapons were soon followed by true sub-machine guns (SMGs), developed as a trench-clearing weapon.

The infantry also learned to fight in a far more dispersed manner than before, using cover whenever possible and shunning long straight lines. In defence it used small independent strongpoints, and in attack it would be based on self-supporting platoons.

Within each platoon, furthermore, a division of function appeared between the 'gun' or 'covering' group – capable of laying down heavy covering fire – and the assault group, whose job was to charge the enemy and bomb out his positions. Despite initial problems with signalling, the new infantry also learned how to co-operate effectively with artillery, armour and air power.

For the next half-century this methodology changed only in details. Anti-armour weapons were introduced: first light KE guns and then, from 1943, bazookas and other types of HEAT launchers. The mortars and light machine guns were technically improved, while a few radios started to make their appearance in each battalion. Motor transport also appeared, to provide mobility behind the front line of combat, although as late as 1945 the German infantry divisions still relied heavily upon horses for their transport.

The second great change in 20th-Century infantry equipment and philosophy was completed as recently as the 1960s, although it had admittedly been prefigured on a small scale in specialist units (for example, the panzer grenadiers and paratroops) during World War II.

Each man was now given an automatic assault rifle and a full NBC suit. His anti-tank capability was enhanced by a new generation of HEAT weapons, in particular the guided missile. Tactical mobility was greatly improved by both APCs and helicopters, which could be supported right up to the target by heavily armed tanks and gunships respectively. Hand in hand with this, the Soviet armies introduced new assault tactics, which took into account the fact that troops could now often ride to the objective in a way that had not been possible with vulnerable soft-skinned lorries.

Alongside this potent and agile infantry an 'elite' corps of special forces, first used in World War II, was further developed and trained to operate in small groups behind the enemy's lines. They were experts in survival under hostile conditions and performed tasks ranging from sabotage and assassination to intelligence-gathering and liaison with resistance workers. They were therefore effectively extending the depth of the battlefield into the enemy's rear areas, in a way not entirely dissimilar from interdiction bombing raids by air forces. Such forces promised to add a whole new dimension to infantry warfare.

tasks to be performed and the specific dangers to be faced by infantry are currently undergoing a new round of transformations – just as they did during World War I and then again around 1960. The infantry is likely to become more specialised and fight in smaller groups, albeit packing more firepower than ever – especially when IFV- or helicopter-mounted weapons are taken into consideration. A task which would once have required a platoon of 30-40 men may now be carried out by a squad or section of eight or 12 men, each divided into two or three 'fireteams' that will similarly be capable of doing the job that previously needed the whole squad.

Which will best protect the infantryman: tactics, or technology?

An example of such a development in today's British Army is the 10-man Warrior-mounted infantry section, which boasts 10 fully automatic weapons, compared with the three machine guns held by a 1945 British platoon (or two in a 1914 battalion) and six in a 1945 German platoon. The section consists of three elements: a lance corporal and two men responsible for driving the vehicle and firing its 30mm Rarden cannon; and two infantry fireteams armed with SA80s – one consisting of a lance corporal and two men, the other of a

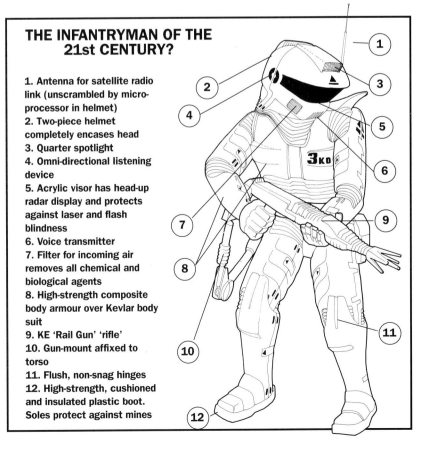

THE INFANTRYMAN OF THE 21st CENTURY?

1. Antenna for satellite radio link (unscrambled by microprocessor in helmet)
2. Two-piece helmet completely encases head
3. Quarter spotlight
4. Omni-directional listening device
5. Acrylic visor has head-up radar display and protects against laser and flash blindness
6. Voice transmitter
7. Filter for incoming air removes all chemical and biological agents
8. High-strength composite body armour over Kevlar body suit
9. KE 'Rail Gun' 'rifle'
10. Gun-mount affixed to torso
11. Flush, non-snag hinges
12. High-strength, cushioned and insulated plastic boot. Soles protect against mines

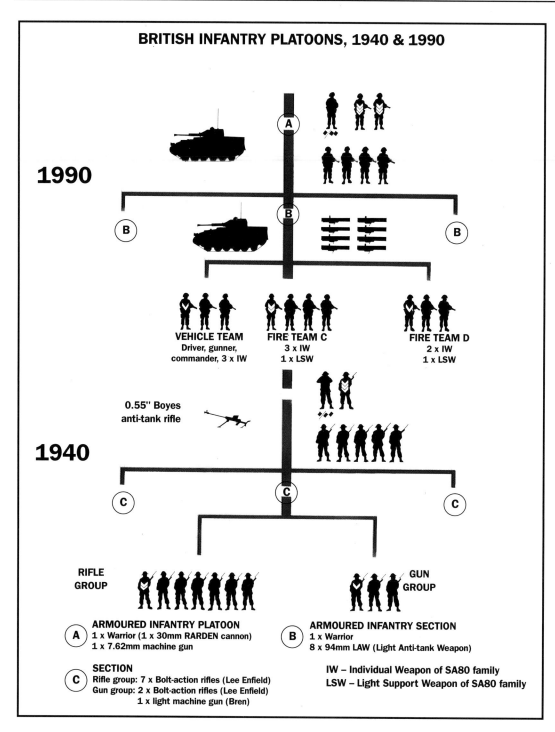

BRITISH INFANTRY PLATOONS, 1940 & 1990

1990

A

B **B** **B**

VEHICLE TEAM
Driver, gunner,
commander, 3 x IW

FIRE TEAM C
3 x IW
1 x LSW

FIRE TEAM D
2 x IW
1 x LSW

0.55" Boyes
anti-tank rifle

1940

C **C** **C**

RIFLE GROUP

GUN GROUP

A **ARMOURED INFANTRY PLATOON**
1 x Warrior (1 x 30mm RARDEN cannon)
1 x 7.62mm machine gun

B **ARMOURED INFANTRY SECTION**
1 x Warrior
8 x 94mm LAW (Light Anti-tank Weapon)

C **SECTION**
Rifle group: 7 x Bolt-action rifles (Lee Enfield)
Gun group: 2 x Bolt-action rifles (Lee Enfield)
1 x light machine gun (Bren)

IW – Individual Weapon of SA80 family
LSW – Light Support Weapon of SA80 family

Left: British infantry platoons, 1940 and 1990. Totals include: Automatic, rifle-calibre weapons: 1940 – 3; 1990 – 37. Anti-armour weapons: 1940 – 1; 1990 – 27+ (94mm LAW is treated as a round of ammo). Vehicles: 1950 – 0; 1990 – 4; Radios: 1940 – 0 or 1; 1990 – 16. Speed: 1940 – 5km/h; 1990 - 75km/h.

Below: The infantry squad of the 1990s. Divided into two fire-teams, and equipped with small calibre automatic weapons, it delivers more firepower than a platoon, three times its size, could muster in World War II.

corporal and three men. One obvious upshot of the concentration of firepower in smaller units is the responsibility this places on junior ranks. A modern infantry section is commanded by a corporal; a World War II platoon (with less firepower) was led by a commissioned officer.

By the same token, a recent US Army prediction foresaw the light infantry battalion of the future as having so much high technology, in both surveillance assets and ATGW, that it could cover the frontage usually defended by a brigade, a formation three times its size. In this particular case an area would be covered by a third of the men required in the past and officers would be cast much more as technicians than as leaders. The actual fighting would be done by the individual

crews of high-mobility multi-purpose wheeled vehicles (HMMWVs, or 'Hummers'), firing Hellfire laser-guided anti-armour missiles against targets designated by robots.

This has important implications for combat leadership. In World War I, it was sometimes said that officers of the rank of major and above were effectively 'non combatants', since they ran the battle from protected shelters set back behind the front line, leaving the day-to-day command of the men in the trenches to company commanders (captains) and platoon commanders (lieutenants). In future warfare this trend may continue still further. Company and even platoon commanders, may find themselves in a relatively sheltered or 'managerial' role – operating computers, logistic links or

When Maxim first produced an effective automatic weapon, he changed the face of the battlefield overnight. Today, the medium and heavy machine gun (Left), of either 5.56mm, 7.62mm or 12.7mm calibre still dominates at short ranges of up to a mile

advanced communication consoles – while responsibility for the prosecution of the actual fighting rests with lance corporals commanding fireteams or half-sections. With increased weapon power and widely dispersed by the speed of the battle, a tactical unit of just four or eight men may well be the largest that can operate independently.

This development promises radical changes in the military pecking order, raising the status of the infantry. In future only the very ablest men will be capable of fulfilling the duties required of a junior infantry commander. As early as the Normandy battles of July 1944, the Allies were giving far too low a priority to the quality of their infantry. As a result, it was either consumed or its cutting edge badly blunted long before it could attain its objectives.

The infantryman must be trained and equipped to fight and win

The problem is still with us today, since the attractive high-tech arms – the air force, armour, engineering and artillery – still tend to take precedence in personnel selection. Thus the infantry may find that it is unable to achieve in practice many of the things that might be technically or theoretically within its grasp, due simply to skill deficiencies.

Elite infantry units will escape this fate because of the high standard of their selection process, but in many armies the line infantry will be unable to cope with the sudden enlargement of its responsibilities. Only a revolution in the way infantry is viewed and thus in the perception of the quality of manpower it requires will avert this possibility.

Yet even the ablest infantrymen will find the modern battlefield a severe test, not least due to communications problems, and the resulting call for him to use his own initiative under extreme

Because it is easier to drop grenades than throw them upwards, and easier to run downstairs than up, the preferred method of clearing buildings is from top to bottom.

Flame is a potent weapon in FIBUA. It is much easier to burn the enemy out of a house than to clear it room by room. The short maximum range of flame throwers is not a limitation, because of the confined nature of the battle.

Some armies believe in bringing artillery into built-up areas in the direct fire role, even using multi-barrel rocket launchers over open sights. Such weapons can be devastating, but they are often vulnerable to small arms and mortar fire.

Ta▮
blo▮
de▮

FIGHTING IN BUILT-UP AREAS

FIBUA is very much an infantry battle. While the other arms play vital supporting roles it is a soldier with rifle and grenades who must fight from building to building and room to room. Fields of fire are usually short, except down streets, and observation difficult. Smoke and dust limit visibility, while rubble inhibits vehicles. The abundance of cover and the distortion of sound by the buildings make locating snipers very difficult, while the comparative openness of the streets requires movement to be within buildings or underground. FIBUA is a three-dimensional battle, with troops fighting up and down buildings and attackers "outflanking" defenders by going through cellars and attics. Sometimes, one side may control the cellars and sewers of a street while the other controls everything above ground level. This type of fighting demands the highest levels of fitness, aggression and determination among the troops, and the highest standard of leadership from junior commanders.

Command and control during FIBUA is particularly difficult. Platoon and section commanders cannot see their men because they are in different rooms and different buildings. Buildings frequently block radio signals.

In FIBUA, the fighting is at very close quarters, with the two sides often in adjacent rooms. One man in a corridor can hold up an entire company, because a building is so confined. At such short ranges, the grenade is the key weapon.

...portant part to play in FIBUA - destroying strong points and ...walls ("mouseholes") for the infantry to enter buildings. The ...n off-route mines and anti-armour weapons to defeat them.

Subterranean passageways, such as sewers, holes between cellars and underground railways, have a vital part to play in FIBUA. They can be casualty evacuation and ammunition resupply routes, or an attacker may use them to get underneath a defender and surprise him.

Below: Lightweight ATGWs such as the MILAN give the individual the power to kill even MBTs over short ranges. The term 'lightweight', however, is strictly relative – these weapons still represent a very heavy individual load for a man on foot, especially one under the stress of battle conditions, and perhaps encumbered by protective clothing to fend off NBC attack

pressure. Dismounted from its vehicles, today's infantry lacks effective personal intercommunication. There are plans to equip infantrymen with personal radios, but for now they are limited to shouted orders and hand signals that cannot convey all the necessary information and instructions. In defensive positions, where the infantry attempts to hide itself in widely dispersed camouflaged positions that separate each man from his comrades, communication of any sort becomes actually impossible. Besides being physically out of touch with their commander, the men feel psychologically isolated.

The infantryman's will to fight and win is still the most important factor

Then there is the challenge of continuous battle. Sensitive electronic equipment will have to be monitored throughout a 24-hour battle, and an exhausted operations officer who dozes over his IR or radar display may miss far more than the traditional sentry dozing behind the front-line wire. Conditions will be even more testing if the battle must be fought closed down in NBC suits.

In some futuristic projections, such as the 1985 US AirLand Battle 2000 (since revised as Army 21), the infantryman is aided in his fight against combat stress by pre-recorded video messages from his unit chaplain, and against boredom by playing computer games. His mail is digitised to be read straight off the computer screen. He is protected from the sight of mutilated bodies by disintegrating foam, and from fatigue, shock and his own inconvenient bodily functions by 'safe' drugs. In some scenarios he even has a personal jet-pack or helipack for flying short distances. (Such packs do exist, but it is surely beyond belief that they will ever be used for anything other than very specialised applications.)

On a more basic level, the front-line soldier will at least enjoy better armour protection than any of his predecessors since the Renaissance. Not only will he have the protection of his IFV, but also personal upper body armour and mine-resistant boots to complement the protective helmet – now made from plastic rather than the traditional steel – and these will go some way towards shielding him from low-velocity rounds and shell, mine or grenade fragments.

New generations of combat dress will contain multi-sensor camouflage features – to reduce the soldier's IR signature, for example – and, looking further into the future, he may have a miniaturised communications console and surveillance sight built into his helmet. His first-aid kit will be more sophisticated than in the past, too. For example, the Falklands conflict of 1982 taught the British the value of saline drips for battlefield first aid. The infantryman will thus be better equipped to treat

wounded comrades, but to do so effectively he will need more extensive training.

A lone infantryman today outguns a World War II section

Infantry armament is also in transition. The future rifleman's personal weapon is likely to fire 'hypervelocity' caseless sabot rounds as do the still-experimental US 5.56/4.32mm Advanced Combat Rifle and the German H&K G11, and carry optical sights like the SUSAT fitted to the British 5.56mm SA80; it might even mount thermal or radar imagers. Automatically-loaded grenade-launchers, more powerful than the combat-proven US 40mm M79s and M16-mounted M203s of the 1960s are in the process of introduction. Already the Red Army has its AGS-17, and the US Marine Corps fields the Mk19. Hand grenades themselves have greater powers of fragmentation than ever, not to mention their diversification into

INFANTRY FIGHTING VEHICLES & APCs

In the past, the Infantry Fighting Vehicle has been little more than an armoured and lightly armed truck, but since the early 1980s, the state of the art has changed considerably. The future IFV may in many ways be a more complex vehicle than the tank itself. While it doesn't have a powerful main gun, it does mount an effective cannon and is set to take on much of the tank's advanced armour and EW hardware. On top of this, the IFV is the 'mothership' for an infantry

squad which will fight either from it, or – more difficult to monitor and control from the vehicle – dismounted. A new generation of personal communications hardware – in development now for many years – looks set to change that, but of course it won't really make the transition from dismounted any easier. The current generation, which must be regarded as technologically transitional or intermediate, includes the following vehicles:-

Name:	1 Marder	2 BMP	3 AMX 10P	4 YW531	5 Bradley	6 Warrior
Origin:	W. Germany	USSR	France	China	USA	UK
Speed:(km/h)	78	56	65	65	78	75
Range (km):	500	440	500	500	500	600
Weight (tons):	28	13	14	12.6	23	25.3
Crew	10	11	11	14	9	10

ARMAMENT:
1: 1 x 20mm, 1 x 7.62mm MG
2: 1 x 73m,m gun or or 1 x 30mm cannon
   1 x Sagger AT or Spandrel missile, 1 x 7.62mm MG
3: 1 x 20mm, 1 x 7.62mm MG
4: 1 x 12.7mm MG
5: Twin TOW AT missiles, 1 x 25mm chain gun, 1 x 7.62mm MG
6: 1 x 30mm, 1 x 7.62mm MG

special applications such as the flash and stun grenades used in hostage rescues. The standard Soviet anti-personnel grenade now comes in two varieties – offensive and defensive, the latter with a larger charge than the former. Portable light anti-tank weapons (LAW) are also much more easily available. While they are not necessarily effective against the frontal arcs of most modern MBTs, they can certainly destroy APCs and IFVs – and can also be used as off-road mines in automatic ambushes, and as first line bunker-busters.

Range, accuracy and rate of fire are the critical factors

To back up these more powerful man-portable weapons, the infantry will be able to call upon a wider variety of heavier weapons too. These will include automatic cannon, AAA and SAMs mounted on IFVs; heavy ATGWs with 'fire-and-forget'

capability; and mortars (themselves automatically fed) firing terminally-guided top-attack anti-tank bombs or anti-personnel cluster munitions. The distinction between 'infantry weapons' and 'artillery weapons' is becoming blurred. Modern infantry weapons are capable of performing many tasks that were once reserved for the artillery, whereas the artillery is itself becoming more discriminating and 'infantry-like' in style, as new munitions allow it to act as a point rather than purely area weapon. The humble mortar in particular has acquired an increased range that puts it very much on a par with the field artillery of earlier eras – and this has given it a new lease of life.

Taken together, this mix of weapons promises to criss-cross the infantry's defensive frontages with a dense and deadly web of fire. In these circumstances, it is hard to see how any attack against alerted infantry can possibly succeed unless it is preceded by a devastating preparatory barrage.

Gas was first used as an agent of war during the second battle of Ypres, in 1915. Despite the danger of contaminating friendly forces, it came back into favour in the mid-1980s, and modern-day troops have to be protected both by clothing and by procedures.

Right: Victims of a gas attack on the Somme, during 1916, await attention at a Regimental Aid Post

Above: A decontamination team sprinkles Fuller's Earth over a simulated casualty to absorb liquid chemical agents

DRAWBACKS OF THE NBC SUIT

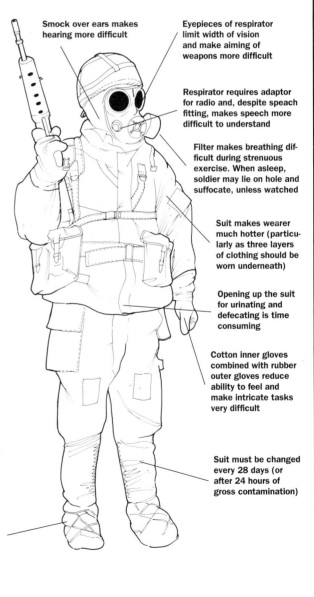

Smock over ears makes hearing more difficult

Eyepieces of respirator limit width of vision and make aiming of weapons more difficult

Respirator requires adaptor for radio and, despite speach fitting, makes speech more difficult to understand

Filter makes breathing difficult during strenuous exercise. When asleep, soldier may lie on hole and suffocate, unless watched

Suit makes wearer much hotter (particularly as three layers of clothing should be worn underneath)

Opening up the suit for urinating and defecating is time consuming

Cotton inner gloves combined with rubber outer gloves reduce ability to feel and make intricate tasks very difficult

Suit must be changed every 28 days (or after 24 hours of gross contamination)

Overboots make running much more awkward and reduce the 'feel' of feet during driving

DEFENCE AGAINST NBC ATTACK

The modern battlefield may become contaminated with nuclear fallout, biological agents or chemical weapons such as mustard gas or nerve agents.

Lethal gas was widely used in Europe between 1915 and 1918, and in the Middle East during the Iran-Iraq war of 1980-88, while non-lethal gas (principally CS) was used by USA in Vietnam, and has been employed by most nations in internal security operations since 1945. Many advanced armies have certainly stocked chemical weapons since they were first developed, despite repeated international attempts to ban them. Biological weapons have been less widely deployed, but were actively used, for example, by the Japanese in China between 1933 and 1945.

As for nuclear warfare, there has fortunately been only one, one-sided, nuclear campaign so far. A complex web of mutual international deterrence has somehow managed to prevent another outbreak, even in unstable areas such as the Middle East. Nevertheless tactical nuclear weapons (TNW) must still

remain an attractive option to any commander of a high-technology army that finds itself outnumbered by a low-tech army. In Korea in late 1950 General Douglas MacArthur wanted to use them against the Chinese; in 1968 it was the turn of the Soviets to contemplate a pre-emptive nuclear strike against the same opponent; and more recently there have been major debates about the potential NATO first use of such weapons as nuclear mines, neutron bombs and nuclear-armed cruise missiles.

All this means that armies have had to take steps to guard their troops and equipment against such weapons. AFVs, for example, are protected from NBC attack by having a slightly higher atmospheric pressure inside than prevails outside. This prevents noxious germs or gases from entering through the inevitable small leaks in the vehicles' outer skin, so that in theory crews do not need to wear protective suits inside the machine. A tank commander will not be able to open his hatch, but otherwise there should be no degradation in per-

formance unless the vehicle is punctured by an anti-tank round.

For the infantry, however, there is a constant requirement to dismount from the vehicle and fight in the open. If they do so in a contaminated area, they will don full protective suits and masks, which seriously degrade combat effectiveness, especially that of commanders, and especially in the attack.

Agility is reduced, breathing becomes more difficult, speech is distorted and hearing reduced, sight is blurred, and bodily functions are impeded. High levels of physical exertion become impossible, even in a cold climate, while the isolation and fear experienced by the soldier are greatly increased. After exposure to radiation, gas or germs, the whole suit must be decontaminated or destroyed, adding yet another unwelcome chore to the infantryman's already crowded programme. A relatively small and 'exemplary' NBC demonstration could thus be a useful way for an army to reduce the tactical efficiency of its opponents.

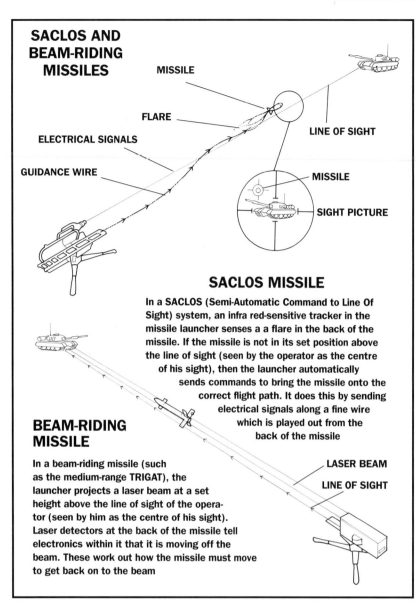

SACLOS AND BEAM-RIDING MISSILES

MISSILE

FLARE

ELECTRICAL SIGNALS

GUIDANCE WIRE

LINE OF SIGHT

MISSILE

SIGHT PICTURE

SACLOS MISSILE

In a SACLOS (Semi-Automatic Command to Line Of Sight) system, an infra red-sensitive tracker in the missile launcher senses a a flare in the back of the missile. If the missile is not in its set position above the line of sight (seen by the operator as the centre of his sight), then the launcher automatically sends commands to bring the missile onto the correct flight path. It does this by sending electrical signals along a fine wire which is played out from the back of the missile

BEAM-RIDING MISSILE

In a beam-riding missile (such as the medium-range TRIGAT), the launcher projects a laser beam at a set height above the line of sight of the operator (seen by him as the centre of his sight). Laser detectors at the back of the missile tell electronics within it that it is moving off the beam. These work out how the missile must move to get back on to the beam

LASER BEAM

LINE OF SIGHT

Right: Fighting in built-up areas is an especially hazardous task, even by battlefield standards. In these circumstances, tanks and armoured vehicles are especially vulnerable to sneak attacks from concealed positions, and are not much more use than a well-employed anti-tank rocket in destroying bunkers and other strongpoints. As usual, the task of protecting the tank falls to infantrymen, positioned out in the open, and with very little protective cover

Below: Early night-vision devices were big and cumbersome. Recent advances in microtechnology have reduced them to the size of a mask, worn over the face

And while infantry anti-tank defences are still based largely upon HEAT technology, which is less effective than KE against modern armour, the sheer volume of fire that even company-size units generate makes them very difficult targets indeed.

The infantry's defensive positions – hasty or long-term – will be further strengthened by mines, both anti-tank and anti-personnel. The directional multi-fragment Claymore mine – a mass killer in many a Vietnam ambush – is only one among many potent types that can be laid either by the infantry itself, by its supporting engineers or by means of artillery bombardment. Just as the infantry of World War I regarded barbed wire as an essential element in any prepared defence, so the infantry of today demands a mass of mines.

Defensive positions combine firepower with obstacles

Infantry defences do not, of course, rely solely upon firepower and weaponry; there are also earthworks and fortifications. Tomorrow's infantrymen will probably have their trenches dug for them by mechanical plant which may be integral to army units themselves or requisitioned from civilian sources. These trenches will need to be deeper and stronger than ever, with increased overhead protection, to withstand the onslaught of modern bunker-busting weapons, such as penetrating cluster munitions, fuel-air explosives (FAE) and LAWs and ATGWs aimed at bunker apertures.

Of these, it is perhaps the fuel-air bombs that pose the biggest potential threat. They dispense liquid droplets that drift, un-noticed, down to the very bottom of a bunker or trench, and then explode, with disastrous results. They threaten to make formal bunker systems obsolete; not least when they are combined with improved surveillance techniques and artillery accuracy.

In theory there is nothing to restrict the size of any given FAE blast, since a single igniter can detonate an unlimited number of FAE bombs, as long as the aerosol 'explosive' is contiguous. Even during the Vietnam War, the Americans were using one CBU-55 igniter linked to a pattern of three evenly distributed BLU-73 FAE bombs. Several rockets or strike aircraft might simultaneously drop FAE canisters onto a particular target, distributing them in a pre-planned pattern for maximum effect. A few moments later, when the droplets have spread, a single igniter detonates them all together. Given enough FAE, the explosion could have the force of a small nuclear bomb.

The buddy system helps reduce stress in the soldier

To counter such threats, defensive infantry must make maximum use of camouflage, concealment, deception and trench siting. The trench systems of the future may well need active EW protection, and even active armour or rapid-firing point-defence guns to counter incoming rounds and missiles. There is also a trend towards constructing the

Above: Men of the French Foreign Legion prepare a 120-RT-61 mortar for firing. Few other armies use heavy mortars any more, preferring instead to rely on artillery batteries, which have considerably greater accuracy. The 120-RT-61, however, can reach out to 13km, weighs just 257kg and can sustain a rate of fire of 12 rounds per minute. Best of all, from the infantry commander's point of view, it is under his direct control, and he can initiate a fire mission with it in just minutes

four-man 'fireteam' slit trench (as used already by the British Army), rather than the more traditional two-man type; partly so that there is an NCO in every trench, and partly to reduce the loneliness, stress and isolation discussed earlier. Of course, if the enemy can accurately locate such a position, a successful hit threatens to take out twice as many defenders in one fell swoop.

There is no mistaking the fact that infantry, in defence, for all its awesome new firepower, remains vulnerable to almost all of its traditional enemies, and especially to concentrated artillery fire. The same is true when it goes on the attack. It will be as lonely and exposed as ever, the moment it breaks cover to assault the enemy. At present there is relatively little that can be done to reduce the footsoldier's surveillance signature when he's moving in the open, except by laying down chaff and smoke. In the absence of any foolproof 'stealth' cover, therefore, he relies as far as possible on the direct protection afforded by the accompanying IFVs.

Armoured IFVs have become an intrinsic and indispensable part of the infantry's tactical battle. The soft-skinned lorry could offer operational mobility only, and could not stay with the troops during the firefight itself. At the battle of Gazala in May 1942, for instance, the British motor transport was in many areas forced to flee the battlefield, because it was too vulnerable above ground on the open surface of the desert.

The APC was the first improvement on the lorry. It first appeared in a useful form during World War

II (though the British had experimented during the last days of the Great War), as the German SdKfz and US M3 half-tracks and the British 'Kangaroo', developed from a turretless tank. At least, thus mounted the infantry could ride to within striking distance of the enemy, safe from shell splinters and ordinary smallarms rounds, went the theory. These vehicles promised great savings in casualties during the approach march, but in the event light anti-tank weapons forced tacticians to think again, for a single penetrating hit on an APC could wipe out an entire section. And thus perished the 'battle taxi'.

Inside an IFV the soldier is protected but performance suffers

The solution seemed to be the modern IFV – a vehicle that can carry a whole section or squad of troops, but which can also fight back strongly during the advance, and all the way into the enemy position. In Vietnam, the Americans improvised such vehicles by mounting several shielded heavy machine guns on the existing M113 APC, calling it the armored cavalry assault vehicle (ACAV). Then the Soviets went one step further, and demonstrated their BMP, which carried a 73mm anti-tank gun and a Sagger anti-tank missile, and had firing ports for the riflemen.

The BMP seemed to represent a formidable mixture of firepower, armour and mobility for the infantry, to give it plenty of punch even against armour; in practice, as the 1973 Yom Kippur War showed, the BMP was alarmingly vulnerable even

MORTARS

When it was first introduced during World War I, the mortar represented a really massive enhancement of the infantry's firepower. Then, it gave the brigade and division an indirect HE fire capability that was hitherto the exclusive preserve of artillery. For the first time infantry could reach into enemy trenches from a distance, using its own weapons.

Today, light (2in) mortars are often used as a platoon weapon. The 81mm mortar, used at battalion level, is a standard piece of man-portable equipment in many armies and enjoys an enviable reputation, although in the Red Army in particular it has been overtaken by heavier, vehicle-mounted mortars, such as the 120mm weapon. This has the effect of a light artillery piece and to Western eyes may appear to be an unnecessary luxury in an infantry unit. However, Soviet tank and motor rifle regiments have their own organic artillery and so are not concerned about co-ordinating indirect fire at a higher or overall level. The 120mm mortar is extra insurance for the infantry.

Mortars are now coming into service that feature automatic loading and have the ability to fire 'smart' munitions, including anti-armour warheads. With a range of more than 6km and double the rate of fire of artillery, such weapons promise to revolutionise infantry firepower yet again.

to relatively light infantry weapons. There have been attempts since then to overcome this vulnerability by fitting heavier armour to purpose-built IFVs, and the time may soon arrive when laminated, Chobham-type armour and reactive tiles become the order of the day – though such vehicles would surely be dauntingly heavy and have less space for troops to ride in. They would perhaps somewhat resemble the Israeli Merkava, a heavily armoured and sophisticated tank which includes a rear passenger compartment for just three men.

Perhaps the single most important tactical question yet to be answered concerning infantry in the assault is: what is the precise relationship between the tank and the IFV? Will the tanks taking the lead be able (or willing) to suppress all the diverse enemy weaponry, harmless to them but lethal to IFVs? Will the IFVs stick too closely to the tanks, making themselves vulnerable to overshots from the tank battle – or will they lag too far behind, in complete safety, but where they can achieve nothing? Will the IFV really be able to suppress the enemy by means of its own firepower – or will it be forced to leave the main fighting to the tanks and revert, in effect, to the old APC role of 'battle taxi'?

The infantry fighting vehicle: death trap, or death dealer?

On balance it seems that today's IFVs are just too vulnerable to too many different weapons for them to follow the tanks up as closely as they must in the assault. They must either take on more armour and counter-measures in their own right, or learn the fieldcraft skills to creep forward using ground cover some distance behind the tanks, having at an earlier point in the battle disgorged their infantry for dispersed action on foot.

Von Clausewitz's celebrated 'Fog of War' is often all too real. Even without artificially created smoke screens, visibility on the battlefield is likely to be restricted, especially after an artillery bombardment has started. However, modern conditions are a vast improvement over those of 200 years ago, when black powder produced so much smoke that everything was obscured. At Waterloo, for example, few infantrymen or artillerymen could see more than 10 yards, once they were in action

THE SQUADRON AND COMPANY GROUP ATTACK

The key to the modern battlefield may well lie in the combination of tanks and mechanised infantry, which offer commanders, at the level of tank squadron and infantry company, a range of options in both attack and defence, some of which are shown in the diagrams.

1A: An infantry company and tank squadron have successfully attacked and moved into an enemy position. With three tanks in the lead, the leading infantry (1) have not dismounted from their IFVs during the assault. But now (2) they debus from their IFVs to clear the position while the reserve platoon (3) and the bulk of the tank squadron (4) provide cover against any counter-attacks.

1B: When the position is cleared,

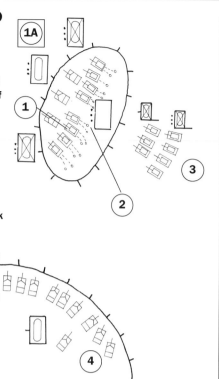

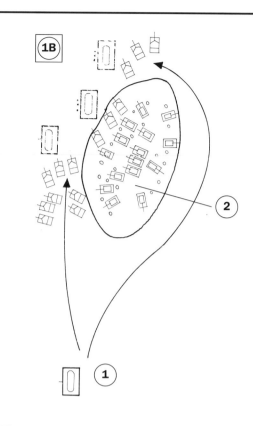

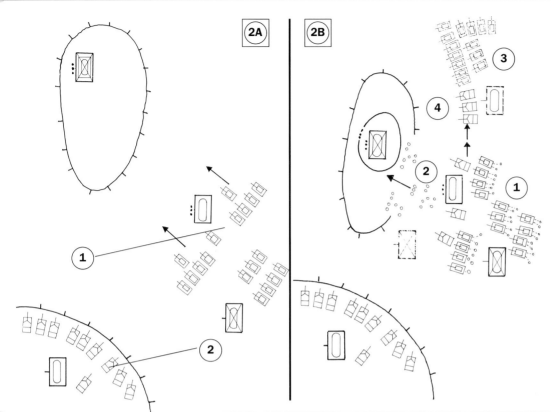

2A | **2B**

the tank squadron (1) moves up in force to form a ring of steel around the objective, while the infantry (2) take up defensive positions – some within trenches and some in their IFVs.

2A: The commander of the attacking force may, however, decide that his support tanks and IFVs (1) will be too vulnerable to enemy fire, even with gunnery support from the bulk of the tank squadron (2).

2B: In this situation, the commander has the option of dismounting his infantry, (1) who will then press home their attack on foot (2) while the IFVs (3) and the support tanks (4) move to the flank to either give covering fire from a new angle or to protect against a counter-attack. Once the position has been taken, then the combined company/squadron will take up defensive positions as in 1B.

It is hard to believe, in the computer age, that the infantry unit commander today still has to rely on shouts and signals to convey increasingly complex instructions to his men. In order to communicate with a higher echelon, which may be located some kilometres away, he must be accompanied by a signaller. This German platoon commander (Left) is awaiting instructions to begin an assault on a built-up area – the last place where one would wish to be held up by poor communications

The whole question of the employment of IFVs and APCs also implies a radical change in the infantry's logistics. No longer can each man simply be issued with five days' rations and ammo and be told to come back when that has run out. The infantry now has vehicles to worry about, with all the problems that generates

Certainly, the IFV can help the infantryman to carry heavier and more diverse weaponry than was convenient in the past, but it exacts a heavy price through its own maintenance requirements, creating a logistic problem every bit as complex as that which faces tank forces. The IFV complicates the infantry commander's task by demanding fuel, its own ammunition and a repair park, thereby inevitably increasing the size of resupply echelons and the 'tail-to-tooth' ratio within each infantry unit. Even though the fighting squads themselves may have become leaner and meaner, they now depend on a greatly inflated rear echelon. This in turn makes them enormously more expensive; hence fewer of them can be fielded. Thus the familiar downward pressures on infantry numbers have by no means disappeared.

The advantages and limitations of the helicopter as a means of transporting infantry have been discussed elsewhere, but it is worth making a 'human' point. From the infantryman's point of view it is a highly disconcerting vehicle. Not only does it hurtle through the air with unexpected twists and turns that can be far more violent than those of an IFV, but its payload area is almost entirely unarmoured and its 'cargo' is thus exposed to enemy firepower. So while the pilot and the helicopter's control systems are well protected, the infantry are almost as vulnerable as they would be in a soft-skinned terrestrial vehicle.

And still the infantry must carry out most of its prime tasks unaided. It must still make its assault on its own feet, relying mainly on its own organic weapons to 'shoot itself forward' on to the objective. At least, in this type of 'conventional' attack the infantry is mercifully released from the vulnerability it enjoys sitting closely packed inside lightly armoured vehicles, but it pays for this by having to advance across open spaces without any protection at all. In such an operation, it may find itself in one of two familiar situations:

Bold man-management is essential to successful infantry actions

On the one hand, the infantry may be able to infiltrate deep into enemy territory, exploiting difficult, under-defended terrain, good intelligence and the power of surprise. This was done systematically by Soviet infantry in their offensives of 1944-45, and less often by the British at around the same time. Boldness brought platoon- or company-size units well behind the enemy's front line before he recognised them as a threat. Under modern conditions of improved 24-hour surveillance such infiltrations may be more difficult than in the past, although the spread of special forces techniques and independent squad tactics may go far towards restoring the balance. And against a demoralised or badly supported enemy, robust infantry can still fight through successfully, as the British triumphantly demonstrated at Goose Green and then around Port Stanley in 1982.

Conversely, a dismounted infantry attack runs the risk of meeting the same fate as did all too many World War I offensives. During the Vietnam

War, for example, in their desperate assaults against US firebases, the North Vietnamese Army (NVA) often found that three battalions were inadequate to capture a single company position, if the latter possessed advanced weaponry, night-vision equipment and air power. At Ap Bau Bang near Route 13 in Vietnam, a US armoured infantry company and six M-48 tanks not only held off two battalions of the 273rd Viet Cong Regiment during the night of 19/20 March 1967, but destroyed them. Three US soldiers died, and so did 227 enemy, whose only additional armament besides their usual AK47 rifles and RPG-7s had been a solitary wheeled 12.7mm machine gun. If an unsupported attack on foot encounters such a solid defence, it is almost doomed to fail, with very heavy casualties. NVA regiments typically lost between 300 and 700 men in a few hours of such fighting; that is, as much as half their effective combat strength.

The will to win makes the difference between success and failure

Yet in any future conflict, where the defender has the capability to counter-attack with AFVs, the losses could easily reach 100 per cent. The success of

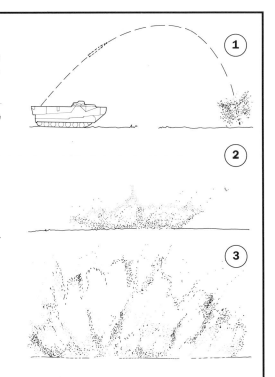

HOW FAEs WORK

1. The launch vehicle fires the FAE (Fuel Air Explosive) rocket, which has an airburst fuze, often in the form of a mechanical probe. This sets off the bursting charge when the rocket reaches a set height.
2. The bursting charge disperses the fuel into an aerosol cloud.
3. Delayed action detonator charges then detonate the cloud, producing a massive overpressure

An example of an FAE is SLU-FAE (Surface-Launched Unit FAE), a 30-barrelled multiple rocket launcher that fires Zuni rockets, each weighing 59kg, to a maximum range of 1000m. Each warhead contains 38.5kg of liquid propylene oxide and the explosion of all 30 warheads produces a 300m, 90kg/cm^3 overpressure

foot-infantry assaults in the Falklands and elsewhere should not blind us to the fact that without tank and artillery support they remain desperate gambles, their outcome determined almost entirely by the enemy's readiness, or lack of it. The unsupported infantry assault may be brilliantly successful, but without the proper back-up it can lead just as easily to sudden death.

There is one type of dismounted infantry assault in which the odds are not heavily weighted in favour of the defending side, however: street fighting, house clearing, or, to give it its official title, Fighting In Built-Up Areas (FIBUA). This has always been an expensive activity – it is scarcely a means of avoiding casualties – but at least it is an activity whose conclusion depends to a large extent on the skill of the attacker, rather than on how lucky he is. In the advance through a town there is far more cover available than in the open field, just as there

Below: It is important to confront troops on exercise with realistic representations of casualties. This man, from 2Bn, Parachute Regiment, on exercise north of the Arctic Circle, in Norway, has apparently suffered a serious leg injury. Only swift medevac will save him from an all-too-real case of frostbite

Below, far left: The (largely) conscript army with which America had to fight the war in South East Asia often resorted to 'recon by fire' – firing blindly on full automatic into any position that looked like it might harbour an enemy

THE CRUCIAL IMPORTANCE OF MORALE

The infantryman has more freedom on the battlefield than any other soldier, but the price he pays for that is solitude, and the need for tremendous self-reliance. When he gets out of his helicopter, APC or IFV to fight, the grunt has only his own legs to carry him forward, his own brains to find cover and his own skills to help him hit the enemy. Alhough he works as part of a team, he has to force his own body forward, up out of the protection of the ground, to close with the enemy. It is his own body too that he has to stop from turning and running away from a hail of enemy fire. He is not surrounded by a steel box that both protects him and carries him forward regardless. In defence, he must force himself not to cower in the bottom of his trench until it is all over.

Wherever he is, he has to keep on fighting, while all around him his mates will be suffering and dying. The sheer noise and confusion of a full-scale infantry battle, with artillery shells screaming and exploding, armour firing and going out of control as it is hit, the racket of small-arms fire – especially that aimed at him personally – can be paralysing, and no amount of training can entirely prepare a soldier for the psychological shock of joining real battle. But through this welter of lethal distractions the infantryman has to plug on to his objective intelligently, bravely, and on his own. About all that can be said in favour of being shot at seriously is that for many soldiers it disposes at once of the real and inevitable fear that preoccupies them in the prelude to actual fighting.

Morale is a highly complex quality. It depends on a great many intangibles, such as team spirit, leadership, training, discipline, and confidence in commanders (at whatever level). But it also depends on technology, for the infantryman must have confidence in his weapons if he is going to fight hard. He must have faith in his hand-held anti-tank weapons, or he will see running as the only alternative to 'terminal track-rash'. He must know that his personal weapon will not fail him at a critical moment, or he will not give it the opportunity to fail – by not firing it at all. And he must be able to dominate the enemy infantry with the firepower in his section if he is to move forward during the 'fight through'.

How effective firepower is depends on how close rounds land to the enemy and the rate at which they are pumped out. Infantry advancing against machine guns that have a much higher rate of fire than their own are immediately placed at a psychological disadvantage – it is that much easier for the enemy to dominate them mentally. American and British infantry faced this situation in northwest Europe in 1944-45. Against the tearing rasp of the German MG 42, all they would hear from within their own section or squad would be the measured hammer of their Browning automatic rifles or Bren light machine guns.

Technology has also increased the importance of individual, as opposed to group, morale. As area weapons have become more effective (a modern 81mm mortar, for instance, is lethal over a far greater area than one of 50 years ago), so dispersion on the battlefield has increased. As a result, the infantryman now fights further from the other men in his section than ever. In darkness, or when he is crawling forward, he can often see none of his friends or leaders. In an NBC suit he is in his own private world, strangely detached from what is happening outside. In all these cases, section commanders can influence their men through words and actions very little. It is up to the individual to keep himself moving forward, to maintain his own morale.

The Germans, who place great emphasis on individual morale, call it 'innerer Feuhrung' – inner leadership or, in British terms, personal conduct. While the Germans have sought to solve the problem from a moral point of view, the Soviets adopted a technological approach. With the introduction of the BMP in the 1960s they had an infantry fighting vehicle that would carry the soldier right on to the enemy position. Through the gunports in the side he could fire his personal weapon, so he did not even have to get on to the ground to fight, but would stay inside where his section commander could keep close control of him and where the machine would keep him moving inexorably forward.

The Soviet Army discovered the folly of this approach in Afghanistan. There, they discovered that the only way to be sure of destroying the enemy was to root out and kill him with grenade and bayonet. To do this requires fire and movement – suppressive fire to keep the enemy's head down, and aggressive forward movement to close with and destroy him personally. Sitting in a BMP blazing away at Afghan guerillas may seem safe and reassuring but, as very few of the rounds hit anything except rocks, it was not an effective response to an ambush. In fact, the infantry inside their BMPs soon ran out of ammunition, allowing the Afghans to move in and destroy both vehicles and occupants.

But by firing their weapons through the gunports, the Soviet troops could feel they were fighting back, while remaining protected by the armour of the BMP. Without gunports, the infantry would have had to debus – get out on the ground – to fight back. Interestingly, the British and French never put firing ports in their latest generation of IFVs, and the US and Germans covered theirs up during 1989-90 in upgrading programmes.

Even when they are being transported, infantry are very vulnerable to air attack, as this sequence of pictures demonstrates

Right: The RAF Jaguar, whose North European scheme camouflage is visible in the foreground, is in the last stage of its attack run against the mixture of armour and soft-skinned trucks to its front

Right: The aircraft itself is long gone before the first of its artificially retarded bombs bursts open and its load of sub-munitions hit the ground around the first of the target vehicles

Right: As the rest of the projectiles land, and the pattern develops, it is obvious that just one aircraft, on one attack run, can easily saturate an area the size of two football pitches

is often protection to be found in the very proximity of the enemy. In these circumstances, the assault troops can come to grips with their opponents on more or less even terms.

FIBUA means clearing the enemy out by any means possible

The only real advantage the defending troops have lies in their ability to use natural obstacles to their advantage, and enhancing them with booby traps, demolitions and ambushes. Given sufficient time, the defenders may even be able to prepare the battlefield more comprehensively, stockpiling stores and planning their fields of fire. Against this, however, the attacking infantry will advance carefully and systematically, 'unzipping' the defence house by house, block by block, street by street, and gradually installing its own lines of communications by 'mouseholing' corridors through internal walls. It can batter the defence by calling on the support of artillery, armoured vehicles and assault guns. Soviet practice even recommends the use of BM21 or BM27 multiple rocket launchers, firing directly, to blow buildings apart from close range. And in Vietnam, the Americans gave FIBUA tacticians extra food for thought when they used 15,000lb 'Daisy Cutter' parachute-delivered bombs in urban operations.

FIBUA takes time, patience and very large numbers of men. Even a relatively small town can swallow up a whole division for several weeks; and in recent decades most countries – in the First, Second and Third Worlds alike – have seen a major proliferation of small towns, suburban developments and concrete laid in all its forms. If a future war involves much fighting over such 'terrain', the shortage of infantry, which has been a recurrent difficulty in all 20th-Century warfare, could become an acute problem. Certainly, the emphasis on armoured operations, which rely on speedy advance, has long made it standard doctrine to bypass any towns that look like becoming potential FIBUA battlefields.

The bigger and older the city, the harder the FIBUA task

Yet FIBUA isn't going to go away. Common sense dictates that as urban developments spread, the need to fight there inevitably increases apace. In any battle, there is always some key ground that cannot be ignored; and in future combat this is more likely than ever to be urban ground. Nor should we forget the severe setback suffered by the Iraqis, when their 1980 *blitzkrieg* became bogged down in Abadan and Khorramshar: an updated version of Hitler's come-uppance when his own 1942 *blitzkrieg* into southern Russia finally ground to a halt at Stalingrad.

To reiterate the basic truth: the infantry will be no less essential on the battlefield of the future than it was on the battlefield of the past, but the job it will have to do will be significantly tougher. In defence, modern infantry is exposed both to

EARLY VERSION OF THE HECKLER & KOCH G11 ADVANCED COMBAT RIFLE (ACR)

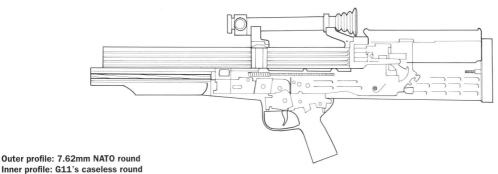

Outer profile: 7.62mm NATO round
Inner profile: G11's caseless round

The magazine is mounted above the barrel for quick loading and an increased magazine capacity of 50 rounds. The G11's outer surface is constructed mostly of carbon reinforced plastic, and so is easier to decontaminate on an NBC battlefield. The outer skin also ensures that the firing mechanism and inner parts are almost completely sealed from dirt

laser-guided artillery rounds of unprecedented accuracy, and to a new generation of bunker-busting weapons. In the attack it faces the bleak choice between the cramped conditions of lightly armoured vehicles and wide deployment on foot without any protection beyond a helmet and a flak jacket. It is scarcely an enviable position, and if things go wrong, the infantry can expect horrific casualties. If, on the other hand, it is handled properly, the infantry will still be the most flexible and most decisive arm on the battlefield. It alone can seize and hold ground – and seizing and holding ground have always been the major requirements for victory.

Above: Instead of armour, the infantryman today relies on trying to blend into the background. The men of this British patrol, its leader equipped with a Nova passive night vision device, are camouflaged so that when they go to ground they will be indistinguishable from the tussocky grass through which they are walking

IS THE INFANTRY DEAD ON ITS FEET?

In the light of emerging technology, it could be said that the infantry has become an anachronism. The reasons:

• Improving surveillance and firepower make the battlefield a more dangerous place than ever for infantry, even when it is dug in

• IFVs were designed to protect the troops, but ironically they are so much more vulnerable than tanks that they may not be able to live at all on the armoured battlefield

• Smaller tactical groups may put too heavy a burden of responsibility on junior NCOs

• Modern armoured infantry has a far greater need for support than the infantry of the past, making it more dependent on uninterrupted supplies

• The huge stress of 24-hour, continuous combat will do more damage to the effectiveness of infantry than direct battle casualties

These arguments can be countered thus:

• A man on foot is far less conspicuous than a vehicle; with modern firepower and small-group tactics he will be able to infiltrate enemy lines to cause great destruction

• IFVs now lend high mobility and heavy armament to each individual infantry squad

• Constantly improving personal armour gives the infantryman enhanced protection

• Improved engineering techniques allow infantry fortifications to be built faster and better than ever

COMBAT ENGINEERING

The sappers (military engineers) gained their name from their original task: 'sapping', or undermining and blowing up, fortifications on behalf of besieging armies. Now their job in the attack is to open the route, improve roads, breach enemy minefields, destroy obstacles and build bridges. In defence, too, it is the engineers who will choose and prepare the position, constructing (or at least, directing the building of) its fortifications, laying out its mines and obstacles, wrecking its approach roads and demolishing key bridges.

Below: Bridging operations are the task most frequently undertaken by combat engineers. These men of the United States Army are maneuvering pontoon sections into place to negotiate a major obstacle

A ir forces, too, need engineers – to repair cratered runways and to build refuelling facilities at forward airstrips, as they did for British Harrier jets in the 1982 Falklands campaign. With hindsight, we can see that had the Argentines used their engineers as effectively, their air force could have based its attack aircraft at Stanley, so increasing their loiter time by a factor of four, with potentially devastating results.

The engineers' business is to change the very landscape of the battlefield if necessary, to channel the direction and shape of combat. Their role is so important that parts of it often spill over into other arms that are not specialised as engineers. For example, mine rollers and scissors bridges are carried by tanks that sappers man but which travel with armoured columns. Artillery or helicopter forces can scatter mines, and crossroads – and even major highways – are kept open by military police. For the sake of convenience in the present chapter all engineer-related tasks will be considered together, and treated as part of an overall 'engineer' approach to the battlefield.

Above: Most bridges will have been destroyed by enemy forces as they fall back. Here, sappers have installed charges which will be detonated remotely as and when the position becomes untenable

Left: While much bridge building is now performed at least semi-automatically, there is still a great deal of hard physical labour to be done

Another problem of definition is that in some – generally conscript – armies the duties of the engineers have been deliberately fragmented. Certain armies make the distinction between 'offensive' (or 'mobility') engineering and 'defensive' (or 'counter-mobility') engineering. Other armies divide their engineers on a rather different basis – into front-line 'combat pioneers' and rear-echelon 'construction troops'.

These arrangements aim to ensure that each type of engineer will immediately have available the specialised skills and equipment he needs for the particular task in hand, and will be able to deploy them very rapidly. They have the corresponding disadvantage of inflexibility. When circumstances

demand that task-trained engineers cross over into other areas of specialisation, they often find it hard to adapt themselves to unfamiliar jobs, and may not have the right equipment readily to hand.

Generally, however, the majority of engineers are ready to turn their hand to anything. This versatility allows them to switch back and forth between offensive and defensive tasks, or between pioneering and construction, according to the dynamics of the battle. They keep a big 'golf bag' of skills and equipment from which they can select the most appropriate 'club' for the task at hand. The problem is that responsiveness may be impaired, and time lost, while a particular 'club' – which means equip-

RESERVE BRIDGE DEMOLITIONS

The first rule of reserve bridge demolition is to clear and then garrison the surrounding area, making sure that all ground, air and water-borne approaches to the objective are carefully watched. The garrison's task is to prevent the enemy seizing the bridge by *coup de main* before it can be demolished. The German offensive into Holland in 1940, for example, included a flying-boat seizure of a key bridge in central Rotterdam, and the US offensive to the Rhine in March 1945 included an armoured infantry seizure of the rail bridge at Remagen. Securing a bridge effectively *always* requires an all-arms effort, and that means protecting against attacks from aircraft, helicopters, armour, infantry and frogmen.

The next task is to wire up the bridge itself for demolition. Timing is of the essence. The bridge must not be blown too soon, because friendly troops may be stranded on the far side or imminent operations across it may be prevented; and it must not be blown too late, because the enemy may arrive in force to seize it. To make sure nothing can interfere, the engineer responsible for blowing the

bridge must remain in close contact with the senior officer responsible for running the general battle.

When the time comes, all friendly troops – including the bridge garrisons – must first be withdrawn from the far bank. This may well prove difficult, since they may be in contact with the enemy, and find it difficult to respond to an order that is at once peremptory, immediate and overriding.

Examples of successful bridge-blowing operations are the demolition of the Obercaeral Bridge on the Rhine, as US troops approached on 2 March 1945, and the destruction of the Arnhem rail bridge in front of 2 Para on 17 September 1944. Such operations do not always go according to plan, however, as the failures at the Sittang Bridge in Burma in February 1942 and at the Remagen Bridge on the Rhine in March 1945 illustrate.

Timing is everything, and the success or failure of the whole operation may easily hang on a split-second decision. The key personnel must be both competent and confident – the middle of a withdrawal is no time for hesitation.

RESERVE BRIDGE DEMOLITION

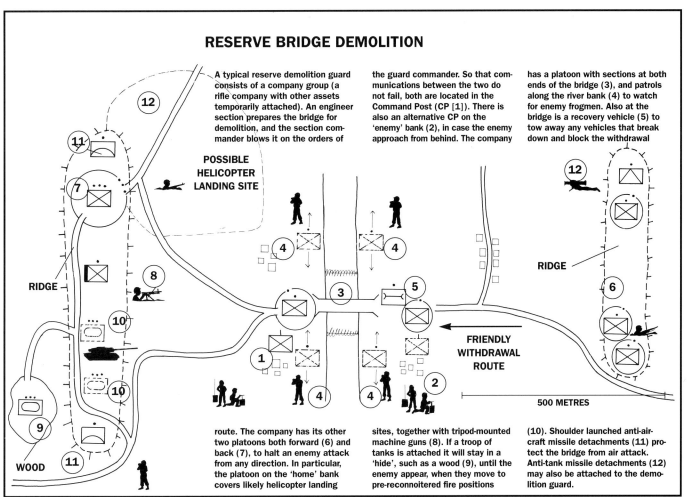

A typical reserve demolition guard consists of a company group (a rifle company with other assets temporarily attached). An engineer section prepares the bridge for demolition, and the section commander blows it on the orders of the guard commander. So that communications between the two do not fail, both are located in the Command Post (CP [1]). There is also an alternative CP on the 'enemy' bank (2), in case the enemy approach from behind. The company has a platoon with sections at both ends of the bridge (3), and patrols along the river bank (4) to watch for enemy frogmen. Also at the bridge is a recovery vehicle (5) to tow away any vehicles that break down and block the withdrawal route. The company has its other two platoons both forward (6) and back (7), to halt an enemy attack from any direction. In particular, the platoon on the 'home' bank covers likely helicopter landing sites, together with tripod-mounted machine guns (8). If a troop of tanks is attached it will stay in a 'hide', such as a wood (9), until the enemy appear, when they move to pre-reconnoitered fire positions (10). Shoulder launched anti-aircraft missile detachments (11) protect the bridge from air attack. Anti-tank missile detachments (12) may also be attached to the demolition guard.

WAYS OF LAYING MINES

With the mine plough (A), the mine passes down a conveyor belt (2), where it is fuzed and then fed into a furrow made by a plough at the front of the trailer (3). Two discs at the back of the trailer then cover the mine with earth (4), and a trailing chain smoothes over the top.

Artillery can deliver instant mine-fields up to 30km behind enemy lines or in front of an attacking enemy, but the mines are small

DELIVERY ROCKET

MINES

ENEMY ARMOURED COLUMN

For even faster laying of minefields, mines can be fired from projectors on helicopters and vehicles, but these are smaller than those laid by ploughs

The simplest, and slowest, way to lay mines is by hand. This usually ensures the best concealment

ment rather than men in this context – is selected and brought into play. On the fast-moving battlefield of the future this shortcoming promises to be extremely serious, as the engineers will find it hard to get sufficient advance warning of future tasks.

The over-riding question is whether or not future 'defensive' engineers will be able to obstruct and block battlefield movement so effectively that operations will cease to be fast moving at all. Will the 'offensive' engineers be able to maintain momentum? Or will they find the sheer scale of obstacles so great that the battle bogs down into immobility, as it did in World War I, in Normandy and in the Iran-Iraq War of the 1980s? It appears that the capacity of engineers to construct obstacles is increasing faster than the capacity of engineers to overcome them. If present trends are projected into the future, therefore, the engineers will become truly 'the decisive arm', insofar as they will be able to make the battlefield all but impassable. This will certainly be so if tracked or wheeled vehicles continue to be the main instruments of future mobility, for such vehicles are the engineers' primary victims and are especially vulnerable to obstacles and mines.

The helicopter, skipping blithely over the traps laid for terrestrial vehicles, is largely immune to engineering 'solutions'. However, it is worth remembering that even in the 1960s, the Viet Cong were already laying anti-helicopter 'windmill' mines

Right: Men of the Royal Engineers operating a bar mine laying vehicle reckon to install up to 600 mines an hour by this method, which has the advantage of placing the munitions in exactly the desired position. On top of the vehicle is a mine-scattering device which operates even faster, but less precisely

Below: Most engineering vehicles are optimised for more than one task. The combat engineering vehicle on the left is fitted with a mine plough and mounts a short-barrelled demolition gun, while the mobile bridge unit is also equipped with a plough

around probable US LZs. These mines are equipped with a small propellor on a vertically-mounted shaft that starts to turn only when there is a strong down-draught, such as that created by the rotors of a helicopter. The rotation of the blade triggers the mine. Another approach was to booby-trap corrugated metal sheets laid out on likely LZs. For the moment, though, the helicopter has tactical problems of its own. It's not yet in a position to seriously challenge tanks and IFVs for the title of primary battle vehicle.

Most combat engineering tasks can be accomplished with civilian tools

Back on the ground, it is clear that civilian earth-moving plant has obvious uses in military engineering operations – particularly in a war fought within a developed nation. There are specialised military machines of this type, such as the British combat engineering tractor (CET) and the US Rome Plow, a bulldozer used in Vietnam to cut away jungle cover alongside roads, but a quick look around today's motorway construction sites or major housing developments reveals that modern civil engineers use vast amounts of heavy-duty earth-moving and landscaping equipment. Today the countryside is positively littered with powerful machines, such as back-hoes, graders, diggers, motor shovels and – especially – bulldozers, with which even a few men can move and re-distribute tonnes of earth in a short space of time. Almost all of these machines would be requisitioned on a battlefield of the future, and deployed within only a few days, building successive layers of anti-tank ditches, fire positions and strongpoints ahead of an attacking enemy spearhead.

The simple anti-tank ditch has not lost its attraction, since the tank's ability to cross such obstacles

has improved not at all since 1916. If anything, the opposite is true, for the tanks of World War I were, after all, specifically designed for that task.

Provided effective fire covers the physical obstacle, the would-be assailant can be prevented from bringing forward his own engineer plant to bridge, fill or breach the gap. A dramatic illustration of this was provided on the Golan heights in 1973, where an Israeli anti-tank ditch halted Syrian armour. When the Syrians brought forward scissors bridges to cross the gap, they quickly became priority targets. Then, when one of the bridges was actually established, it had the effect of drawing all the tanks towards it, thus channelling them into a narrow area that rapidly became a killing zone.

Even quite small obstacles, covered by fire, present a huge problem

Of course, things are not always that simple. Also in the October 1973 War, first the Egyptians (on 9 October) and then the Israelis (on 15/16 October) crossed the much bigger anti-tank obstacle of the Suez Canal. In neither case, however, did the defenders cover the crossing sites effectively with fire. The Egyptian operation at the very start of the war was able to exploit strategic surprise, massive fire superiority and the poor positioning of defending strongpoints in the Bar Lev Line.

Above: The cheapest way to clear and neutralise mines is by hand. Metal detectors have been in use for almost 50 years, but the new generation of mines have so few metal parts that they are undetectable by these means

Right: It's a simple enough matter to fit MTBs with mine ploughs, and use them to clear a way through anti-personnel minefields for an infantry advance. They are even effective against the older types of anti-tank mine

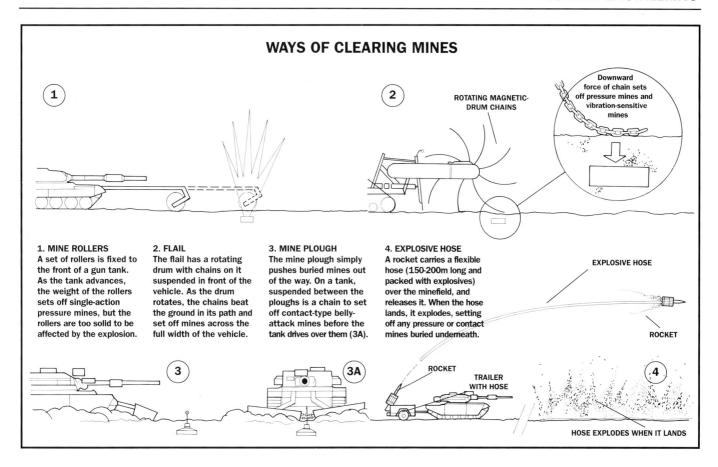

WAYS OF CLEARING MINES

1. MINE ROLLERS
A set of rollers is fixed to the front of a gun tank. As the tank advances, the weight of the rollers sets off single-action pressure mines, but the rollers are too solid to be affected by the explosion.

2. FLAIL
The flail has a rotating drum with chains on it suspended in front of the vehicle. As the drum rotates, the chains beat the ground in its path and set off mines across the full width of the vehicle.

3. MINE PLOUGH
The mine plough simply pushes buried mines out of the way. On a tank, suspended between the ploughs is a chain to set off contact-type belly-attack mines before the tank drives over them (3A).

4. EXPLOSIVE HOSE
A rocket carries a flexible hose (150-200m long and packed with explosives) over the minefield, and releases it. When the hose lands, it explodes, setting off any pressure or contact mines buried underneath.

ROTATING MAGNETIC-DRUM CHAINS

Downward force of chain sets off pressure mines and vibration-sensitive mines

EXPLOSIVE HOSE

ROCKET

ROCKET

TRAILER WITH HOSE

HOSE EXPLODES WHEN IT LANDS

When it came to the Israelis' turn, 10 days later, there was certainly greater apparent urgency about the operation, but even though the crossing site itself was still undefended by Egyptian troops on the ground, the cumbersome bridge came very close to being destroyed by enemy shelling during its vulnerable approach march. If the Israeli operation had encountered even slightly more active opposition, it would surely have failed. So although both sides successfully managed to cross the Suez Canal in 1973, it is clear that water obstacles still retain their traditional position as a major impediment to armoured mobility. As well as demanding complex engineering solutions, they funnel advancing troops and vehicles into a defined area that quickly becomes a killing ground.

Water obstacles, either natural or man-made, are the most effective

The idea of swimming or 'schnorkelling' with armoured vehicles, pioneered in World War II, gained further ground after the war as an alternative to bridging, but seems to be in decline, since it is now apparent just how cumbersome, complicated –

Below: When all else fails, the infantryman will be expected to clear a way through minefields literally by hand, searching in front of him with a probe – such as his bayonet – and then unearthing the munition for subsequent destruction or re-use. This method, however, can be very dangerous, as some of today's mines have anti-tilt and anti-lifting devices

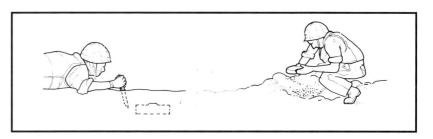

TREE BLOWDOWNS

Small demolition charges or judicious use of the chain saw can drop trees very quickly, creating major obstacles in forest areas and wooded or *bocage* countryside. Similarly, cratering charges soon render roads impassable, and a little firepower easily keeps them that way.

Both tanks and IFVs can often negotiate forest and woodland quite effectively, but well-sited expedient obstacles can equally stop them dead. In Vietnam, especially, the Americans started out regarding the jungle as 'off limits' to armoured forces, but soon found that even though armoured 'punches' were out of the question, much of the terrain was passable to single tanks and ACAVs. In contrast, the Soviet Army has long sought to exploit terrain that appears impassable, but that may only be extremely difficult. The Red Army can be expected to push tanks through deep forest as a matter of course, and so defending engineers must be equipped to use the forest's own resources to create effective obstacles. Siting the obstacle is as important as the block itself; there's no point in dropping trees or cratering the road if a simple diversion is possible. A road passing between earth banks is an obvious target for cratering, and if there are trees growing on the banks, so much the better. Dropping them over the craters makes the engineers' job considerably more than twice as difficult.

Most bridgeable obstacles are small enough to be covered in a single span. Above: The double span of the FV4205 AVLB (Armoured Vehicle Laying Bridge) extending bridge allows vehicles of up to 54 tons to cross obstacles in just minutes

Left: The US M60 AVLB (Advanced Vehicle Launched Bridge) can be positioned even more rapidly to span narrower ditches. The tank chassis is manoeuvred into the ditch and the accompanying vehicles simply drive over it

and dangerous – it can be in practice. Even light shrapnel can rip apart flotation screens, while the demands of amphibious operation greatly distorts a vehicle's suitability for its original purpose. Worst of all is the problem of finding gently sloping ingress and egress sites. It is more often the sharp profile of a river or canal's banks, rather than its width, that makes it difficult to cross. And where nature does not provide such natural defences, there are the engineers, always ready to make good the deficit.

Combining two sorts of obstacles more than doubles the effect

Nevertheless, bridging and ferrying techniques have certainly improved since 1945 – not least in the Soviet Army, whose rapidly laid and flexible PMP pontoon equipment the Egyptians used to such excellent effect in 1973. All armies that may have to operate in theatres criss-crossed by waterways are well equipped with assault boats and a wide range of ferries, allowing them to mount *coup de main* crossings by relatively small forces very quickly. Furthermore, if it is accepted that artillery capabilities all round have improved in recent years, then preparatory fire to help seize a bridgehead, and defensive fires to help hold it, will be that much more effective. (It is also true, of course, that the same advances in artillery technology on

stop here. The very best obstacles to an attacker consist not just of wire, mines, ditches, water obstacles or tree blowdowns, but of a combination of them all. An attacker caught in a maze of all these obstructions will have to bring up all the correct engineering counter-measures, in the right order, to deal with them properly – an exponentially more difficult task than dealing with any one obstacle by itself.

The engineers' preparation of the battlefield goes far beyond building obstacles. In their successful 1973 battle on the Golan Heights, the Israelis benefited enormously from preparing their own tanks' fighting ground with the help of bulldozers. Each tank was dug a series of scrapes, in one of which it would begin the battle lurking turret down (not unlike the 'wild rabbit' tanks that were dug into the British defences of March 1918). When fighting began, each tank would fire from its cover, then move to one of its alternative scrapes – thereby combining mobility with field fortification.

Armoured bulldozers accompany the tanks on to the battlefield

The US M1 Abrams MBT is accompanied in the field by fast armoured bulldozers that are specifically designed to provide similar fieldworks almost on demand. This shrewd American initiative thus institutionalises the greatly increased potential of engineer work on the modern battlefield. It at last promotes the bulldozer to an integral role in the armoured combat team, and implies that earthmoving is every bit as important as firepower.

Buildings, too, provide both cover and protection. It's a simple matter for a tank to push through

the opposing side will make both crossing points and boats more hazardous than ever.)

Waterways remain disproportionately easy to defend, provided that existing bridges can be demolished in good time. There are two basic kinds of tactical demolition work. The first is preliminary demolition, which helps create obstacles to an enemy advance (and can help channel it into a killing zone of the defender's own choosing) and should be complete before battle is actually joined. The second is reserve demolition, in which engineers prepare bridges, buildings and so on for blowing up, but actually destroy them only in response to a tactical need or as a last resort.

Once battle is joined the most important rule of all seems to be that communication must be maintained between higher operational commanders and the engineers responsible for the demolition itself. As radio communications are likely to be seriously degraded in future warfare, it is increasingly doubtful whether tactical demolitions will be timely and effective, if only because of the difficulty in transmitting the destruction order. This apart, the increasing physical power of modern explosives will be an advantage in dealing with old, solidly built, stone bridges and modern concrete ones (the physical strength of modern steel and suspension bridges is a matter of design, not materials)

The power of defensive engineering does not

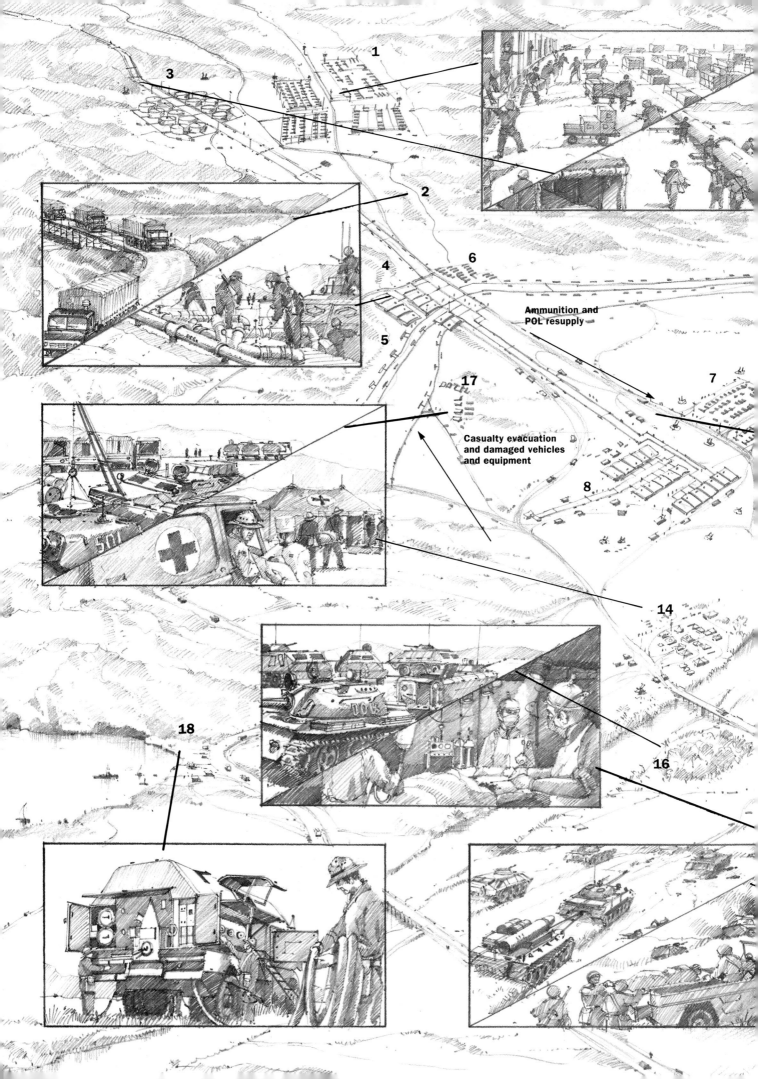

1

3

2

4

5

6

Ammunition and
POL resupply

7

17

Casualty evacuation
and damaged vehicles
and equipment

14

8

18

16

THE LOGISTICS CHAIN

A modern army needs a steady flow of ammunition, POL (Petrol, Oil and Lubricants), spares, rations and medical supplies sent up to the front-line troops, who need to send their casualties and damaged vehicles and equipment back to the rear for treatment and repair. In the Soviet army each level of command sends supplies to its subordinate units as it sees fit, pushing forward supplies to those units which are advancing rapidly, and all but neglecting those which are not doing so well. Supplies are usually sent to the theatre of operations or army group (known in the Soviet army as a "front") by ship, train or (to a limited extent) by aircraft. They are unloaded at the front-level-supply base (1) (150-200km behind the front line) and transferred to trucks for the move forward (2). If possible, front-level supply bases receive their POL through pipelines (3), and special construction brigades build pipelines forward (4) to supply the army-level (equivalent to British and US "corps") supply bases (5), where POL is stored in flexible blivets (plastic storage tanks). Each army has two to three of these POL depots, and one or two ammunition depots (6), all 50-100km behind the front line. From here, 5-15 ton trucks carry the ammunition forward to the divisional supply bases (7), 25-30Km behind the front line. Mobile pipeline-laying units may be able to extend a pipeline to the POL depots of each of the 3-5 divisions in an army, otherwise the POL will go by tanker. These depots are also 25-40km behind the front line (8). From these depots, ammunition is ferried forward to regimental, battalion and company ammo points by 3-5 ton trucks. Artillery is a particularly voracious consumer of ammuntion (10). The POL transport company of the divisional transport battalion ferries fuel forward to the four regimental POL points, one of which is shown at (11). Both ammo and POL supply points are 10-15km behind the front line.

Battalion vehicles evacuate wounded from the battlefield (12), back to a battalion aid post, and from there to a regimental aid post (13), 6-10km behind the front line. Here emergency surgery improves on the very limited work that the battalion aid post can do. The regimental aid post also classifies casualties for further evacuation, with those that are likely to survive going back by ambulance to MASH (Mobile Army Surgical Hospitals) (10-14km behind the front line) or divisional field hospitals (14).

Damaged vehicles receive a similar rearward evacuation. ARVs (Armoured Recovery Vehicles) of the battalion pull them out of battle (15). ARVs are usually based on tank hulls, and take the damaged vehicles back to a battalion repair point. If a vehicle cannot be repaired quickly (30-60min, in action), battalion vehicles take it to a regimental collection point. From there, regimental vehicles tow it back to a regimental repair point (16), about 15km behind the front line. If regimental assets cannot repair the vehicle, then it is taken back to a divisional collection point. From there, divisional vehicles take it back to a divisional repair point, 25-40km behind the front line (17). This is repeated up the chain of command.

Supplying water to front-line troops can be a logistical nightmare in desert conditions, and the Soviet engineers have a variety of water-drilling, desalination, purification and chlorination vehicles (18).

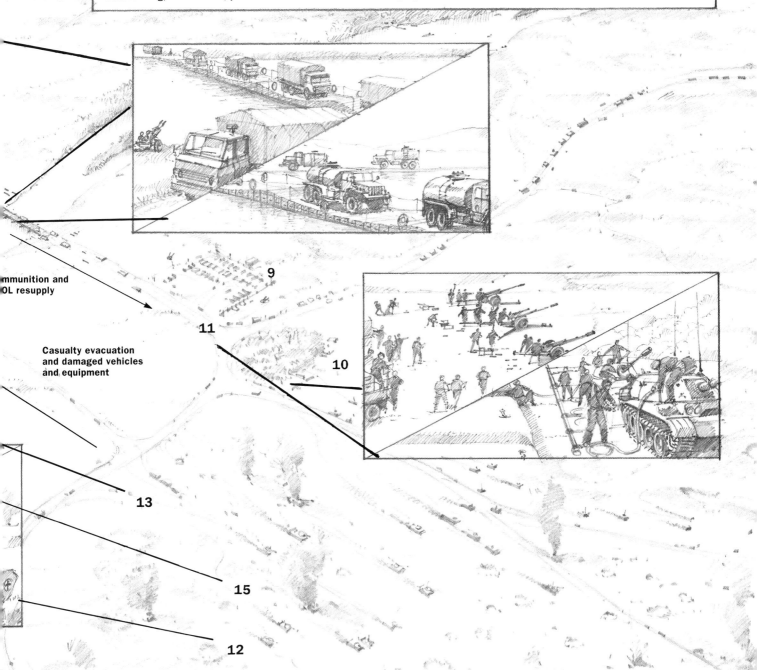

ammunition and
POL resupply

Casualty evacuation
and damaged vehicles
and equipment

9

11

10

13

15

12

EXPLODING UNDERGROUND HOSEPIPE DITCHES

One proposed 'non-provocative defence' for NATO is the preparation of a latent anti-tank ditch along frontier lines, similar to some of the demolitions prepared under British airfields in 1940. Empty pipes would be buried underground and connected to pumping stations full of liquid explosive slurry. In peacetime the system would be invisible and safe, and would interfere very little with agriculture. On the outbreak of hostilities the pipes would be filled with the explosive, then detonated. An instant anti-tank ditch would be created that linked into a system that could well stretch for hundreds of kilometres. All it would need then is a garrison, mines and firepower protection.

The chief weakness of this concept is that the enemy would surely identify it during construction, and would target it for early attack.

Above: In the fierce fighting behind the Normandy beachhead, German elite units made good use of expedient obstacles, littering the streets of towns and villages with rubble interlaced with damaged vehicles and felled trees

the rear wall of a house, using the intact facades as cover. There will probably even be ready-made fire apertures. Even when such surgical conversion of local buildings is impossible, the plentiful and instant supply of rubble from a totally collapsed house can be quickly moulded into an AFV nest that is just as good as a tank scrape or artillery berm dug from bare earth.

Defensive engineering operations are often planned long in advance

Building infantry fortifications on the future battlefield will be faster than ever, partly due to the increased availability of plant and materiel in situ, but also because military engineers have adopted the prefabricated building as enthusiastically as their civilian counterparts. Entire command bunkers may be brought up on lorries, then lifted into holes in the ground and covered with earth. Even the lowly infantryman benefits: there are ready-made roofing sections for trenches, on which earth may be quickly spread to provide overhead cover.

Manned anti-tank ditches and their associated fieldworks still have a lot to offer the defender, but

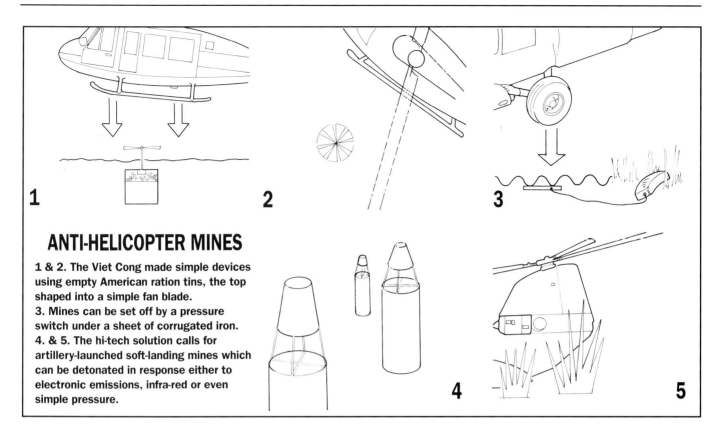

ANTI-HELICOPTER MINES

1 & 2. The Viet Cong made simple devices using empty American ration tins, the top shaped into a simple fan blade.
3. Mines can be set off by a pressure switch under a sheet of corrugated iron.
4. & 5. The hi-tech solution calls for artillery-launched soft-landing mines which can be detonated in response either to electronic emissions, infra-red or even simple pressure.

Not all Sapper tasks are carried out on the battlefield. Static installations, such as the fuel supply to Gibraltar (below) are also the Engineers' responsibility

even with modern techniques and machinery, they take a long time to build. They are not the work of a few minutes, like an air-delivered scattered minefield, or of a few hours, like a more formal minefield or an obstacle constructed of blown down trees. A light wheeled tractor (LWT) will dig out earth at a rate of only about 25m³ an hour; a combat engineer tractor (CET) will do the job about three times as fast. But these works need supporting minefields and bunkers to protect their defenders. Each of

these greatly increases the number of engineer tasks involved, which ties up precious engineer resources and stretches their tactical responsiveness.

Full-blown anti-tank lines must therefore be planned many hours or even days in advance. This is not ideal in a fluid battle of manoeuvre, least of all when enemy surveillance can detect the field-works in plenty of time to change the axes of advancing armoured spearheads. Given the newly-acquired long range accuracy of modern artillery weapons, the engineers constructing such lines will surely come under early attack, even many miles behind the front line. Just like the infantry, they will need greater armour protection for their vehicles, and a new approach to camouflage.

Fixed defensive installations are obvious targets

There is much to be said for making extensive engineer preparation of the battlefield before hostilities actually start, but the suspicion of anything that promises to act like the Maginot Line of 1940 or the Bar Lev Line of 1973 – both of which were fixed systems of obstacles and fortifications that had been fully mapped by the enemy, and were relatively expensive to garrison – still lingers. Static linear defences have acquired a bad name for these good reasons, and there is now further opposition to them from the general public: their power to disfigure the landscape is quite awesome, and is less acceptable in peacetime than it has ever been.

In theory, however, such defences should still offer a great deal of additional security, and at the least have the important effect of delaying an attacker. All they seem to need is adequate man-power and firepower to cover the obstacles, and an operational doctrine that sees the works as part of a mobile, rather than of an entirely static, battle. When the Germans made their famous outflanking march around the Maginot Line in May and June 1940, their victory owed much more to failures by the Anglo-French mobile forces in Belgium than to failures by the French engineers who built the fortifications. The very fact that the Germans chose to outflank the line, instead of assaulting it, is the sincerest possible tribute to its intrinsic strength.

Roads are much more difficult to mine quickly than open country

Defensive engineer preparations may legitimately be seen as 'non-provocative' or 'non-aggressive'. Even in periods of high tension they are no more than symbolically threatening, insomuch as they act only against an aggressor's desire to 'get his retaliation in first'. Conversely, offensive engineer preparations – those that seek to open highways into the very heart of a potential enemy's defences – must fall into a quite different category, since, like tanks, helicopters and rockets, they imply a projection of power into his territory.

Mines fall somewhere between 'defensive' and 'offensive' engineer preparations. They are defensive insofar as they help to hold ground, but edge into the offensive to the extent that they can now be laid rapidly, and hence enjoy a certain measure of 'mobility'. Modern minefields can be carried by advancing spearheads, and then quickly put down to secure the flanks or prevent a counter-thrust. By the same token, however, a defending force may also lay them quickly in front of an attacking spearhead, to buy time while the defence is consolidated. In both cases, the purpose of the minefield is to slow down the battle and bog it into the mire.

Engineers, with their specialised heavy plant and equipment, are often called in to help with even mundane maintenance tasks.
Right: A combat engineering tractor uses its jib to extract the engine from an APC

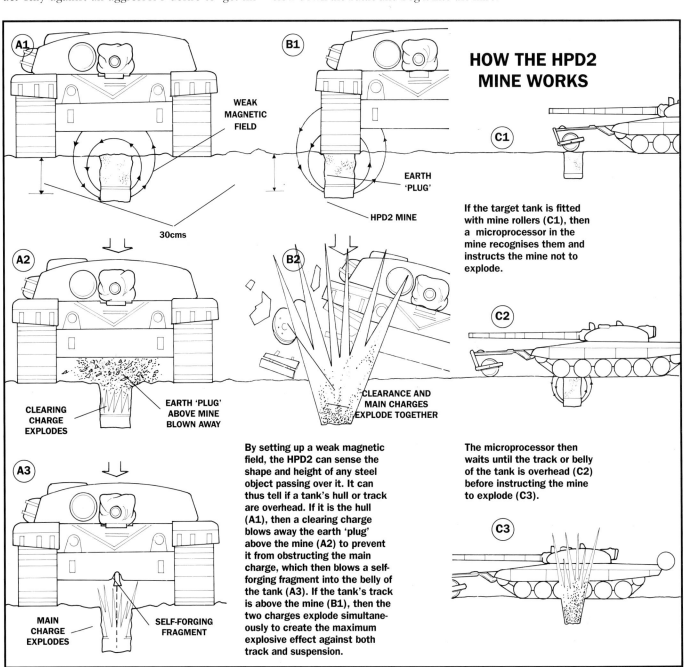

A1

WEAK MAGNETIC FIELD

30cms

A2

CLEARING CHARGE EXPLODES

EARTH 'PLUG' ABOVE MINE BLOWN AWAY

A3

MAIN CHARGE EXPLODES

SELF-FORGING FRAGMENT

B1

EARTH 'PLUG'

HPD2 MINE

B2

CLEARANCE AND MAIN CHARGES EXPLODE TOGETHER

HOW THE HPD2 MINE WORKS

C1

If the target tank is fitted with mine rollers (C1), then a microprocessor in the mine recognises them and instructs the mine not to explode.

C2

The microprocessor then waits until the track or belly of the tank is overhead (C2) before instructing the mine to explode (C3).

C3

By setting up a weak magnetic field, the HPD2 can sense the shape and height of any steel object passing over it. It can thus tell if a tank's hull or track are overhead. If it is the hull (A1), then a clearing charge blows away the earth 'plug' above the mine (A2) to prevent it from obstructing the main charge, which then blows a self-forging fragment into the belly of the tank (A3). If the tank's track is above the mine (B1), then the two charges explode simultaneously to create the maximum explosive effect against both track and suspension.

The smallest devices of all are remotely deployed mines (RDMs). These are scatterable anti-tank and anti-personnel mines, and can be laid by engineer projectors, fired from field guns, scattered from rockets or dropped from helicopters. They are by far the fastest mines to lay, but their method of delivery does not allow them to be dug in. They also have the embarrassing habit, for a route-denial weapon, of bouncing off concrete or tarmac road surfaces, and they can easily be seen if they do not. On metalled roads this renders them almost entirely useless, but they are wickedly effective in soft ground such as sandy desert, and in vegetation or crops, as is demonstrated by the massive toll of casualties – men, women, and children alike – that they took during 10 years of fighting in Afghanistan.

The current types of scatterable mine should really be regarded as grenades with sophisticated fusing. No bigger than a tennis ball, and not yet fully effective against armour, they are capable of blowing the tracks off a tank and wrecking its suspension. Even today, as a quick-reaction answer to armoured breakthroughs, such mines have massive potential, which promises to revolutionise not just mine warfare but the whole shape of the battlefield.

The next largest mines are the anti-personnel weapons that can be dug in by hand. They are capable of being laid very quickly and efficiently – perhaps 3000 mines supplied by a single vehicle can be sown in a night by a platoon of infantry or troop of engineers.

Some mines are very smart indeed. This anti-tank mine (below) can be pre-programmed to tell one type of vehicle from another from its electro-magnetic emissions

After these relatively small devices come the real tankbusters, which weigh between eight and 15 kilogrammes. Just one is fully capable of destroying anything on tracks, and a platoon or troop can dig in between 500 and 1000 of these in a night. The World War II experience on all battle fronts showed that the supply of mines tended to run out before the opportunities to use them, and in future wars it may well be this purely logistic factor that prevents mine weapons from fulfilling their potential. Many modern AT mines do at least incorporate features that allow them to be dug up and relocated should the combat zone move away from their original site.

Conventional AT mines were already playing a major part in moulding the battlefields of 1942-45, as much through fear of them even when they were not present as by the damage they caused when they were. Not that there was any shortage of them in reality. The Red Army laid 222 million mines in the course of the war, and in north west Europe they caused 22 per cent of all tank casualties. In Vietnam, they accounted for 73 per cent of tank casualties.

Mines were the Falklands infantryman's worst enemy

And now conventional mines have been joined in the armoury by a number of more advanced systems that use automated techniques. The British bar-mine layer, for example, is an armoured vehicle that buries mines at the rate of about 10 per minute. Such automatic distribution methods are admittedly less effective than doing the job by hand, but the sheer volume of ordnance that can be employed more than makes up for that shortcoming.

The simplest solution is often best – don't look for mines

More discriminating mines are also coming into service. A small camouflaged plastic suitcase resting inoffensively behind a clump of wayside bracken may now be able to distinguish between passing M113 APCs or ACAVs, and M1 Abrams tanks. Still more frightening, it may even be able to spot the difference between the infantry version of the M113 and the command post M577A1 version of the very same vehicle. Even then, it may have been told to wait for a second echelon, and go for a deeper target. Once it has identified its optimum victim, whatever it may be, it will unleash a devastating volley of white-hot self-forging fragments.

An example of such a weapon is the extended-range anti-armour munition (ERAM), which responds to the IR and heat signature of a tank to 'pop up' two Skeet sub-munitions that then go for 'top-armour attack'. The lethal collaboration of the microchip, the bombmaker and the armoured engineer promises to scatter the battlefield with automated booby traps like these to such an extent that

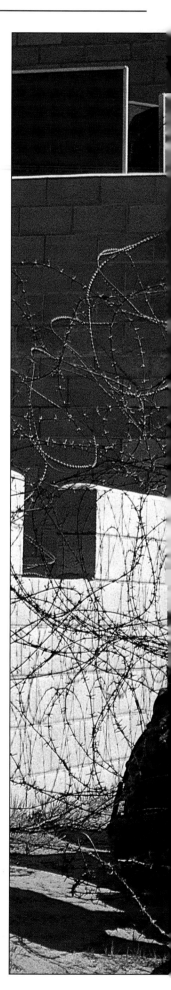

Right: Even the ubiquitous barbed-wire entanglement is a murderous obstacle if it can be covered by fire. This mixed force of US 82nd Airborne and Britons from 2 Para are bogged down in their attempts to clear the houses of a small town by a relatively shallow band of wire

Left: Speed is of the essence if you want to stay alive in FIBUA. This three-man house-clearing team will perform formation acrobatics, even though heavily laden with kit, to cut the time during which they are exposed

no-one will be able to move and survive unless very greatly improved countermeasures can be found.

To defeat mines, engineers have traditionally used metal detectors – but the modern mine is often non-metallic and therefore impossible to locate by this means. Prodders or bayonets are more effective in this case, but their use is enormously time-consuming. Tank forces use mine rollers and flails – but the new discriminating mines will not necessarily be affected by such treatment. One advanced solution is to use a fuel-air explosive barrage that will detonate large areas of mines by massive overpressure, such as the 30-tube US surface-launched fuel-air explosive (SLUFAE) system, designed to make gaps in mine belts at ranges up to 1km.

WILL ENGINEERS MAKE THE BATTLEFIELD IMPASSABLE?

Engineers can turn the battlefield into one huge traffic jam, say some. Their reasons:

- The increasing availability of advanced earthmoving equipment and pre-fabricated bunker structures

- The increase in urbanised areas makes it easier to find cover and obstacles that the engineers can improve

- New scatterable mine systems and automatic minelaying devices will be deployed at unprecedentedly short notice to counter enemy advances

- Smart mines will pick and choose their targets, adding elements of surprise and unpredictability to apparently safe routes

The counter argument says:

- Improved mobile bridging and ferrying systems will outwit engineer obstacles

- Increased air-mobility will let infantry and even medium artillery fly over obstacles

- Better anti-mine equipment, including FAEs, will let attacking columns move swiftly through minefields

- A fast-moving battle would not leave the engineers time to prepare the terrain against attackers

- Engineers working in depth will be under increased threat from long-range weapons, which will prevent them doing their job properly

CASUALTIES AND REFUGEES

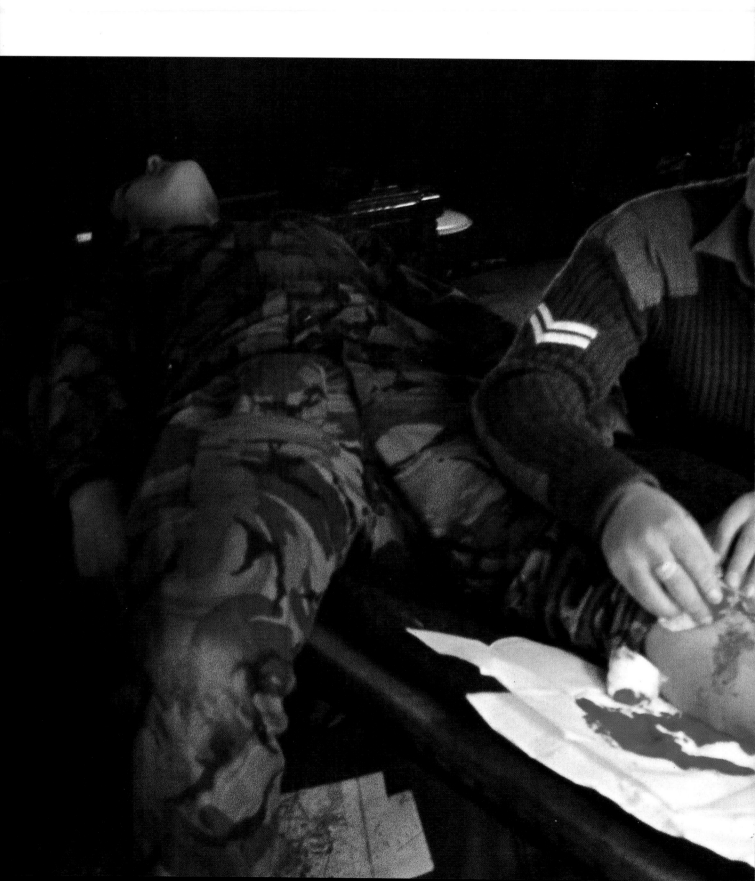

The 18th-century Prussian military theorist General Karl von Clausewitz taught that war is 'the continuation of politics by other means' – in other words, war is primarily about the resolution of political differences, and knows no limitations. As such it can easily degenerate in practice into mass killing. This in turn may spill out beyond the boundaries of the military battlefield altogether, producing vast numbers of civilian casualties and even more refugees.

Below: Military medicine is a very specialised branch of the science. As well as wounds occasioned as a result of fighting, huge numbers of accident victims also have to be treated

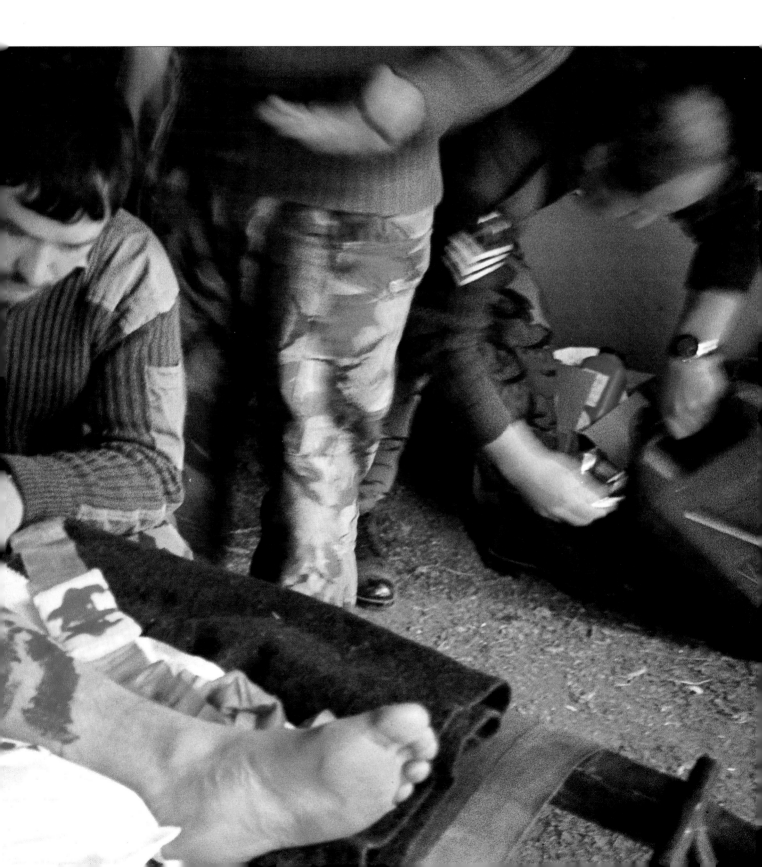

Above: It is extremely difficult to treat a casualty effectively on the field of battle – all the combat medic tries to do is immobilise the wounded part to prevent further trauma, make the patient as comfortable as possible and call for evacuation. However, such have been the advances in evacuation procedures following the development of the helicopter, that the casualty's chances of survival are far greater than they were even 30 years ago

Even such seemingly simple concepts as 'key military terrain', or 'ground of tactical importance', are themselves crammed with unstated assumptions about the people who may happen to live on the terrain in question. What is merely 'high ground' to the soldier may perhaps turn out to be a bare hillside far from habitation – but it may equally turn out to be an irreplaceable jewel of a medieval monastery, as happened at Monte Cassino in 1944. Alternatively it may be a less celebrated but more heavily populated site; a school, perhaps, or a hospital.

Any sort of fighting in built-up areas (FIBUA) – as in Caen in 1944, Stalingrad in 1943, Hue in 1968, Khorramshar in 1980 or Beirut in 1982 – automatically results in enormous numbers of civilians killed, wounded and missing. Interdiction bombing or shelling against bridges, or installations sited in built-up areas will usually have the same effect. Only precision-guided munitions (PGMs), such as the 'smart' laser-guided bombs and electro-optical guided bombs that destroyed the Thanh Hoa and Paul Doumer bridges in North Vietnam in April and May 1972 promise to reduce the civilian death toll.

We can take some comfort from the fact that modern warheads tend to be smaller and far more discriminating than the immense, but scarcely-aimed, showers of HE and incendiaries that were so prolifically scattered across European cities during World War II. We are fast approaching a time when hyper-accurate, tailor-made aerial weapons will be able to search around any given grid-square, and then hit a specific point target with surgical precision. Manual guidance methods have already achieved that sort of accuracy on occasion: on 18 February 1942, specialist crews flew a handful of Mosquitoes on a low-level mission to blast away a precise section of the walls around Amiens prison to release members of the French Resistance. In 1973, Israeli F4 Phantom jets were able to make a pinpoint attack on the Damascus Ministry of Defence building, and on 7 June 1981, the IAF destroyed an Iraqi nuclear reactor outside Baghdad.

While such accuracy is rare in the world of aerial bombardment, it may yet become commonplace. The new microchip-equipped target-homing munitions promise to be yet more discriminating than the most expert aircrew, and may lead to an almost complete avoidance of civilian casualties.

FIBUA automatically results in enormous civilian casualties

On the other hand, current plans for Emerging Technology (ET) cluster weapons, which spread hundreds of bomblets, mines and/or terminally-homing anti-tank 'pucks' all over every 'potential deep choke point', will have exactly the opposite effect. Such weapons are by nature less discriminating than warheads that are individually aimed, however poorly; hence they will inevitably put civilians at risk. In a new era of precision-guided munitions, it seems that we are simultaneously entering a time of massed cluster-shell, cluster-bomb or cluster-rocket strikes that aim to interdict whole areas. Some commentators have even congratulated arms manufacturers on developing the capacity to cause devastation almost on a nuclear scale without the implications of radioactivity!

However, the modern battlefield will not see HE bombardment on the scale of the two World Wars, so it is possible that future warfare won't destroy towns in quite the same wholesale manner. Towns are themselves less concentrated and tightly packed than they used to be, and industrial areas are often dispersed in the suburban sprawl rather than being concentrated in the highly populated inner city. Nevertheless the level of urban destruction may still be high, and it will be made still higher by requisitions.

Chemical or biological weapons will have serious environmental effects

In a future war the armies will requisition a greater proportion of civilian equipment than ever before. No longer will it be merely a matter of flour, meat and vegetables that are taken: it will also be POL, JCBs, cars, trucks and the entire telephone network. Trees and bridges will be blown down, and buildings blown up, to help put as many obstacles as possible in the enemy's way. It will take a very long time indeed for the urban landscape to recover from a modern war – or even from a war mobilisation.

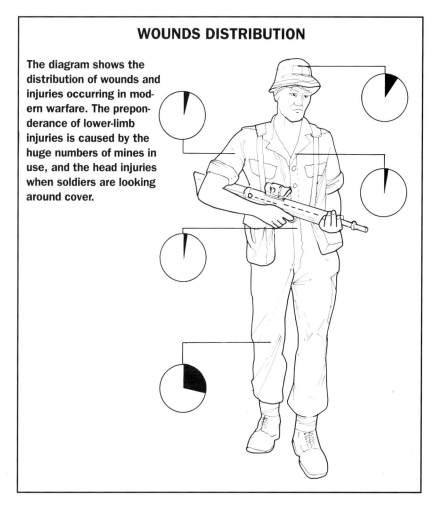

WOUNDS DISTRIBUTION

The diagram shows the distribution of wounds and injuries occurring in modern warfare. The preponderance of lower-limb injuries is caused by the huge numbers of mines in use, and the head injuries when soldiers are looking around cover.

Right: The huge battlefield cemeteries of WWI tell the gruesome story of mass death in their own graphic way. This is Serre Road, on the Somme. The Commonwealth War Graves Commission looks after this site, and thousands like it, in 130 countries around the world

SACRIFICING EFFICIENCY FOR PROTECTION

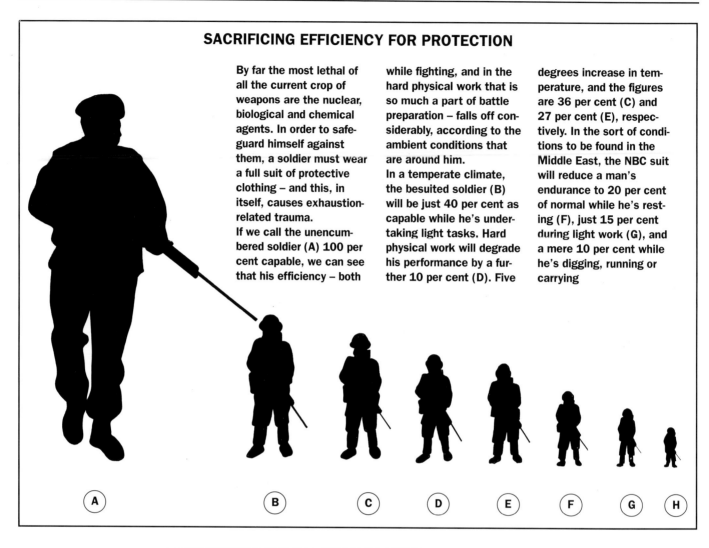

By far the most lethal of all the current crop of weapons are the nuclear, biological and chemical agents. In order to safeguard himself against them, a soldier must wear a full suit of protective clothing – and this, in itself, causes exhaustion-related trauma.

If we call the unencumbered soldier (A) 100 per cent capable, we can see that his efficiency – both while fighting, and in the hard physical work that is so much a part of battle preparation – falls off considerably, according to the ambient conditions that are around him.

In a temperate climate, the besuited soldier (B) will be just 40 per cent as capable while he's undertaking light tasks. Hard physical work will degrade his performance by a further 10 per cent (D). Five degrees increase in temperature, and the figures are 36 per cent (C) and 27 per cent (E), respectively. In the sort of conditions to be found in the Middle East, the NBC suit will reduce a man's endurance to 20 per cent of normal while he's resting (F), just 15 per cent during light work (G), and a mere 10 per cent while he's digging, running or carrying

Right: Not all the Americans who fought in Vietnam have been accounted for; some are still listed simply as 'missing'. Just how these men disappeared is impossible to know for sure, but there are three main areas of possibility. Many were captured and either died in captivity and were simply forgotten, while some, it is suggested, are still in captivity. Some certainly absconded, and have effectively disappeared – probably by means of false identities. The remainder were probably vapourised, or reduced to tiny unidentifiable portions, by massive weapons effect

If chemical or biological weapons are used, they may have still more serious environmental effects. Many countries have experimented with agents such as anthrax, even though they have been banned by the 109-nation UN Convention of 1972. As shown by the case of Gruinard Island – the site of British experiments with anthrax in World War II and declared free of contamination only in 1989 – such agents are not only deadly, but often very persistent. More flexible, but with apparently rather wider international acceptability, is the chemical warfare (CW) arsenal. This includes non-lethal weapons such as were used by USA in Vietnam during the 1960s: CS gas and 'Agent Orange'. More lethal types were used during the 1980s by the USSR in Afghanistan, and by Iraq in the Gulf War, including persistent mustard gas – a blistering agent.

Low persistance non-lethal gas is a very attrtactive weapon

Under sufficient pressure, any nation might be tempted to resort to nerve ('G' or 'V') agents. While there are moves to ban these weapons, proposed controlling conventions have never been signed – and in any event such agreements have not always been effective. Modern technology allows the weapons to incorporate a variety of tactically useful

Left: The Americans lost almost 60,000 men in Vietnam. The name of every one is inscribed on the Vietnam Veterans' Memorial, a wall of polished black marble in Washington DC. In front of it stands a statue of three infantrymen: one Anglo-Saxon, one Black and one Hispanic. The monument has become a place of pilgrimage for Americans, with as many visitors as longer-established sites in Washington such as the Lincoln Memorial.

TRIAGE

Triage – division into three categories – is a time-honoured principle of military medicine. In what might be called 'normal' times a field aid post will try to give maximum care and attention to all its patients; but if it comes under heavy pressure from large numbers of casualties, as the British did at San Carlos for a time during the Falklands war of 1982, a system of priorities may have to be applied.

This system is the triage, and under it the wounded will be divided into those who seem certain to die, those who can be saved with difficulty, and those who are only lightly wounded. Resources will be concentrated on the middle category, while patients in the other two will merely be made comfortable. The system is intended to ensure that the maximum number of casualties will be saved.

The same principle applies to vehicles and equipment – for instance, damaged AFVs – though here just two categories are used. A front-line unit's repair facilities may concentrate solely on those that can be put back on the road within 24 hours. The rest may either be cannibalised for spare parts, or sent back to a rear area repair shop, depending on the resources available and the state of the roads.

features – but they are also features that may spell grim death to combatants and non-combatants alike.

Recent US research has concentrated on developing safe ways to handle these weapons. Binary systems, composed of two chemicals that are harmless when stored separately in shells or rockets, but combine on impact to form nerve gas, are particularly popular. Modern nerve agents can be made non-persistent, to allow friendly forces to use the ground within half an hour of a CW attack. But for other tasks, such as airfield denial, the older, persistent type of gas would still find favour with many. In windy, rainy conditions these may remain dangerous for up to 36 hours, but in cold and calm weather they could be lethal for as long as four months.

Chemical weapons used in Europe would treble civilian casualties

As far as civilians are concerned, chemical warfare spells disaster. Civilians do not have access to the protective suits and decontamination equipment enjoyed by soldiers. It has been calculated that a war in Europe that called on chemical weapons would treble the number of civilian casualties that might be expected in a conventional conflict. It may be that civilians would rarely find themselves in areas that had been specifically targeted, but even so the chemicals would soon spill out of the battlefield into populated areas – for they are notoriously easily affected by the vagaries of the weather.

There is another problem with civilian casualties, insofar as they are not usually assessed, reported or commemorated with quite the same attention to detail that is lavished upon casualties who happen to be wearing uniform. Soldiers who are killed in action (KIA) come from a bureaucracy that is expert at taking roll calls and checking rosters of those on active duty every day. But the average

civilian town may keep only relatively vague annual lists of telephone subscribers, householders or taxpayers. Soldiers wear metallic 'dog-tags' to identify them, while civilians rarely carry anything more durable than flammable plastic credit cards or paper driving licenses.

More important still is the difference in the symbolic and political significance of a soldier who 'offers the ultimate sacrifice', and a civilian who just 'got caught in the crossfire'. In low intensity warfare, the press may raise a storm over the latter while ignoring the former; but the situation is entirely reversed as soon as the warfare increases in intensity. The fallen soldier will then be held up

Above: South African troops, fighting with Montgomery's Eighth Army during the North African campaign, prepare to clear a house. Whenever fighting comes to built-up areas, the amount of collateral damage sustained is enormous Right: Aerial and artillery bombardment can turn an inhabited area into a desert. This is Heligoland after the Allies took it in 1945

THE SCALE OF BATTLE

The size and duration of individual battles has increased considerably. The battlefield at Agincourt (A) was 500 metres wide, the engagement took just six hours, and cost 20,000 lives. Waterloo (B) took place over a four-kilometre front, lasted for 10 hours, and cost 65,000 dead. By 1916, and the Battle of the Somme (C), the fighting front was almost 50km long, the battle lasted for four and a half months, and the death toll was 1,200,000 men. The Battle of Normandy (D), which started with the D-Day landings on 6 June 1944, ranged over 120km, took 10 weeks, and cost 450,000 casualties

ANTI-PERSONNEL MUNITIONS

The changeover from large single anti-personnel bombs to cluster munitions means that there is far less energy wasted in sending fragments high up in to the air, where they do no good. A cluster bomb covers a larger area much more economically

NOTES
The outer semi-circle denotes the lethal area of a 250lb fragmentation bomb.
Each of the smaller semi-circles represents the lethal area of a modern cluster sub-munition or hand grenade.
The dotted line shows the range of a modern grenade launcher. The 150m semi-circle shows the lethal area of a modern defensive grenade, while the inner semi-circle shows the lethal area of a WWII Mills Bomb

Each bomblet has the same effect as an infantry grenade – a destructive radius of perhaps 75 metres. Even a good ball player would have trouble throwing a grenade that far, so the light-weight launcher was developed to project a grenade up to 250 metres

150 m

600 m

as a shining example for succeeding generations, while the civilian victim may often appear more as an unwelcome reproach against a government that has failed to protect him.

Civilian wounded are also likely to be cared for less effectively than soldiers wounded in action (WIA). The reason is that civilian hospitals generally have fewer facilities for sudden influxes of wounded than do the medical echelons in advanced armies – and if the armies are already fully occupied with their own WIA they will have no surplus capacity left over for civilians.

Modern warfare produces more burns than gunshot wounds

Military medicine has made huge advances in the last three decades. Vietnam showed how rapid helicopter casualty evacuation ('medevac' or 'casevac') can save the lives of unprecedented numbers of WIA: estimates of the survival rate among the wounded airlifted from Vietnam battlefields range from 82 to 98 per cent, though we can never know how many of them would have been saved by treatment in situ followed by surface evacuation.

Advances in civilian medicine have also spun-off benefits for those WIA. Ultrasonic scanners, for example, can help locate plastic shrapnel fragments that fail to show up on X-ray. In the Falklands war of 1982 the survival rate of WIA was increased still

Above: The Americans' Hearts and Minds programme in Vietnam attempted – with limited success – to establish bonds of trust and acceptance between themselves and the indigenous population

Right: The airborne gunships, Spooky, Shadow and Spectre – based on the C-47 Dakota, the C-119 Flying Boxcar and the C-130 Hercules, respectively – proved to be terrifyingly effective as their miniguns laid down a sheet of fire that could cover every square inch of a football pitch in a matter of moments. This time-exposure photograph reveals every minigun burst as a solid stream of fire

BOMBERS AND BOMB LOADS

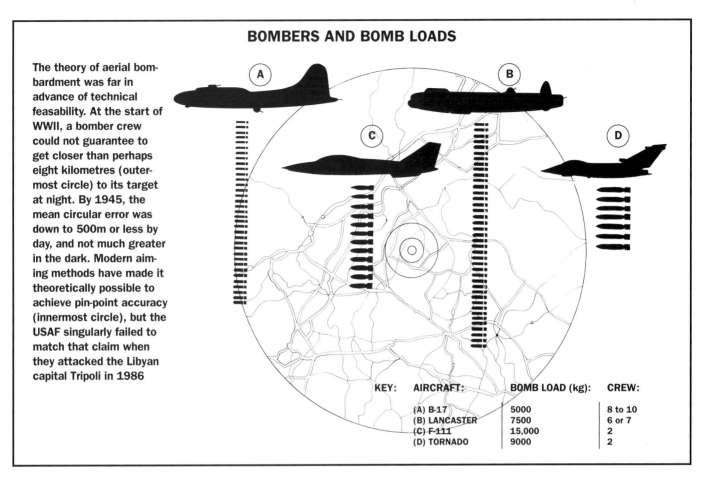

The theory of aerial bombardment was far in advance of technical feasability. At the start of WWII, a bomber crew could not guarantee to get closer than perhaps eight kilometres (outermost circle) to its target at night. By 1945, the mean circular error was down to 500m or less by day, and not much greater in the dark. Modern aiming methods have made it theoretically possible to achieve pin-point accuracy (innermost circle), but the USAF singularly failed to match that claim when they attacked the Libyan capital Tripoli in 1986

KEY:	AIRCRAFT:	BOMB LOAD (kg):	CREW:
(A)	B-17	5000	8 to 10
(B)	LANCASTER	7500	6 or 7
(C)	F-111	15,000	2
(D)	TORNADO	9000	2

further by advances in the treatment of wounds gained in the Royal Victoria Hospital, Belfast, during the Northern Ireland 'troubles'. Still more important, a very high level of first aid training among all the infantry soldiers meant that instead of a single medic per platoon there were effectively 30, yet how many soldiers are going to take time out of the battle to come to the aid of a wounded civilian?

The sensitivity to any friendly casualties is noticeably rising

Some concern about civilian casualties in modern warfare may be misplaced. It is actually possible that modern improvements in weaponry will not, after all, bring an overall increase in the numbers of either killed or wounded per day of combat. We should recognise that the fearsomeness of many of these weapons has more to do with media hype than it does with reality. This comes about not just through the arms industry's own self-serving advertising – which is prodigious – but also through the appetite of the media for new sensational stories.

Technological warfare, almost by definition, originates in highly developed societies where life is relatively soft. Such societies have an escalating horror of all forms of hardship, destruction and death, and their sensitivity to any hostile weaponry or friendly casualties is noticeably rising, especially when the casualties are 'innocent civilians' and, perhaps surprisingly, even when they are professional soldiers whose stock in trade is death and destruction.

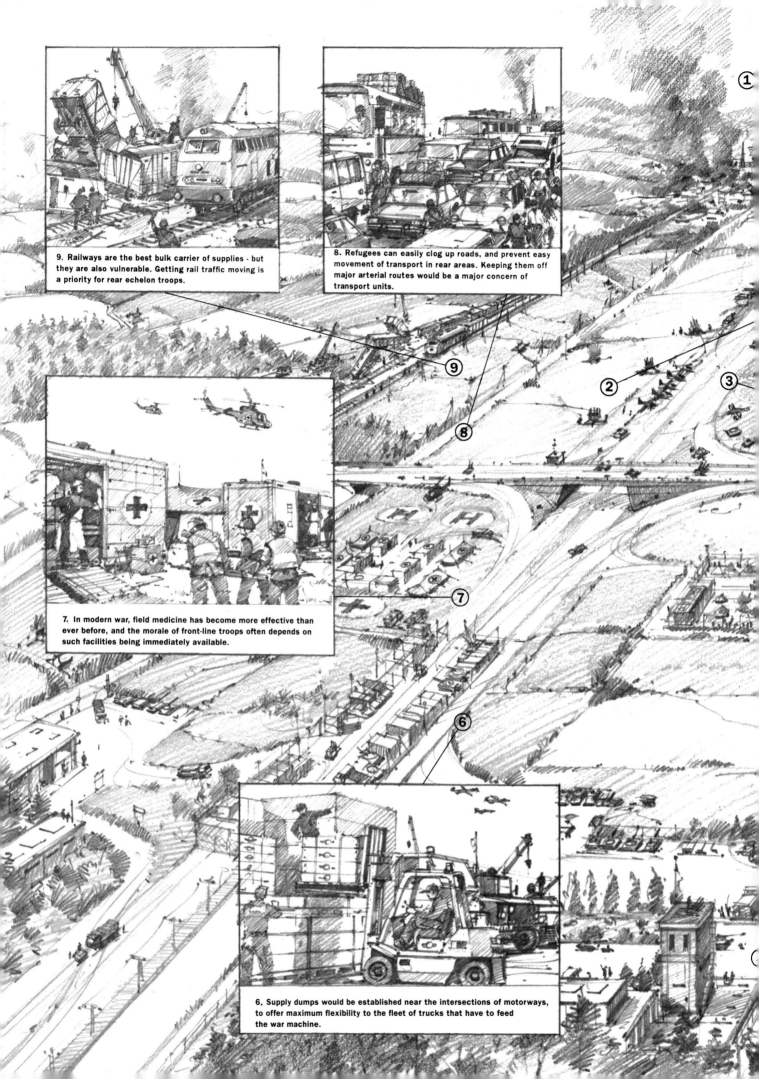

9. Railways are the best bulk carrier of supplies - but they are also vulnerable. Getting rail traffic moving is a priority for rear echelon troops.

8. Refugees can easily clog up roads, and prevent easy movement of transport in rear areas. Keeping them off major arterial routes would be a major concern of transport units.

7. In modern war, field medicine has become more effective than ever before, and the morale of front-line troops often depends on such facilities being immediately available.

6. Supply dumps would be established near the intersections of motorways, to offer maximum flexibility to the fleet of trucks that have to feed the war machine.

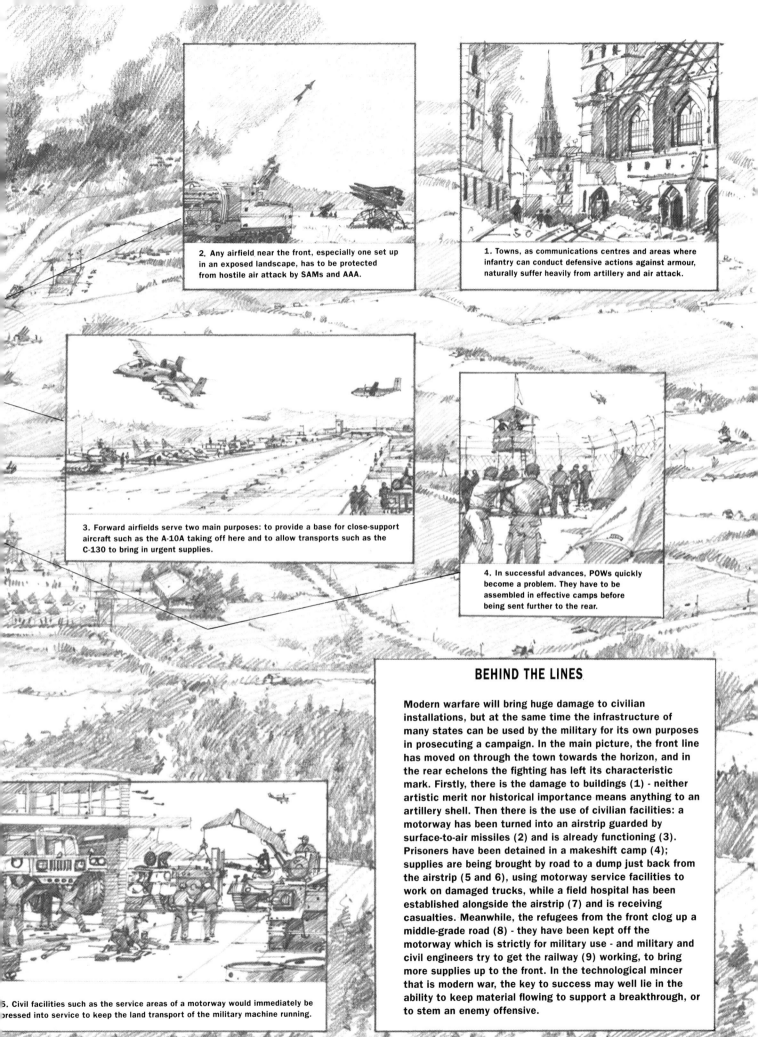

2. Any airfield near the front, especially one set up in an exposed landscape, has to be protected from hostile air attack by SAMs and AAA.

1. Towns, as communications centres and areas where infantry can conduct defensive actions against armour, naturally suffer heavily from artillery and air attack.

3. Forward airfields serve two main purposes: to provide a base for close-support aircraft such as the A-10A taking off here and to allow transports such as the C-130 to bring in urgent supplies.

4. In successful advances, POWs quickly become a problem. They have to be assembled in effective camps before being sent further to the rear.

BEHIND THE LINES

Modern warfare will bring huge damage to civilian installations, but at the same time the infrastructure of many states can be used by the military for its own purposes in prosecuting a campaign. In the main picture, the front line has moved on through the town towards the horizon, and in the rear echelons the fighting has left its characteristic mark. Firstly, there is the damage to buildings (1) - neither artistic merit nor historical importance means anything to an artillery shell. Then there is the use of civilian facilities: a motorway has been turned into an airstrip guarded by surface-to-air missiles (2) and is already functioning (3). Prisoners have been detained in a makeshift camp (4); supplies are being brought by road to a dump just back from the airstrip (5 and 6), using motorway service facilities to work on damaged trucks, while a field hospital has been established alongside the airstrip (7) and is receiving casualties. Meanwhile, the refugees from the front clog up a middle-grade road (8) - they have been kept off the motorway which is strictly for military use - and military and civil engineers try to get the railway (9) working, to bring more supplies up to the front. In the technological mincer that is modern war, the key to success may well lie in the ability to keep material flowing to support a breakthrough, or to stem an enemy offensive.

5. Civil facilities such as the service areas of a motorway would immediately be pressed into service to keep the land transport of the military machine running.

This relatively modern perception can seriously distort policy-making and strategy. For example: the USA was persuaded to pull out of Vietnam mainly because of the 20,000 dead she had suffered in the four years leading up to the Tet Offensive of 1968, even though she was claiming to have inflicted around twenty times that total on the enemy – not all of whom, it was suspected even at the time, were necessarily combatants. In 1973 Israel was deeply unhappy with the result of the Yom Kippur war when she lost 3000 dead as the price of a double victory, over both Egypt and Syria. She had been hoping, perhaps, for a result closer to that of June 1967: around 1000 dead in return for a spectacular doubling of her territory.

Advancing armies always spread a wave of terror ahead of them

The most tragic feature of the modern battlefield is perhaps the flood of refugees, evacuees, orphans and displaced persons that it generates. Advancing armies always spread a wave of terror ahead of them, and this is likely to become more intense in future. The proliferation of civilian news media might be expected to contribute to the spread of terror in a war zone, but this is unlikely to be the case; these (VHF) means of

Right: One notable feature of modern conflict is the number of friendly nationals caught up in hostilities on foreign soil. The US Air Force airlifted many US citizens out of Grenada after the island was invaded

Left: The British Government has taken great pains to keep the conflict in Ulster inside the civilian structure, though this has meant turning the police force there into a paramilitary organisation. The British Army in Ulster has quite restricted powers, and is always said to be acting in support of the civilian authorities

communication will be rendered inoperable by electronic warfare even more quickly than will military communications.

Nevertheless, the lifestyles and expectations of civilian populations in developed countries, and their massive access to motor vehicles, will tend to create both a greater desire to escape and a more widespread attempt to do so. Something of this sort was seen in the prompt Catholic exodus from Belfast in August 1969, in response to an outbreak of violence that – by comparison with the harsh standards of wholesale conventional warfare – can only be described as minor.

Pitiful streams of refugees were a heart-rending feature of many European campaigns during World War II. They have often reappeared in subsequent conflicts, such as the Arab-Israeli war of 1967 or the American war in Vietnam. The scale and intensity of the refugee problem will surely be greater in any future conflict that takes place in industrialised countries – and from the armies' point of view this will be significant in two very different ways.

In the first scenario the sad columns of refugees may be treated as unfortunate victims of an unfortunate circumstance: helpless people to be succoured and aided in every way possible, even if – irritatingly to distant staff officers – they block roads and interrupt military operations. This was a problem for the Western allies during the 1940 campaign in France, when the Germans, it was suggested, tried to create tactical obstacles by deliberately herding refugees into traffic nodes, such as cross-roads, using fighter ground attack (FGA) aircraft to nudge them along with regular strafings.

In any future war this traffic problem would be greatly intensified, just because the sheer volume of traffic of all kinds, military or civilian, will be so much greater. However, the first few passes by modern FGA planes – which might charitably be expected to be seeking purely military targets – may well clear major roads of absolutely all traffic, regardless of its origins or its intentions.

A refugee needs just as much food and shelter as a combat soldier

When, during World War II, the Allies invaded Italy, France and then Germany herself, the Western armies accepted considerable tactical disruption because of their soldiers' generally well-meaning relations with civilians. A refugee needs just as much food and shelter as a combat soldier or a prisoner of war (POW), and the Western Allies' resources were seriously stretched by their policy of taking whatever care they could of the disrupted civilian population. Nevertheless, they felt it was

BATTLE & DATE	CASUALTIES (both sides combined)	DAYS	CASUALTIES (per day)
Borodino 1812	74,000	1	74,000
Leipzig 1813	127,000	4	31,750
Waterloo 1815	63,000	1	63,000
Antietam 1862	22,000	1	22,000
Gettysburg 1863	45,000	3	15,000
Gravelotte 1870	33,000	1	33,000
Somme 1916 First day:	61,000	1	61,000
Whole battle	1,200,000	140	8571
Verdun 1916	750,000	300	2500
2nd Alamein 1942	35,000	12	2916
October War 1973 Syrian front:	7000	19	370
Canal front:	11,000	19	579
Total in war:	18,000	19	949
Lebanon Invasion 1982	11,000	70	157

LETHALITY v LOSSES

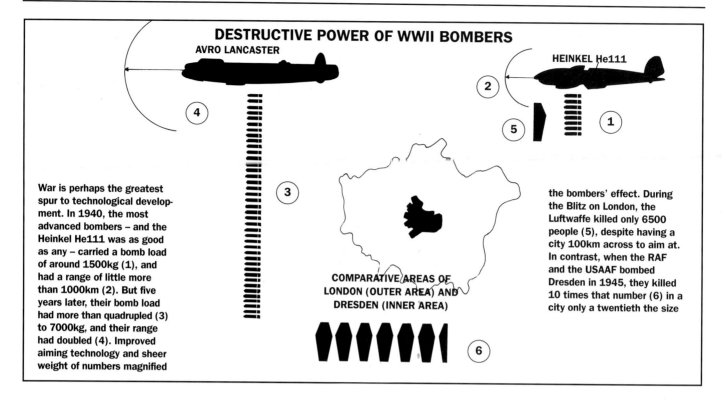

DESTRUCTIVE POWER OF WWII BOMBERS

AVRO LANCASTER

HEINKEL He111

COMPARATIVE AREAS OF LONDON (OUTER AREA) AND DRESDEN (INNER AREA)

War is perhaps the greatest spur to technological development. In 1940, the most advanced bombers – and the Heinkel He111 was as good as any – carried a bomb load of around 1500kg (1), and had a range of little more than 1000km (2). But five years later, their bomb load had more than quadrupled (3) to 7000kg, and their range had doubled (4). Improved aiming technology and sheer weight of numbers magnified

the bombers' effect. During the Blitz on London, the Luftwaffe killed only 6500 people (5), despite having a city 100km across to aim at. In contrast, when the RAF and the USAAF bombed Dresden in 1945, they killed 10 times that number (6) in a city only a twentieth the size

---

only proper to devote considerable manpower, and a major administrative effort, to civilian government and rehabilitation. This consisted of 'G5' staffwork functions, which imposed unexpected non-tactical pressures on the military, not to mention the far-reaching political implications that were involved for the future state of Europe.

The whole problem of refugees is a major burden to any fighting army

There were occasions when the Allied commanders deliberately avoided targets of enormous psychological significance simply because of the drain that the dislocation and disruption to the civilian population would have imposed on their fighting resources. It has even been suggested that Allied Supreme Commander Dwight D. Eisenhower resisted the flamboyant, francophile General George Smith Patton's insistent demands that he be allowed to march on Paris (as he could easily have done) for just that reason. Eisenhower was aware that feeding the population of Paris would have starved his own troops, and so he planned to bypass the city. Other commentators have a more romantic explanation: that the honour should fall to the men of the Free French Army. In the event, the people of Paris rose and liberated themselves – leaving the French capital to be entered, in due course, by General Jacques Leclerc's Second French Division, and French civil problems to be shouldered by Frenchmen.

In Vietnam, the Americans made great efforts to avoid fighting in built-up areas if they could possibly help it; but even in rural areas they were seriously embarrassed by the large masses of refugees that the war created. Vast tracts of the country became depopulated, with tactical maps being dotted with the word 'abandoned' beside many a hamlet.

There can be no doubt that the whole problem of refugees – even if it is to some extent actually a self-created problem – is a major and most unwelcome burden to any fighting army. Soldiers do not feel happy when they are in close proximity to civilians, especially unhappy civilians.

The problem is far worse for the civilians, however, in the second scenario for civil-military relations within a war zone. This is the still bleaker prospect of an invading army that sees itself as a positive scourge upon an alien and hostile population. In this case there is an assumption of unadorned power. The invading army invades and rules, while the local population is expected to cringe, turn its face to the wall, and simply accept its fate. The invading army may inflict almost limitless atrocities and indignities upon its victims, as did first the German army in Russia and then in turn the Russian army in Germany, during World War II.

The Khmer Rouge have exploited refugees with ruthless cynicism

In these circumstances any column of refugees may look to a prejudiced army much more like a 'legitimate target' than an 'innocent victim'. There is probably no army in the world that can honestly say that, under the stress, frustration and frequent ambiguity of 20th-Century combat, it has never at some time or another turned its guns on entirely innocent civilians.

The moral and practical difficulties and dangers faced by both military and civilians in conflicts where the enemy depends absolutely on the civil population for its sustenance have been illustrated with chilling clarity by such incidents as the massacre of Vietnamese men, women and children at My Lai in March 1968 and the slaughter of Palestinians by Lebanese Christian militia at Chabra

The current spate of 'troubles' in Ulster is now in to its third decade. An entire generation has grown up in the Province without ever knowing the true meaning of peace. From one side of the Province to the other – from Derry's Bogside (Top) to Belfast's Divis Flats (Right) – the helicopter and the armoured car are an accepted part of everyday life

and Chatila in September 1982. In the fighting in Cambodia since 1979, the Khmer Rouge have exploited refugees with ruthless cynicism, herding them thousands at a time in front of their own advances or positions as a human buffer against opposing government forces.

Faced with such an invader, harassed civilians will – like the Vietnamese, the Afghanis and the Palestinians – almost certainly turn their hands to civil disobedience, resistance work and what is today often known simply as 'terrorism'. Fifty years of resistance campaigning, cold war and limited war have brought an unprecedented degree of sophistication to the skills of today's partisan and saboteur. Better and more compact explosives, better timers, better mines, new light anti-tank weapons and carefully rehearsed ambush drills – all these, and much more, allow even a tiny handful of experts to wreak havoc in an unwary invader's soft logistic rear.

Conventional armies have their own private guerrilla forces

To counter this threat, troops will have to be diverted from front-line tasks to guard key points and convoys against attack. Active sweeps will have to be mounted to hunt down saboteurs. The problem is made doubly difficult for an invading or occupying army by the modern logistic and command infrastructure, whose increasing complexity is making it steadily more fragile and vulnerable. Selective sabotage thus threatens to become more important to the general battle than it has ever been in the past.

Conventional armies have their own private guerrilla forces as well, of course. Small special forces teams, who have been trained to infiltrate deep into enemy territory, live off the land and make their attacks effective will be operating on both sides of any future conflict, with or without local support. But if local people do support such troops to the full, these teams will enjoy a far greater freedom of movement – and, provided the war lasts for more than a few days, soldiers on clandestine operations can recruit large numbers of partisans from the local population. US Green Beret 'A' teams in Vietnam, for example, were each able to mobilise a complete company of Montagnard soldiers to fight the Viet Cong and the North Vietnamese Army.

The best defence against random attack is often simple alertness

But if 'conventional' soldiers can organise guerrilla warfare, it follows that they can also combat it. The spread of international terrorism since the late 1960s has done much to prepare and warn the world's armies against this kind of threat. Experience says that the best defence against random attack is often simple alertness, enhanced by surveillance aids. Frontier and security lines can today be wired up to monitor foot traffic electronically – almost as effectively as a house can be wired up with burglar alarms. The Americans, for example, have made extensive use of remote sensors to monitor illegal immigrants across their frontier with Mexico. The Israeli frontier with Lebanon has been made so secure that infiltrators must apparently now use somewhat exotic means, such as gliders, to penetrate the cordon at all.

But it will almost always be a minority of civilians who take up arms against an invading army. Many will find quieter if often very effective ways of obstructing hostile soldiers who try to take over their lives, through disinformation, lack of co-operation and general bloody-mindedness. But most civilians will suffer, and by and large suffer worse than soldiers, in any future conflict, for the simple reason that the people in whose name and over whose land a major war is fought will not only find that most of their country's resources will be diverted to the military, but that the military will regard civilian interests, even survival, as secondary to winning the immediate battle, the current campaign or the whole war. That is the great irony of the history of warfare, and there is no reason to suppose it will be different in the future.

Until the next major conflict, we will not know the truth behind the conflicting claims of armies and armament manufacturers. But of one thing we can be absolutely certain: any new major war will produce casualties on a scale impossible to comprehend. The fact that many of them will be 'innocent' civilians, who just happen to be in the wrong place at the wrong time, makes the projection even uglier and harder to bear. But bear it we must, for man has less chance of achieving truly peaceful co-existence with his fellows than he has of flying through the air unaided.

When guerrilla forces come up against conventional troops, with their superior firepower and training, losses can be horrendous

Left: A trooper of the United States Army's 101st Airborne Division checks the bodies of three Viet Cong, killed at An Khe, in Binh Dinh Province, in September, 1967

Above: Money is sometimes a more potent weapon than any gun or bomb. In a country whose economy has been destroyed by war, it is often easier to buy friends than win them. This pregnant woman, also photographed in the aftermath of the fighting around An Khe, worked on the construction of a new base for the American 1st Air Cavalry Division

WILL CIVILIANS SUFFER MORE IN A FUTURE WAR?

The future battlefield promises to spill over into civilian life as never before. The reasons why:

• If persistent NBC agents are used in a future war, they will be a major threat to civilians and to the ecology

• Long-range ET cluster weapons used over towns may dispose of enemy troops there, but will kill many more civilians in the process

• Armies will requisition more material and equipment from civilians than ever before, and disrupt the landscape more with engineer work

• More advanced long-range weaponry will bring much wider areas of the countryside, and quiet suburban areas too, into the front line of battle

• Medical resources will be in short supply, and will soon be overloaded if civilian casualties are high

• Civilians may be used as mass hostages by a ruthless enemy

• Rear echelons, lodged in ostensibly 'safe' areas with a high civilian population, are more vulnerable than ever to attack by special forces, partisans and ET weapons

• The sheer speed of developments on the highly flexible battlefield of the future is bound to involve unintended but inevitable civilian casualties

• History teaches that the people in whose name so many wars have been fought are the ones who suffer most from the realities of taking up arms

On the other hand, civilians may escape the many of the horrors of the next major war, for these reasons:

• Armies may avoid using persistent NBC agents, either for fear of retaliation in kind or because non-persistent types are tactically more appropriate. In other words, they will want to keep their options open and be able to fight again safely over the same ground if the need arises.

• More smart weapons and discriminating warheads will limit damage to military targets

• Increasingly lethal weaponry, and public awareness of it, may paradoxically lead to people taking more precautions and counter-measures against them, so reducing overall casualties

• Vaunted and feared advanced weaponry may in fact be in short supply, so limiting the scale of battle: relatively normal civilian life may be able to continue around a bogged-down mutual front line

• Medical techniques have improved so much that simple but effective treatment can be brought to most civilian as well as military battle casualties

• Improved counter-terrorist techniques will help protect rear areas, and the civilians in them, against clandestine attack.

CONCLUSION

Many of the changes we have discussed, in weaponry and in tactics, are already under way. Even the interim results of this exercise show that the precise balance of advantage between attack and defence, between small squads and big battalions, is harder to predict now than it has been at any time since the end of hostilities in 1945. Without having to accept all the claims that have been made for the various ET weapons, it does seem clear that they are going to make the waging of war very different indeed from what it once was.

One stark difference between assumption and reality will certainly be apparent in the field of communications. Battle management revolves around the flow of information through tactical VHF radio nets. New (and some not so new) developments in electronic warfare will probably make normal VHF traffic impossible, leaving commanders with a bleak choice between antiquated motorcycles and their despatch riders and advanced microwave radio links. Each of these imposes its own limitations. With less efficient communications the tactical commander will be less able to react quickly to changes in circumstances.

And yet the flip-side of the electronic coin – modern surveillance systems – will ensure that tomorrow's battlefield will be bristling with targets 24 hours a day. At first glance this would seem to assist the attacker, by revealing all the lurking defender's traps and ambushes. However, stationary troops and vehicles can still be concealed against even the most modern surveillance. To that extent, it is the attacker, pumping out heat from his

Left: Lasers are finding wider and wider uses on the battlefield, but one of the most potent is as a target designator. The operator can be mobile, like this one, or in a secure position – all that matters is his view of the battlefield. The designator will operate out to the limits of his vision, and the target he illuminates ('sparkles' is the general term) is vulnerable to attack from the ground or the air

ARMOURED VEHICLES 1920-1990

Since the armoured vehicle first appeared on the battlefield, in 1916, there has been a divergence of opinion as to whether it should be a mobile strong-point or an armoured truck. Both have their adherents, but to the infantryman, the prospect of not having to make his way on foot, and unprotected, through the beaten zone has a certain inevitable attraction!

Over the 75 years of its life so far, the APC/IFV has changed out of all recognition – but then, so have all other weapons systems

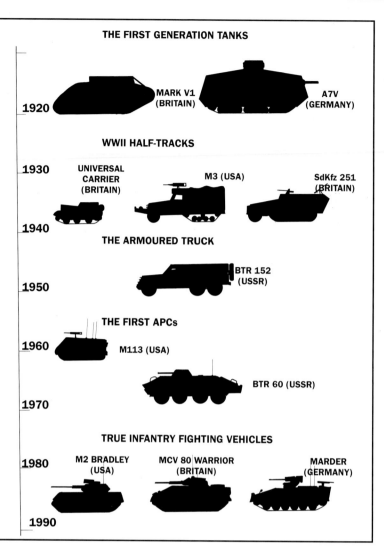

THE FIRST GENERATION TANKS

1920 MARK V1 (BRITAIN) A7V (GERMANY)

WWII HALF-TRACKS

1930 UNIVERSAL CARRIER (BRITAIN) M3 (USA) SdKfz 251 (BRITAIN)

1940

THE ARMOURED TRUCK

1950 BTR 152 (USSR)

THE FIRST APCs

1960 M113 (USA)

BTR 60 (USSR)

1970

TRUE INFANTRY FIGHTING VEHICLES

1980 M2 BRADLEY (USA) MCV 80 WARRIOR (BRITAIN) MARDER (GERMANY)

1990

The turret of an Armoured Fighting Vehicle would never pass muster as a civilian workplace. Cramped and fume-filled, it can be a nightmarish place, straight out of an updated illustration from Dante's *Inferno*. The British Abbot (Below), with its 155mm gun, is by no means the biggest SPG, but it is exemplary. The artillery crewman's job is physically arduous enough out in the open; when he has to do it in the confines of a turret, it's more difficult still

moving vehicles, who will be visible and who must expose himself as he goes into action, while the defender remains invisible.

Logistics have always been a major constraint on military operations, but the future battle promises to escalate this problem into an absolute crisis. An average infantry division in World War II could often make do with only tens of tons of supplies a day, but a modern armoured brigade demands hundreds of tons a day. Admittedly the system distributing such a weight of fuel, ammunition and food has improved enormously since 1945, but there is still the haunting fear that it will break down with unnerving speed in the crucible of real war, real traffic jams and real enemy interdiction strikes. The latest, fast-moving MBTs, in particular, consume fuel so rapidly that they soon lurch to a very ignominious halt without constant re-supply.

The modern army consumes and expends at a monumental rate

The air battle is equally likely to degenerate into stalemate. Pre-emptive strikes by a determined aggressor will make airfields not only unusable in the crucial first few hours of war, but irreparable, since CW weapons will make them effectively uninhabitable too. The few remaining VSTOL tactical strike aircraft will then be too thinly spread to be of decisive use, and will be at the mercy of interdiction strikes against their supply echelons. In the air, too, the electronic war is likely to wreck the subtlest plans for tactical and strategic air strikes, as jamming renders communications, IFF equipment and navigation aids useless. The vaunted 'stealth' aircraft may be undetectable by enemy radars, but their electronic invisibility has had to be paid for in terms of speed and, if their communications are scrambled, they become extremely expensive fire-and-forget weapons flying what amount to suicide missions.

All these gloomy prognostications apply to both sides in a high-technology war, in the air or on the ground. The leading lights of the military-industrial complex on both sides may have designed armies and air forces into a corner from which the only escape is a primitive, bare-knuckle fight. In that case, the outcome on the future battlefield will depend on the traditional skills in fieldcraft, cunning and sheer bravery that have characterised infantry regiments since time immemorial. The high-tech war of the future may, ultimately, be won by superior skills in what one Falklands veteran bluntly called 'gutter fighting'.

There is, of course, another, and grimmer, way out of such a stalemate. If one – or worse, each – side has nuclear weapons on hand and a reasonable

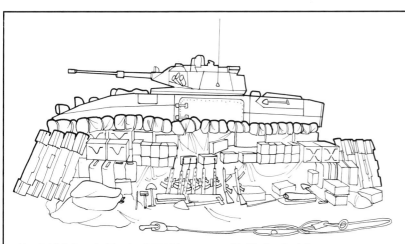

The British Army's Warrior, MCV-80, has a crew of three and a fighting complement of seven. The basic kit for these 10 men occupies much of the vehicle, though some of it – such as sleeping bags – is quite welcome as protective padding.

Each man has his own basic kit, packed into a bergen. He is also personally responsible for his weapon – either an SA-80, for the infantryman, or a Stirling SMG for the vehicle crewman. In addition, there are eight LAW anti-tank rockets and as many grenades, claymore mines and packets of C4 explosive as are available.

Add water, rations and spare fuel, and it's obvious that resupplying even one vehicle – let alone a whole squadron – will be a major task.

chance of delivering them to their targets, the temptation to cut the Gordian knot of a mired battlefield with a single devastating nuclear strike would be hard to resist. It is now, to everyone's relief, less likely than ever that such an intractable state of affairs, and the temptation of a nuclear solution, will come to pass between the old Eastern and Western power blocs. But lesser powers might well become entangled in a such a mutually losing war, as did Iraq and Iran between 1980 and 1988, and one or the other may in future possess nuclear weapons.

Technology can only take the infantryman so far

For 50 years there has been a frantic race to devise and perfect new antitank weapons, to the point that there is now a truly awesome array of different types, some of them with equally awesome range. The tank's armour and EW counter-measures have also greatly improved over the same period, and an alert tank crew can still probably survive the test of battle. Nevertheless, this newly enforced alertness and the general complexity of the tank's tasks on the battlefield will surely increase the strain on its

1. AWACS aircraft are able to survey huge areas of airspace and control the air assets.

2. Tactical Reconnaissance is the oldest use of airpower. Manned reconnaissance aircraft are still an important means of gathering information.

7. Close Air Support has the most visible influence on the ground battle. It is also the most dangerous for the pilots involved.

3. Defensive Counter-Air seeks to prevent the enemy entering friendly airspace and carrying out his mission.

4. Offensive Counter-Air takes the fight to the enemy. Its effectiveness was amply demonstrated in 1967 by the Israeli Air Force.

5. Battlefield Air Interdiction can be devastating, particularly if the attack is directed at choke points such as passes or bridges.

6. Airlift is one of the least glamorous aspects of air operations, but where there are few roads it is vital to the ground war.

AIRPOWER AND THE LAND BATTLE

1. Controlling the airpower and providing early warning of enemy aircraft throughout the depth of the battlefield, AWACS (Airborne Warning And Control System) aircraft fly at 30,000 ft, well behind friendly lines.

2. Tactical Reconnaissance missions give the ground commander a much wider picture of the battlefield in front of him than he could ever obtain for himself, finding targets for attack missions and other weapons systems.

3. Defensive Counter-Air tasks include Combat Air Patrols (CAPs), which fly over the battlefield and wait for enemy aircraft to appear, and Interception, which is a sortie in response to a specific enemy attack.

4. The most effective way to prevent the enemy using his airpower is to destroy his aircraft on the ground, or to destroy the airfields he needs to support them—particularly the vulnerable runways. This is one of friendly airpower's Offensive Counter-Air (OCA) tasks and is usually performed by high-technology strike aircraft, such as Tornado IDS, F-111 and Su-24 Fencer.

5. Battlefield Air Interdiction (BAI) attacks the enemy's second echelon, hitting enemy units when they are most vulnerable. It delays follow-on forces, slows down reinforcement of success and reduces combat effectiveness.

6. Airlift can bring vital men, equipment and stores into the theatre of operations faster than any other means of transport. Aircraft also allow casualties to be evacuated quickly. Transport aircraft can be used for Special Forces insertion and for dropping paratroopers, either to seize an objective or for rapid reinforcement of a threatened area.

7. Close Air Support (CAS) targets enemy forces in contact with friendly troops, or in close proximity to them. It requires excellent co-ordination between the men on the ground and the pilots flying the sortie, as it is all too easy to bomb the wrong side. A forward Air Controller (FAC) therefore controls the strike by radio, either from the ground or from a light aircraft or helicopter. CAS may be a crucial factor in holding a vital position or restarting a flagging thrust.

crew, who can hardly avoid knowing that a single moment's inattention could be fatal. And their ability to react quickly in a fast-moving mobile battle will also suffer, especially if communications are in disarray.

Still more serious, there will be far fewer chances for the many relatively lightly-armoured vehicles – such as IFVs – to continue to live on the battlefield. They are now every bit as vulnerable to enemy weapons as were the unarmoured transport lorries of World War II. This development promises to separate the tanks from the infantry, destroying their mutual support, with potentially catastrophic consequences.

The infantry is likely to fight in smaller groups with higher firepower and protection than in the past. But this will impose greater demands on the individual soldier and his squad leader. And, for all his advanced protection, the individual infantryman remains a fragile and vulnerable creature, however well infantry units can take appalling punishment and still stay in the fight. If a soldier on foot moves in the open and is detected, he is as good as dead. If he hides in a trench, napalm, white phosphorous, multiple rockets or FAE may seek him out. If he moves in an IFV or a helicopter, he may become a very crackable egg among too many others in a very permeable basket. If he jumps into a town to

The most puissant weapon on today's battlefield is the surface-to-surface missile. In its most powerful form, it will hurl a tactical nuclear weapon in to the fighting area from the comparative safety of the rear echelon. In the case of Iraq's *Al Abbas*, developed from the Soviet Scud-B (Above), this could be perhaps as much as 900km away. The US Army's Pershing and Lance (which is also deployed by the British Army), and the French Pluton battlefield support missile fulfil the same requirement, though their range is shorter.

There is some doubt as to the true terminal accuracy of all these systems, and in real deployment they would probably be used as area saturation weapons. Due to their great range, they are almost certain to be the medium of dissemination for chemical and biological weapons, should they ever be used. At the other end of the scale, man-portable surface-to-air missiles, such as the Javelin (Left), enable even infantrymen to kill sophisticated aircraft. This triple-tubed launcher can be set up in just minutes

play a part in FIBUA he may well succeed in his enterprise – but he will need a lot of comrades at his side, and a very long timescale.

Helicopters certainly have much to offer on the future battlefield. As infantry transports they give an exponential increase in speed and a flexibility that is mercifully unaffected by ground obstacles. Unfortunately, however, the helicopter remains essentially an unarmoured, soft-skinned vehicle that happens to be able to fly. It may look like a fast-mover to the grunt on the ground, but in the context of the air battle (through which it has to fly), the helicopter is helplessly slow. It is fair to say that the helicopter today is even more vulnerable to

Below: The AGM-65 Maverick is perhaps the most sophisticated anti-tank weapon in the US Air Force's armoury. The television camera in its nose scans the target area, allowing the operator to designate a point target. The missile's computer will then home in on that point, even if it moves in the meantime

Left: The Pluton battlefield tactical nuclear weapon. The French-built Pluton can carry two different kinds of warhead. Depending on which one is fitted, the missiles have a range of between 19km and 120km.

213

Above: But no matter what, war still resolves, in the end, to two groups of individuals fighting for possession of a few square yards of territory

TIME TAKEN TO TRANSMIT A SECURE MESSAGE

It has often been suggested that that objects and events grow to fill the space available to them. In the military context, this has always meant exploiting technology to the limit of its development. At the end of the 18th Century, it took three months to get the simplest secure message from London to Singapore. During the 19th Century, successive developments brought that time down to three or four days, if everything worked perfectly. Even as recently as WWII, it still took hours, yet today, it is simply a matter of picking up a telephone and dialling the number. A message relayed by satellite can go round the world almost as quickly as it can go to the next town by land line.

ground-to-air and air-to-air weapons than the IFV is to AT weapons. Helicopters may well be admirably suited to wearing down a tank attack as snipers or as reconnaissance fire controllers, but they surely cannot hope to survive very long as infantry transport much beyond the enemy's front line, and certainly not in the absence of air superiority.

As for artillery, the future battlefield promises to be completely dominated by long-range indirect fire. The 'deep battle' is a vital part of modern artillery practice, and can now be conducted with devastating accuracy. Gun and rocket fire will scour through what used to be the enemy's secure rear area, and will extend the battlefield 70km or more beyond the FLOT. The main problems facing the guns – and so many other new weapons – will be surveillance and logistics. Just as our guns will be able to see deep into the enemy's rear, so the enemy will be able to see them and pick them off. And the quicker they can identify targets, the quicker they're likely to expend their precious loads of ammunition.

Provided they can avoid the attention of artillery, engineers will be able to make even greater changes to the future battlefield than they could ever have done in the past. Massed ranks of earth movers will create deep layers of anti-tank

ditches and bunkers; minelayers will go forward to create lethal obstacles, and tree blowdowns will soon make any forest impassable. Against this kind of prepared battlefield it is hard to see how any mechanised army can possibly hope to move.

The most advanced weaponry may well prove to be unworkable

There are at least three key factors that may unblock this apparent log jam. Perhaps the most likely is that one side will run out of resources much sooner than the other. Unlike the situation that occurred in 1915, the 'shell shortage' in a future war may not apply to both sides simultaneously. The side with sufficient reserves of ammunition and POL will then continue to press its attack. The army left in this fortunate position may not be the most advanced technologically, however: the rate of consumption of supplies promises to be much higher with sophisticated weapons than with more basic ones.

Second, it may well turn out that the most advanced weaponry proves to be unworkable. Peacetime armies swelled out to their wartime establishment by conscripts and volunteers may lack sufficient numbers of adequately skilled soldiers to keep

Left: Gone are the days when the infantrymen had to guess at the range of their target. Now, laser rangefinders such as this reel off the distance to the nearest metre, as far as the amplified eye can see

Left: Static installations, such as airfields, have always qualified for a higher standard of protection. Rapier, shown here, is acknowledged to be one of the best of the medium-range surface-to-air missile systems. There is also a vehicle-mounted system in service with the British Army and the RAF, which extends the weapon's umbrella right up to the forward edge of the battle area

THE SHRINKING WEAPON

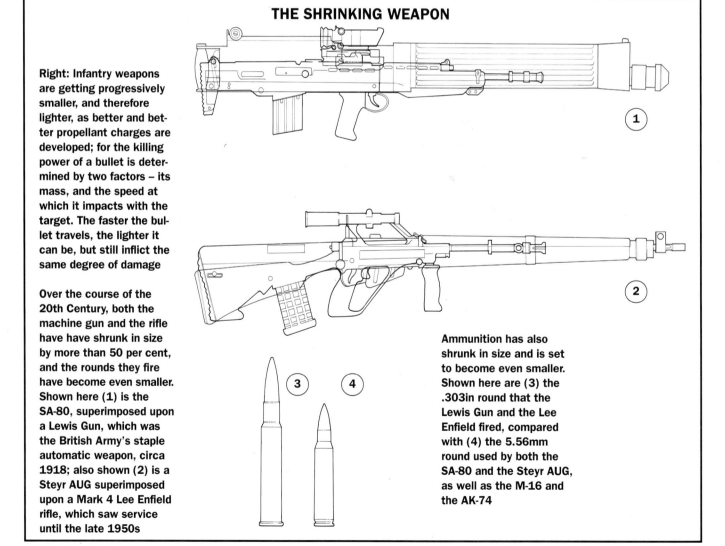

Right: Infantry weapons are getting progressively smaller, and therefore lighter, as better and better propellant charges are developed; for the killing power of a bullet is determined by two factors – its mass, and the speed at which it impacts with the target. The faster the bullet travels, the lighter it can be, but still inflict the same degree of damage

Over the course of the 20th Century, both the machine gun and the rifle have have shrunk in size by more than 50 per cent, and the rounds they fire have become even smaller. Shown here (1) is the SA-80, superimposed upon a Lewis Gun, which was the British Army's staple automatic weapon, circa 1918; also shown (2) is a Steyr AUG superimposed upon a Mark 4 Lee Enfield rifle, which saw service until the late 1950s

Ammunition has also shrunk in size and is set to become even smaller. Shown here are (3) the .303in round that the Lewis Gun and the Lee Enfield fired, compared with (4) the 5.56mm round used by both the SA-80 and the Steyr AUG, as well as the M-16 and the AK-74

Aircraft, too, are changing their shape. If the F-117A Stealth Fighter seems outlandish, it's a fair bet that tomorrow's aircraft will be even more extreme. Above: MacDonnell Douglas's contender for the next generation of multi-role fighter aircraft, the YF-23, is not designed to the same criteria as the F-117 at all, yet it has some of the same lines

the equipment working properly, and there may not be the time in war to train new experts to keep pace with combat losses. The battlefield may break apart simply because of a shortage of skills. And the technology itself may prove unsatisfactory. In 1967 and 1968 the much-heralded dawn of electronic battlefield surveillance in Vietnam turned out to be something of a damp squib. In the 1973 October War, the equally trumpeted ATGW 'revolution' also produced disappointing final statistics. Primitive bazookas proved to be better tank killers than sophisticated wire-guided missiles. Such experiences should lead us to treat the claims of the weapons manufacturers with – at the very least – considerable caution.

Third, a very effective answer to trenchlock may be found in the traditional methods of deception and surprise, or *maskirovka*. This can allow highly mobile spearheads to penetrate deep into an unsuspecting opponent's territory before he has a chance to set up his firepower and obstacles. The best technological weaponry in the world is useless if its operators are unaware that they are at war with anyone. The best air force will be grounded if its runways are cratered and mined before the aircraft have taken off. Nor will even overwhelming numerical superiority help a defender who has already been overrun by the time his troops manage to struggle out of their barracks.

If there should be a high-technology war in the 1990s, its early days will see many mistakes. Key items may be missing from the inventories, and weapons that exist only on paper may be urgently

needed on the battlefield. The soldiers who have to use the most advanced weapons may not understand them fully, which will hinder still further their ability to break through the enemy's position. However, if the war continues long enough the armies will learn new tricks, and will find how to get the best out of what is available. There will also be crash development programmes and a mobilisation of scientific and industrial talent. We may then see not just the present new generation of weaponry deployed in the field, but its successor as well.

WWI was horrific, but casualties were light by modern standards

Just what will that next generation of technology look like? Doubtless there will be a continuing enhancement of 'smart' indirect-fire artillery, and a final realisation of the truly deep battle at long range. Airfields may become a thing of the past, and an army's whole rear area, previously regarded as secure, may be right in the firing line. On the other hand, incoming missiles and warheads may be vulnerable to rapidly reacting point defences, perhaps using DEW or electromagnetic rail guns. Then again, the RPV and the remotely-controlled tank will surely be able to fire without exposing the location of their human operators. And, perhaps even more important, a proliferation of stealth technologies will go far towards restoring the classic 'empty battlefield' of the early 20th century.

BIBLIOGRAPHY

Many of the most important details for this subject appear in the military periodical press, rather than in books. Only a few of the relevant articles can be mentioned here, but in general the reader is referred especially to back numbers of *International Defense Review* for the hardware, and *Military Review* for the doctrines and tactics.

J Albright, J A Cash & A W Sandstrum, *Seven Firefights in Vietnam* (Vietnam Studies Series. Department of the Army, Washington DC 1970)

J R Alford, *Mobile Defense, the Pervasive Myth* — (King's College thesis, London 1977)

Anon, *Lessons of Lebanon* in *Defence Attache* No 4, 1982, p23 ff

Anon, *Operations: FM 100-5, 20 August 1982* (Headquarters, Department of the Army, Washington DC)

Anon, *German Defense Tactics Against Russian Break-Throughs* (US Army Department 20-233, Washington DC, October 1951)

M de Arcangelis, *Electronic Warfare* (Blandford, Poole, Dorset 1985)

J B A Bailey, *Field Artillery and Firepower* (Military Press, Oxford 1989)

F Barnaby, *The Automated Battlefield* (Sidgwick & Jackson, London 1986)

F Barnaby & M ter Borg, *Emerging Technologies and Military Doctrine* (Macmillan, London 1986)

C Bellamy, *The Future of Land Warfare* (Croom Helm, London 1987)

C Bellamy, *Red God of War* (Brassey, London 1986)

R G S Bidwell, *Gunners at War* (Arms & Armour, London 1970)

R G S Bidwell, *World War 3* (Hamlyn, London 1978) (fiction)

R G S Bidwell & D Graham, *Firepower* (Allen & Unwin, London, 1982)

J Bradley, *The Illustrated History of World War 3* (Omega, Leicester 1982)

C Campbell, *War Facts Now* (Fontana, London 1982)

T Clancy, *Red Storm Rising* (Collins, London 1987) (fiction)

H Coyle, *Team Yankee* (Presidio Press, San Novato, Calif. 1987) (fiction)

H Coyle, *Sword Point* (Penguin, London 1989) (fiction)

M Creveld, *Fighting Power* (Arms & Armour, London 1983)

P Dickson, *The Electronic Battlefield* (London 1976)

E Dinter, *Hero or Coward?* (Cass. London 1985)

E Dinter and P Griffith, *Not Over by Christmas* (Bird, Chichester 1983)

T N Dupuy, The Evolution of Weapons and Warfare (First published 1980; Jane's edn, London 1982)

J Ellis, *The Sharp End of War* (David & Charles, Newton Abbot, Devon 1980)

J A English, *On Infantry* (First published Praeger, New York 1981; new edn 1984)

ESECS, *Strengthening Conventional Deterrence in Europe*, the report of the European Security Study (Macmillan, London 1983)

C D'Este, *Decision in Normandy* (Pan edn, London 1984)

J J Ewell & I A Hunt, *Sharpening the Combat Edge* (Vietnam Studies series, Department of the Army, Washington DC 1974)

H Faringdon, *Confrontation* (RKP, London 1986)

R S Friedman, *Advanced Technology Warfare* (Salamander, London 1985)

R A Gabriel, *Military Incompetence: why the American military doesn't win* (Hill & Wang, New York 1985)

R A Gabriel, *Operation Peace for Galilee* (Hill & Wang, New York 1984)

L H Gann, ed., *The Defense of Western Europe* (Croom Helm, 1987)

P Griffith, *Forward Into Battle* (New Edn, Crowood, Ramsbury Wilts. 1990)

P Griffith, *Countering Surprise by Mobility — a concept for armoured warfare on the Central Front* in *The Sandhurst Journal of Military Studies* vol 1, no 1, 1990

B Gunston and M Spick, *Modern Fighting Helicopters* (Salamander, London 1986)

J Hackett, *The Third World War* (Sidgwick & Jackson, London 1978) (fiction)

H Halberstadt, NTC — *A Primer of Land Combat* (Presidio Press, San Novato, Calif. 1989)

N Hannig, *The Defense of Western Europe with Conventional Weapons* in *International Defense Review* vol 15, no 3, April 1982, pp 1439-1442

J P Harris & F H Toase, eds, *Armoured Warfare* (Batsford, London 1990)

J H Hay, *Tactical and Material Innovations* (Vietnam Studies series, Department of the Army, Washington DC 1974)

C Herzog, *The Arab-Israeli Wars* (Arms & Armour, London 1982)

C Herzog, *The War of Atonement* (Weidenfeld & Nicholson, London 1975)

R Holmes, *Firing Line* (Cape, London 1985. Published in USA as *Acts of War*)

Mary Kaldor, *The Baroque Arsenal* (Deutsch, London 1982)

L Lavoic, *Is the Tank Dead?* in *Defense & Diplomacy* Vol 7, No 5, May 1989, p 16

R G Lee, *Introduction to Battlefield Weapons Systems and Technology* (2nd edn, Brassey's 1985)

R Lopez, *The Airland Battle 2000 Controversy — Who is being short-sighted?* in *International Defense Review*, 1983 no 11, pp 1551-6

T T Lupfer, *The Dynamics of Doctrine: The Changes in German Tactical Doctrine During the First World War* (US Army Command and General Staff College, Fort Leavenworth, Kansas 1981)

E Luttwak & D Horrowitz, *The Israeli Army* (Lane, London 1975)

J J G Mackenzie & B H Reid (eds) *The British Army and the Operational Level of War* (Tri-Service, London 1989)

K Macksey, *Tank Warfare, a History of Tanks in Battle* (Hart-Davis, London 1971)

K Macksey, *First Clash — Combat Close-up in World War Three* (Arms and Armour, London, 1985) (fiction)

E von Manstein, *Lost Victories* (first published 1955, translated Methuen, London 1958)

J Marriott, *Weapons Technology* (RUSI and Brassey's, London 1975)

S L A Marshall, *Men Against Fire* (New York 1947)

S L A Marshall, *Infantry Operations & Weapons Usage in Korea* (E C Ezell ed, Greenhill, London 1988)

R Mason, *Chickenhawk* (first published 1983, Penguin edn, London 1984)

J J Mearsheimer, *Maneuver, Mobile Defense and the NATO Central Front* in *International Security* vol 6, no 3, winter 1981-2, pp 104-22

J J Mearsheimer, *Why the Soviets Can't Win Quickly in Central Europe* in *International Security* vol 7, no 1, Summer 1982, pp 3-39

F W von Mellenthin, *Panzer Battles* (trans Betzler, Cassell, London 1955 and Okiahoma University 1956)

C Messenger, *Armies of World War 3* (Bison, London 1984)

D Middleton, ed, *Air War Vietnam* (USAF, reprinted London 1978)

D Miller and C F Foss, *Modern Land Combat* (Salamander, London 1987)

D M O Miller and others, *The Balance of Military Power* (Salamander, London 1981)

R Ogorkicwicz, *Countermeasures for Tanks: Beating smart munitions* in *International Defense Review* 1989, No 1

D E Ott, *Field Artillery, 1954-73* (Vietnam Studies series, Department of the Army, Washington DC 1975)

P Paret, ed., *Makers of Modern Strategy* (Princeton University, 1986)

R Peters, *Red Army* (W H Allen, London 1989) (fiction)

R L Pfaltzgraff jr. U Ra'anan, R H Shultz & I Lukes, eds, *Emerging Doctrines and Technologies* (Lexington, Mass. 1988)

A J Pierre, ed, *The Conventional Defense of Europe* (Council on Foreign Relations, New York 1986)

R R Ploger, *U S Army Engineers, 1965-70* (Vietnam Studies series, Department of the Army, Washington DC 1974)

G G Prosch, *Israeli Defense of the Golan*, an interview with Brigadier General Avigdor Kahalani in *Military Review* vol 59, no 10, Oct 1979, pp ;2-13.

U Ra'anan, *The New Technologies and the Middle East: Lessons of the Yom Kippur War and Anticipated Developments* in G Kemp et al, eds, *The Other Arms Race* (Lexington, Mass 1975), pp 79-90

W R Richardson, *FM100-5: the Air-Land Battle in 1986* in *Military Review*, vol 66, no 3, March 1986, pp 4-11

G F Rogers, *The Battle for Suez City* in *Military Review* vol 59, no 11, November 1979, pp 27-33

P Sabin, *The Third World War Scare in Britain* (Macmillan, London, 1986)

B F Schlemmer, *The Raid* (MacDonald & Jane's, London 1976)

D A Starry, *Extending the Battlefield* in *Military Review*, vol 61, no 3, March 1981, pp 32-50

D A Starry, *Mounted Combat in Vietnam* (Vietnam Studies series, Department of the Army, Washington DC 1978)

J J Tolson, *Airmobility, 1961-71* (Vietnam Studies series, Department of the Army, Washington DC 1973)

P Towle, ed., *Estimating Foreign Military Power* (Croom Helm, London 1982)

T Wintringham & J N Blashford-Snell, *Weapons and Tactics* (Pelican edn, London 1973)

Zaloga, *Red Thrust* (Brassey's, London 1989)

GLOSSARY

AA: Anti-Aircraft
AAA: Anti-Aircraft Artillery
AAM: Air-to-Air Missile
ACAV: Armoured Cavalry Assault Vehicle
AD: Air Defence
ADP: Automated Data Processing
AFV: Armoured Fighting Vehicle
ALARM: Air-Launched Anti-Radiation Missile
ALB: AirLand Battle
APC: Armoured Personnel Carrier
APFSDS: Armour-Piercing Fin-Stabilised Discarding Sabot
ARA: Aerial Rocket Artillery
ASM: Air-to-Surface Missile
ASMP: *Air-Sol Moyenne Portée* (French medium-range air-to-surface missile)
AT: Anti-Tank
ATF: Advanced Tactical Fighter
ATGW: Anti-Tank Guided Weapon
ATM: Anti-Tank Missile
AWACS: Airborne Warning And Control System

BAI: Battlefield Air Interdiction
BATES: Battlefield Artillery Target Evaluation System

C³I: Command, Control, Communications and Information
CAP: Combat Air Patrol
CAS: Close Air Support
Casevac: Casualty evacuation
CB: Counter-Battery
CET: Combat Engineer Tractor (British)
CFE: Conventional Forces in Europe
CFV: Cavalry Fighting Vehicle (eg the M3 Bradley)
CP: Command Post
CPB: Charged Particle Beam
CW: Chemical Warfare

Desant: Soviet parlance for a 'fire and forget' raid – mounted by parachute, helicopter, AFV, landing craft or any other means – that strikes deep into the enemy rear
DEW: Directed Energy Weapon (or 'death ray')

DIVADS: DIVisional Air Defence System
DROPS: Demountable Rack Offloading Pickup System

ECM: Electronic Counter Measures
EHF: Extremely High Frequency
ELF: Extremely Low Frequency
EMP: Electro-Magnetic Pulse
EOCM: Electro-Optical Counter Measures
ERAM: Extended Range Anti-armour Munition
ERFB: Extended Range Full Bore
ET: 'Emerging Technology' (ie the whole range of new systems soon to be available to the battlefield commander in the new age of the micro-chip)
EW: Electronic Warfare

FAAA: *Fuerza Aérea Armada Argentina* (Argentinian naval air force)
FAC: Forward Air Controller
FAE: Fuel-Air Explosives
FEBA: Forward Edge of the Battle Area
FGA: Fighter Ground Attack aircraft
FIBUA: Fighting In Built-Up Areas
FISTV: FIre Support Team Vehicle
FLIR: Forward Looking Infra-Red
FLOT: Front Line of Own Troops
FO: Forward Observer
FOFA: Follow-On Forces Attack
FSB: Fire Support Base

GCHQ: Government Communications HeadQuarters
GMR: Graduated Mobilization Response

HE: High Explosive
HEAT: High Explosive Anti-Tank
HESH: High Explosive Squash-Head
HF: High Frequency
HMMWV (or 'Hummer'): High Mobility Multi-purpose Wheeled Vehicle (ie the successor to the jeep)
HPM: High Power Microwave
HUD: Head-Up Display
HVAPFSDS: High-Velocity Armour-Piercing Fin-Stabilised Discarding Sabot

HVM: High-Velocity Missile
IAF: Israeli Air Force
IFF: Identification Friend or Foe
IFV: Infantry Fighting Vehicle
Interdiction: deep strikes designed to cut off the enemy on the battlefield from supplies and reinforcements coming from the rear
INS: Inertial Navigation System
IO: Information Overload – a 'fatal disease'
IR: Infra-Red

JSTARS: Joint Surveillance and Target Attack Radar System (a US surveillance system for operational depth)
JTACMS: Joint TACtical Missile System (a US cruise missile carrying anti-tank sub-munitions)

KE: Kinetic Energy
KIA: Killed In Action

LANTIRN: Low-Altitude Navigation and Targeting Infra-Red for Night
LAW: Light Anti-tank Weapon
LF: Low Frequency
L of C: Line of Communication
LOH: Light Observation Helicopter
LRSOM: Long Range StandOff Missile (a US cruise missile for attacking static targets)
LWT: Light Wheeled Tractor
LZ: Landing Zone

MBFR: Mutual Balanced Force Reductions
MBT: Main Battle Tank
MF: Medium Frequency
MG: Machine Gun
MIA: Missing In Action
(M)ICV: (Mechanised) Infantry Combat Vehicle (the same as an 'IFV' – see above)
MLRS: Multiple Launch Rocket System
MTU: Soviet scissors bridge mounted on tank chassis
MV: Muzzle Velocity

NATO: North Atlantic Treaty Organisation
NBC: Nuclear, Biological and Chemical
NTC: National Training Center
NVA: North Vietnamese Army
NVG: Night Vision Goggles

OKH: German Army High Command in World War II
OMG: Operational Manoeuvre Group
OP: Observation Post
OPV: Observation Party Vehicle
PBW: Particle Beam Weapon

PGM: Precision Guided Munition
PLO: Palestine Liberation Organisation
PLSS: Precision Location Strike System
PMP: Soviet ferry-cum-pontoon-bridge that comes in sections that can be bolted together to make any length of bridge.
POL: Petrol, Oil and Lubricants
POW: Prisoner Of War

RAP: Rocket-Assisted Projectile
RDM: Remotely Deployed Mine
RPG: Rocket Propelled Grenade
RPV: Remotely Piloted Vehicle (or 'drone')
RV: Rendezvous

SAM: Surface-to-Air Missile
SDI: Strategic Defense Initiative (popularly known as 'Star Wars')
SEP: Specific Excess Power
SHF: Super High Frequency
Sigint: Signals intelligence
SLAR: Side Looking Airborne Radar
SLUFAE: Surface LaUnched Fuel Air Explosive
SMG: Sub-Machine Gun
SP: Self-Propelled
SPG: Self-Propelled Gun
SUSAT: Sight Unit Small Arms Trilux

TGSM: Terminally Guided Sub-Munition
TGW: Terminally Guided Weapon
TMM: unarmoured Soviet truck-mounted scissors bridge
TNW: Tactical Nuclear Weapons
TO & E: Table of Organisation & Equipment
TOW: Tube-launched, Optically tracked, Wire-guided anti-tank missile

UAV: Unmanned Aerial Vehicle
UHF: Ultra High Frequency
USAF: United States Air Force
USMC: United States Marine Corps
UV: Ultra-Violet

VC: Viet Cong
VHF: Very High Frequency
VLF: Very Low Frequency
VSTOL: Vertical/Short Take-Off & Landing
VT: Variable Time

WAAM: Wide-Area Anti-armour Munition
WIA: Wounded In Action
WP: White Phosphorus
WSO: Weapons Systems Officer

INDEX

Equipment has been indexed according to standard NATO designations. Page numbers in *italics* refer to photographic captions; page numbers in **bold** refer to diagrams and box features.